M000169290

Vertex Pharmaceuticals
130 Waverly Street
Cambridge, MA 02139

PHARMACOPHORE
PERCEPTION, DEVELOPMENT,
AND
USE IN DRUG DESIGN

IUL Biotechnology Series

PHARMACOPHORE

PERCEPTION, DEVELOPMENT, AND USE IN DRUG DESIGN

edited by

OSMAN F. GÜNER

INTERNATIONAL UNIVERSITY LINE
La Jolla, California

Library of Congress Cataloging-in-Publication Data

Pharmacophore perception, development, and use in drug design / edited by Osman F. Güner
    p.cm—(IUL Biotechnology Series; 2)
    ISBN 0-9636817-6-1 (hardcover)
      1. Drugs—Structure-activity relationships. 2. Drugs—Design.   I. Güner, Osman F., 1956- II. Series.

RM301.42.P48 1999
615'.19—dc21

                    99-088143
                    CIP

© International University Line, 2000
Post Office Box 2525,
La Jolla, CA 92038-2525, USA

Library of Congress Catalog Card Number 99-088143

Printed in the United States of America

10 9 8 7 6 5 4 3 2 1

ISBN   0-9636817-6-1 $109.95   Hardcover

Contents

Contents

Preface

Perceiving a pharmacophore is the most important first step towards understanding the interaction between a receptor and a ligand. In the early 1900s, Paul Ehrlich offered the first definition for a pharmacophore: "a molecular framework that carries (*phoros*) the essential features responsible for a drug's (*pharmacon*) biological activity".[1] That definition of a pharmacophore remained unperturbed for over 90 years. The current widely used definition was presented by Peter Gund in 1977: "a set of structural features in a molecule that is recognized at a receptor site and is responsible for that molecule's biological activity".[2] This modern definition is remarkably loyal to the earliest definitions.

It is only appropriate, then, that this books starts with the "Evolution of the Pharmacophore Concept in Pharmaceutical Research" in Chapter 1, written by Peter Gund who also developed the first 3D searching software, Molpad, and the first ideas for computational pharmacophores.[2] It took 15 years for the commercial 3D searching software to become available following its original publication by Gund, Langridge, and

---

[1] Ehrlich P: *Dtsch Chem Ges* 1909, **42**:17.
[2] Gund P: *Prog Mol Subcell Biol* 1977, **5**:117-143.

Wipke.[3] John Van Drie, on the other hand, was involved with the development of two commercial 3D searching software applications: one of the earliest ones, Aladdin, and the latest one, Catalyst®. He has also been active and forward-looking in his work with pharmacophores as, for example, "shrink-wrap pharmacophores,"[4] and in his program Dante.[5] It is only appropriate, then, to end this book with Chapter 27 on the "Future Directions in Pharmacophores Discovery," written by John Van Drie.

The information provided in between these two chapters is pretty much everything you would want to know about pharmacophores, and probably more.

The Part II of the book is dedicated to analog-based pharmacophores. Your editor, Osman Güner, presents an elementary introduction to the concept of pharmacophores in Chapter 2, entitled "Manual Pharmacophore Generation: Visual Pattern Recognition." The analog-based pharmacophore development is then introduced with the description of the Active Analog Approach by Denise Beusen and Garland Marshall in Chapter 3: "Pharmacophore Definition Using the Active Analog Approach."

This information is followed by a detailed description in Chapters 4 through 10 of various pharmacophore development and 3D-QSAR software by the pioneers in this area, their inventors, and current developers. Yvonne Martin describes and critically evaluates one of the earlier pharmacophore development software products, DISCO, in Chapter 4 entitled "DISCO: What We Did Right and What We Missed." Chapter 5 describes a common-feature based alignment software, "HipHop: Pharmacophores Based on Multiple Common-Feature Alignments," written by Omoshile Clement and Adrea Mehl. Gareth Jones, Peter Willett, and Robert Glen describe one of the recent alignment and pharmacophore software in Chapter 6: "GASP: Genetic Algorithm Superimposition Program." Stephen Cato then describes how to perceive pharmacophores in Chapter 7 with "Exploring Pharmacophores with Chem-X." Moving onto the predictive model generation software, Erich Vorpagel and Valery Golander describe the importance of negative activities in Chapter 8

---

[3] Gund P, Wipke WT, Langridge R: *Proc Intl Conf on Computers in Chem Res and Educa*, Ljubljana, 1973:5/33.

[4] Van Drie J: *J Chem Inf Comput Sci* 1997, **37**:38-42.

[5] Van Drie J: *J Comput-Aided Mol Des* 1997, **11**:39-52.

entitled "Apex-3D: Activity Prediction Expert System with 3D-QSAR." Robert Clark, Joseph Leonard, and Alexander Strizhev emphasize the importance of molecular alignment in Chapter 9: "Pharmacophore Models and Comparative Molecular Field Analysis (CoMFA)." Finally, Hong Li, Jon Sutter, and Rémy Hoffmann bring the description of the methodology under Catalyst/HypoGen in Chapter 10 entitled "HypoGen: An Automated System for Generating 3D Predictive Pharmacophore Models."

Chapters 11 through 17 involve various applications of analog-based pharmacophores and success stories. Chapter 11 introduces some scoring techniques for pharmacophores and hit lists including "Metric for Analyzing Hit Lists and Pharmacophores," written by Osman Güner and Douglas Henry. Different database querying strategies are introduced by Osman Güner, Marvin Waldman, Rémy Hoffmann, and Jong-Hoon Kim in Chapter 12 entitled "Strategies in Database Mining and Pharmacophore Development." Evaluation of automated methods is presented in Chapter 13, "Pharmacophore Modeling by Automated Methods: Possibilities and Limitations," by Morten Langgård, Berith Bjørnholm, and Klaus Gundertofte. A successful example of the identification of novel structures is provided by James Kaminski, Dinanath Rane, and Marnie Rothofsky in Chapter 14 entitled "Database Mining Using Pharmacophore Models to Discover Novel Structural Prototypes." Other successes with pharmacophores are described in Chapters 15 through 17 with "Predicting Drug-Drug Interactions *in Silico* using Pharmacophores: A Paradigm for the Next Millennium" by Sean Ekins, Barbara Ring, Gianpaolo Bravi, James Wikel, and Steven Wrighton. "Feature-Based Pharmacophores: Applications to Some Biological Systems" by Rémy Hoffmann, Hong Li, and Thierry Langer; and "Pharmacophore Definition of Retinoid-X-Receptor Specific Ligands" by Steven K. White.

Part III deals with more recent ideas on receptor-based pharmacophores. It starts with "Receptor-Based Pharmacophore Perception and Modeling" in Chapter 18 by Venkatachalam, Paul Kirchhoff, and Marvin Waldman, Followed by Chapter 19 where Bert Thomas IV, Diane Joseph-McCarthy, and Juan Alvarez describe "Pharmacophore-Based Molecular Docking." Successful applications of receptor-based pharmacophores are presented in the next two Chapters 20 and 21: "Pharmacophores Including Multiple Excluded Volumes Derived from X-Ray Crystallographic Structures of Nuclear Receptors: Their Application in 3D Database Searching and 3D-QSAR" by Mikael

Gillner and Paulette Greenidge, and "Docking-Derived Pharmacophores from Models of Receptor-Ligand Complexes" by Renate Griffith, John Bremner, and Burak Coban. The complications arising from the flexibility of the receptor structure is covered by Kevin Masukawa, Heather Carlson, and Andrew McCammon in Chapter 22 entitled "Technique for Developing a Pharmacophore Model That Accommodates Inherent Protein Flexibility: An Application to HIV-1 Integrase."

Part IV provides new ideas and algorithms in pharmacophore development. It starts with a contribution from Sandra Handschuh and Johann Gasteiger in Chapter 23 entitled "Pharmacophores Derived from the 3D Substructure Perception." Isaac Bersuker, Süleyman Bahçeci, and James Boggs present "The Electron-Conformational Method of Identification of Pharmacophore and Anti-Pharmacophore Shielding" a novel perspective towards pharmacophore identification. Ali Özkabak, Mitchell Miller, Douglas Henry, and Osman Güner discuss the concept of pharmacophore optimization in Chapter 25, "Development and Optimization of Property-Based Pharmacophores." An enhancement to predictive pharmacophore model generation, "Effect of Variable Weights and Tolerances on Predictive Model Generation," is introduced in Chapter 26 by Jon Sutter, Osman Güner, Rémy Hoffmann, Hong Li, and Marvin Waldman

Finally, Chapter 27 provides a closing with John Van Drie's perception of the future directions in this area.

If you are new to this area, you should start with Chapters 1, 2, 3, and 27 for an introduction; then move on to the desired software discussions, DISCO at 4, HipHop at 5, GASP at 6, Chem-X at 7, Apex-3D at 8, CoMFA at 9, and HypoGen at 10. If you feel you still need to be persuaded that these approaches are effective, you will want to read Chapters 14, 15, 16, and 17 for some real-world success stories.

Seasoned database searchers who want to improve their skills should first understand the limitations outlined in Chapter 26, and then enrich their portfolio of different querying techniques with Chapter 25. Finally, they can learn how to analyze their hit lists by reading Chapter 11.

If the receptor structure is available and you want to use it to improve your pharmacophore models, different techniques in this area are described in Chapters 18 and 19 and successful applications of receptor-based pharmacophores are presented at sections 20 and 21. You should also read chapter 22 to appreciate the conformational flexibility of the receptor structure and its impact on pharmacophore models.

If you are involved in development of software tools in this area, several new ideas and algorithms are detailed in Chapters 23, 24, and 26. If you are interested in automating the pharmacophore optimization process, Chapter 25 provides good ideas and Chapter 11 provides some scoring functions that can be used for this purpose.

To get the full picture of pharmacophores, it is always good to go back and read Chapters 1 and 27 for a historical perspective and future directions.

In closing, consider the history of aviation with the very first flight taking place in the early 1900s and, the moon landing a mere 50 years later. Contrast this to the first use of the term "pharmacophore." It was first used in early 1900s as Peter Gund explains in Chapter 1; however, the meaning of the definition remained remarkably unperturbed during its close to 90 years of existence. Today, pharmacophores are considered one of the most important types of "information" that can be obtained from receptor-ligand interactions. Yet, quite surprisingly, this book is the first book that has the word "pharmacophore" in its title. We therefore wanted to be very comprehensive in this first volume, covering all aspects of pharmacophore perception, development, and use in drug design. We hope that you will find this book useful to bring your computer-aided drug design endeavor to a higher level.

Happy discoveries...

Osman F. Güner

Contributors

Juan C. Alvarez
Biological Chemistry Department,
Wyeth Research,
87 Cambridge Park Drive,
Cambridge, MA 02140, USA
jalvarez@genetics.com

Süleyman Bahçeci
Department of Chemistry and Biochemistry,
The University of Texas at Austin,
Austin, TX 78712, USA
suleyman@eeyore.cm.utexas.edu

Isaac B. Bersuker
Department of Chemistry and Biochemistrry and College of Pharmacy
The University of Texas at Austin,
Austin, TX 78712
bersuker@eeyore.cm.utexas.edu

Denise D. Beusen
1118 Dunston Drive,
St. Louis, MO 63146, USA
beusen@i1.net (eye-one-dot-net)

Berith Bjørnholm
Department of Computational Chemistry,
H. Lundbeck A/S
Ottiliavej 9,
DK-2500 Valby, Denmark
bbj@lundbeck.com

James E. Boggs
Department of Chemistry and Biochemistry,
The University of Texas in Austin,
Austin, TX 78712, USA
james.boggs@mail.utexas.edu

Gianpaolo Bravi
Glaxo Wellcome R&D,
Medicines Research Centre,
Gunnels Wood Road,
Stevenage, Herts SG1 2NY, UK
gb94807@ggr.uk.com

John B. Bremner
Department of Chemistry,
University of Wollongong,
Northfields Avenue,
Wollongong, NSW 2522, Australia
john_bremner@uow.edu.au

Heather A. Carlson
Department of Chemistry and Biochemistry,
University of California at San Diego,
9500 Gilman Drive,
La Jolla, CA 92093-0365, USA
hcarlson@ucsd.edu

Stephen J. Cato
Oxford Molecular Group Inc.,
11350 McCormick Rd.,
Executive Plaza 3, Suite 1100.
Hunt Valley, MD 21031-1045, USA
scato@oxmol.com

Robert D. Clark
Tripos, Inc.,
1699 S. Hanley Road,
St. Louis, MO 63144, USA
bclark@tripos.com

Omoshile O. Clement
Molecular Simulations Inc.,
9685 Scranton Road,
San Diego, CA 92121, USA
oclement@msi.com

Burak Coban
Zonguldak Karaelmas University,
Department of Chemistry,
Zonguldak, 67100 Turkey
bc70@hotmail.com

Sean Ekins
Lilly Research Laboratories,
Lilly Corporate Center,
Drop Code 0825,
Indianapolis, IN 46285, USA
ekins_sean@lilly.com

Johann Gasteiger
Universität Erlangen-Nürnberg,
Computer-Chemie-Centrum,
Institut für Organische Chemie,
Nägelsbachstrasse 25,
D-91052 Erlangen, Germany
Gasteiger@ccc.chemie.uni-erlangen.de

Mikael Gillner
Karo Bio AB, Novum,
S-141 57 Huddinge, Sweden
Mikael.Gillner@karobio.se

Robert C. Glen
University Chemical Laboratory,
University of Cambridge,
Lensfield Rd.,
Cambridge, CB2 1EW, UK
rcg28@cam.ac.uk

Valerie Golender
Mutek Solution, Ltd.,
24 Hachoroshet street,
Or-Yehuda, 60200, Israel
valery@actcom.co.il, valery@mutek.com

Paulette Greenidge
Thrombosis Research Institute,
London, SW3 6LR, UK
paulette@tri-london.ac.uk

Renate Griffith
Department of Chemistry,
University of Wollongong,
Northfields Avenue,
Wollongong, NSW 2522, Australia
renate_griffith@uow.edu.au

Peter Gund
Pharmacopeia Inc.,
CN5350 Princeton, NJ 08543, USA
pgund@pharmacop.com

Klaus Gundertofte
Department of Computational Chemistry,
H. Lundbeck A/S
Ottiliavej 9,
DK-2500 Valby, Denmark
kgu@lundbeck.com

Osman F. Güner
Molecular Simulations Inc.,
9685 Scranton Road,
San Diego, CA 92121, USA
osman@msi.com

Sandra Handschuh
Universität Erlangen-Nürnberg,
Computer-Chemie-Centrum,
Institut für Organische Chemie,
Nägelsbachstrasse 25,
D-91052 Erlangen, Germany
Handschuh@ccc.chemie.uni-erlangen.de

Douglas Henry
MDL Information Systems, Inc.,
14600 Catalina Street,
San Leandro, CA 94577-6604, USA
dough@mdli.com

Rémy Hoffmann
Molecular Simulations SARL,
Parc Club Orsay Université,
20 rue Jean Rostand,
91893 Orsay Cédex, France
remy@msi-eu.com

Gareth Jones
Arena Pharmaceuticals Inc.,
6166 Nancy Ridge Drive,
San Diego, CA 92121, USA
GJones@arenapharm.com

Diane Joseph-McCarthy
Biological Chemistry Department,
Wyeth Research,
87 Cambridge Park Drive,
Cambridge, MA 02140, USA
djoseph@genetics.com

James Kaminski
Schering-Plough Research Institute,
2015 Galloping Hill Road,
Kenilworth, NJ 07033, USA
james.kaminski@spcorp.com

Jonghoon Kim
R&D Center,
Cheil Jedang Corp.,
522-1 Tokpyong-ri Majang-myon
Ichon-si Kyonggi-do, Korea
kjh@cheiljedang.com

Paul Kirchhoff
Molecular Simulations Inc.,
9685 Scranton Road,
San Diego, CA 92121, USA
paulk@msi.com

Thierry Langer
University of Innsbruck,
Institute of Pharmaceutical Chemistry,
Innrain 52a,
A-6020, Innsbruck, Austria
Thierry.Langer@uibk.ac.at

Morten Langgård
Department of Computational Chemistry,
H. Lundbeck A/S
Ottiliavej 9,
DK-2500 Valby, Denmark
mol@lundbeck.com

Joseph M. Leonard
Tripos, Inc.,
1699 S. Hanley Road,
St. Louis, MO 63144, USA
jleonard@tripos.com

Hong Li
ChemInnovation Software, Inc.
8190-E Mira Mesa Blvd., #108,
San Diego, CA 92126, USA
henryl@cheminnovation.com

Garland R. Marshall
Center for Molecular Design, Box 8036,
Washington University School of Medicine
700 S. Euclid, St. Louis, MO 63110, USA
garland@ibc.wustl.edu

Yvonne C. Martin
Pharmaceutical Products Division,
Abbott Laboratories,
100 Abbott Park Road,
Abbott Park, IL 60064-6100, USA
yvonne.c.martin@abbott.com

Kevin M. Masukawa
Department of Chemistry and Biochemistry,
University of California at San Diego,
9500 Gilman Drive,
La Jolla, CA 92093-0365, USA
kmasuka@itsa.ucsf.edu

J. Andrew McCammon
Department of Chemistry and Biochemistry, Department of Pharmacology,
University of California at San Diego,
9500 Gilman Drive, 4202 Urey Hall,
La Jolla, CA 92093-0365, USA
jmccammon@ucsd.edu

Adrea Trope Mehl
Molecular Simulations Inc.,
100 N. State Street, Studio # 400,
Ephrata, PA 17522, USA
adrea@msi.com

Mitchell A. Miller
NetGenics, Inc.
1717 E. 9th Street,
Cleveland, OH 44114, USA
mmiller@netgenics.com

Ali G. Özkabak
MDL Information Systems, Inc.,
14600 Catalina Street,
San Leandro, CA 94577-6604, USA
alio@mdli.com

Dinanath Rane
Schering-Plough Research Institute,
2015 Galloping Hill Road,
Kenilworth, NJ 07033, USA
dinanath.rane@spcorp.com

Barbara J. Ring
Eli Lilly & Co.,
Lilly Corporate Center
Indianapolis, IN 46285, USA
ring_barbara_j@lilly.com

Marnie L. Rothofsky
Schering-Plough Research Institute,
2015 Galloping Hill Road,
Kenilworth, NJ 07033, USA
marnie.mcguirk@spcorp.com

Alexander Strizhev
Tripos, Inc.,
1699 S. Hanley Road,
St. Louis, MO 63144, USA
strizhev@tripos.com

Jon Sutter
Molecular Simulations Inc.,
9685 Scranton Road,
San Diego, CA 92121, USA
jms@msi.com

Bert E. Thomas IV
Biological Chemistry Department,
Wyeth Research,
87 Cambridge Park Drive,
Cambridge, MA 02140, USA
bthomas@genetics.com

John H. Van Drie
Pharmacia & Upjohn,
301 S. Henrietta Street,
Kalamazoo, MI 49001
vandrie@mindspring.com

C. M. Venkatachalam
Molecular Simulations Inc.,
9685 Scranton Road,
San Diego, CA 92121, USA
venkat@msi.com

Erich R. Vorpagel
Pacific Northwest National Laboratory,
Environmental Molecular Sciences Laboratory,
3335 Q Avenue, MS K8-91,
Richland, WA 99352, USA
erich.vorpagel@pnl.gov

Marvin Waldman
Molecular Simulations Inc.,
9685 Scranton Road,
San Diego, CA 92121, USA
marvin@msi.com

Steven K. White
Ligand Pharmaceuticals,
10275 Science Center Drive,
San Diego, CA 92121, USA
swhite@ligand.com

James H. Wikel
Lilly Research Laboratories,
Eli Lilly & Co.,
Indianapolis, IN 46285, USA
jimw@lilly.com

Peter Willett
Department of Information Studies,
University of Sheffield,
Western Bank, Sheffield, S10 2TN, UK
p.willett@sheffield.ac.uk

Steven Wrighton
Eli Lilly & Co.,
Lilly Corporate Center,
Indianapolis, IN 46285, USA
wrighton_steven_a@lilly.com

PART I

✦

The Origins of Pharmacophore Research

✦

- **Evolution of the Pharmacophore Concept in Pharmaceutical Research**

1

Evolution of the Pharmacophore Concept in Pharmaceutical Research

Peter Gund

Abstract

Early explorations on the relationship between chemical structure and biological activity led to the postulation of drug-receptor theory by Ehrlich, Langley, and others around the end of the nineteenth century. A tenet of the theory was that certain functionality of the active molecules, called a pharmacophore, conferred the activity. Later it became clear that the disposition in 3-dimensional space of the functionality, in a pharmacophoric pattern, was also important. The first computer program to find such patterns, and a prototype database of modeled structures for searching, were created at Princeton University in 1974. This chapter briefly traces the rise of commercial pharmacophore searching and discovery software, and large structure databases, from these origins; and suggests some areas of likely further development.

1

Evolution of the Pharmacophore Concept in Pharmaceutical Research

Peter Gund

Pharmacopeia Inc., Princeton, New Jersey

Since before the start of recorded history, mankind has sought to treat illnesses and infirmities. There are two major traditions for this early pharmaceutical research: the empirical discovery of healing potions and poultices, and the use of transformed or altered materials for medicinal purposes. Those who preferred natural medicines followed the teachings of Galenus (A.D. 131-200), a Roman naturalist who contended that herbal mixtures could cure all conceivable health problems.[1] Those willing to use unnatural materials followed an alchemical tradition, which probably derived from metallurgy, and which reached its highest medical incarnation in the work of Paracelsus in the sixteenth century. Alchemists taught that suitably refined and transformed materials, such as the mythical "philosopher's stone" dissolved in a little wine, could cure human ills, restore youthfulness, and prolong life.[2] Both traditions have continued to modern times, with blurring of the borders as active principals of naturalists' concoctions have been isolated and improved synthetically.

Louis Pasteur demonstrated in the middle of the nineteenth century that many diseases were caused by microbes or parasites. Researchers recognized that materials could be tested on these micro-organisms to identify compounds likely to help against disease. Also around this time, organic chemists began studying the synthesis of coloring agents, since several synthetic dyes made by Perkins and others had been commercial successes. These researchers discovered that it was often possible to leave the molecular skeleton of the dye compound intact and vary the attached functional groups in order to obtain a variety of colors and related properties. That part of a molecule essential for imparting color was termed a "chromophore."

Near the end of the nineteenth century, during his M.D. thesis research, Paul Ehrlich discovered that different dyes selectively stained different tissues. In this way he discovered eosinophils and basophils (white blood cells named by their affinity to eosine and basic dyes). He similarly identified mast cells and three types of erythrocytes. He discovered dyes which specifically stained tubercle bacillus and malarial plasmodia, and demonstrated that the latter dye (methylene blue) could cure a patient of malaria. Around 1903, Ehrlich began testing dyes and other compounds for their ability to kill trypanosones, a microorganism that causes African sleeping sickness and other serious diseases. He and others discovered three different classes of effective drugs, as well as the phenomenon of drug resistance: Some trypanosomes became resistant to the drugs of one class while retaining sensitivity to drugs of the other classes. Later Ehrlich embarked on the first large-scale project for synthesis and testing of potential chemotherapeutic agents, and his 606th compound, an arsenical which he named Salvarsan, proved to be a highly effective treatment for syphilis. He coined the term "chemotherapy" to describe the use of such synthetic agents to treat disease.

Ehrlich had earlier studied the effect of toxins, such as diphtheria toxin. He suggested that they had "haptophoric" groups, which allowed them to be attached to the cell, and separate "toxophoric" groups which caused the toxic effect. (Much the way that dye molecules have groups, separate from the chromophore, that "fix" the dye to fabric). Ehrlich initially resisted extending this idea to drug molecules, because many drugs did not seem to combine irreversibly with the cells the way toxins do. But he soon began to argue that cells had "chemoreceptors" (e.g., an arsenoreceptor which bound arsenicals), and that drugs had to bind to these receptors before they could exert their medicinal effect. Ehrlich coined the term "pharmacophore" to describe the groups of a drug molecule that are essential for imparting biological activity.[3]

Ehrlich assumed that chemoreceptors were involved in normal physiological functions, and therefore existed in all cells. Thus he realized that the search for the "magic bullet" which killed the microbe without effect on the host was doomed to failure; the best researchers can hope to do is maximize efficacy and minimize toxicity.

John Langley contributed to the theory by noticing that nicotine and curare appeared to combine with and compete for the same protoplasmic substance involved in eliciting muscle action. In work published in 1905, he called this cell constituent a "receptive substance," and speculated that many drugs and poisons acted by a similar mechanism.[4]

Ehrlich and Langley (among others) thus developed a somewhat simplistic "drug-receptor" formulation of drug action, which envisioned a "lock and key" type of interaction.[5] They developed this into a quantitative model, which "explained" the observed receptor on- and off-rates for particular ligands. Drug-receptor theory thus became one of the fundamental tenets of pharmacology.

As molecular structure concepts were developed early in the twentieth century, including conformational and chirality effects on structure and reactivity, there was increasing success in "explaining" the effect on bioactivity of varying the ligand's structure. Similarly, it became clear that the presence of pharmacophoric groups was insufficient for activity—they needed to be presented to the receptor in an acceptable geometry for "recognition." Kaufman and Kerman[6] distinguished between topologic and topographic pharmacophoric patterns. Topologic patterns refer to the connectivity between the atoms and/or groups, in a graph theoretical sense; topographic patterns refer to the arrangement of the molecular components in three-dimensional space. In an influential book, Korolkovas[7] listed a great many pharmacophoric patterns that had been suggested to be associated with bioactivity.

Confidence in drug-receptor theory grew much stronger when the crystal structures of ribonuclease and other enzymes became available. The dihydrofolate reductase enzyme crystal structure, with the anticancer drug methotrexate bound to it, was particularly revealing.[8] As the number of known protein structures has grown, many more structural models have been generated based on their homology to known crystal structures.

Another conceptual breakthrough related to the question of whether chemical forces were sufficient to explain drug-receptor action and other aspects of pharmacology, or whether some additional "vital force" had yet to be discovered. A careful analysis of intermolecular forces by Wolfenden[9] provided a rationale for explaining rates of drug-receptor action and enzyme catalysis through chemical forces alone. This has evolved into the very elaborate present-day calculations of ligand-receptor binding energy, which take into account solvation effects, the dynamic motion of ligand and receptor, and linear free-energy perturbation estimation of the effects of structure alterations.

The pharmacophores summarized by Korolkovas, and in later reviews by Gund,[10,11] Humblet and Marshall,[12] and others, represented a new paradigm for medicinal chemists to summarize their insight into the effects of chemical structure on bioactivity. By looking at structures of active and inactive analogs (topologic patterns), and considering the possible three-dimensional structures of these molecules (topographic patterns), they could often postulate a pharmacophore as the "essence" of the structure-activity knowledge they had gained. Initially, topographic patterns were postulated based on measuring distances on a Dreiding model of a molecule, or by computing the distances in small molecule crystal structures. Determining whether a putative pharmacophoric pattern was present in some other potential ligand, however, was a tedious and difficult undertaking. It became obvious that a computer program could facilitate this process.

An early attempt at such a program was developed at Princeton University in the early 1970s.[10,13] This work defined the concepts of pharmacophoric pattern chirality; pharmacophore orientation and accessibility (which govern the ability of the pattern components to approach complementary receptor functionality); pharmacophore indefiniteness (ability to accommodate multiple atom types at a site, and pattern variability due to allowed ranges of interatomic distances). It also emphasized the importance of computer graphics to aid the medicinal chemist in evaluating and understanding the pharmacophoric patterns.

This early work recognized, but did not solve, the general problem of defining the pharmacophoric patterns for computerized searching. Generating the pharmacophore as a list of atom pairs and their allowed distances did not assure correspondence to a physically realizable pattern: this problem was later solved by Crippen[14] using the technique of distance geometry. An easier pharmacophore definition method was to abstract and edit the coordinate positions of the important functionality from a 3D structure of an active ligand. General interfaces for defining pharmacophores were created in commercial products from MDL Informations Systems, San Leandro CA (MACCS-3D and ISIS-3D); Oxford Molecular Group, Oxford U.K. (Chem-X); Tripos Inc., St. Louis MO (DISCO); and Molecular Simulations, San Diego CA

(Catalyst). The problem of defining pharmacophores by complementarity to receptor structures has been attacked by such programs as DISCO (available from Tripos), and Ludi and MCSS (available from Molecular Simulations).

Similarly, it was recognized early on that one needed a large database of 3D molecular structures that could be searched for the presence of pharmacophores. In addition to molecular crystal structures, a number of databases of "theoretical" 3D molecular structures have since become available from MDL Information Systems (e.g., Available Chemicals Directory ACD-3D) and others, or could be generated as needed by application of such programs as CONCORD (available from Tripos).

A major advance involved solving the difficult problem of automatically detecting a pharmacophore from a collection of compounds tested against an assay. This was solved in the program Catalyst (available from Molecular Simulations Inc.) and its variant, HIPHOP, which automatically find common pharmacophores among active compounds in a multiconformation structure database (also generated by Catalyst).

Another major effort has focused on dealing with the steric environment of molecules fulfilling a pharmacophoric pattern; the pattern may be used to align the structures, then a surface can be "draped" over the active molecules to define an allowed region. Among the several programs that deal with this problem, is Catalyst/Shape (Molecular Simulations Inc.).

Recent efforts have focused on making the methods more efficient for application to databases of thousands or even millions of compounds, such as the Chemical Abstracts Services (Columbus, OH) 3D database of published compounds and of large combinatorial chemistry-generated libraries.

In summary, the last 30 years have seen remarkable progress in the development of computer-assisted methods of discovering molecules with useful biological properties. However, empirical screening is also making a comeback, due to advances in high-throughput screening (HTS) and high-throughput synthesis (parallel chemistry, combinatorial chemistry). The so-called "rational" methods are also providing important guidance in selection of compounds for screening (data mining) and for design of promising compounds and libraries for testing. The drug-receptor theory of drug action has given rise to the techniques of mechanism-based design, pharmacophore-based design, structure-based design, SAR-based design, cheminformatics-based design, and others described in the following chapters of this volume. As these techniques evolve further, and are coupled with improved experimental techniques, there is every reason to believe that development of new therapies will continue to accelerate.

References

1. Burger A: **History and economics of medicinal chemistry.** In: *Medicinal Chem* 3rd Edit., part I. Burger A, ed., New York: Wiley, 1970:4.

2. Burkhardt, T: *Alchemy.* Baltimore: Penguin Books, 1971.

3. Ehrlich P: **Über den jetzigen Stand der Chemotherapie.** *Chem Ber* 1909, **42**:17. Quoted by Ariens, EJ: **Molecular Pharmacology, a Basis for Drug Design.** *Progr Drug Res* 1966, **10**:429.

4. 4. Parascandola J: **Origins of the receptor theory.** *Trends in Pharmacol Sci* 1980, **1**:189-192.

5. Clark AJ: *The Mode of Action of Drugs on Cells.* London: E. Arnold & Co., 1933.

6. Kaufman JJ, Kerman E: **Quantum chemical and other theoretical techniques for the understanding of the psychoactive action of phenothiazines.** In: *The Phenothiazines and Structurally Related Drugs.* Forrest, I.S., Carr, C.J., Usdin, E., eds., New York: Raven, 1974:55.

7. Korolkovas A: *Essentials of Molecular Pharmacology. Background for Drug Design.* New York: Interscience, 1970.

8. Mathews DA, Alden RA, Bolin JT, Filman DJ, Freer ST, Hamlin R, Hol WG, Kislink RL, Pastore EJ, Plante LT, Xuong N, Kraut J: **Dihydrofolate reductase from** *Lactobacillus Casei.* **X-ray structure of the enzyme-methotrexate-NADPH complex.** *J Biol Chem* 1978, **253**:6946-6954.

9. Wolfenden R: **Transition state analog inhibitors and enzyme catalysis.** *Ann Rev Biophys Bioeng* 1976, **5**:271-306.

10. Gund P: **Three-dimensional pharmacophoric pattern searching.** In: *Progress in Molecular and Subcellular Biology*, vol. 5, Hahn, F.E., ed., Berlin: Springer-Verlag, 1977:117-143.

11. Gund P: **Pharmacophoric pattern searching and receptor mapping.** *Ann Reports Med Chem* 1979, **14**:299-308.

12. Humblet C, Marshall FR: **Pharmacophore identification of receptor mapping.** *Ann Reports Med Chem* 1980, **15**:267-276.

13. Gund P, Wipke W.T, Langridge R: **Computer searching of a molecular structure file for pharmacophoric patterns.** In: *Proc Intl. Conf on Computers in Chem Res and Educa,* Ljubljana, July 12-17, 1973, Amsterdam: Elsevier, 1974, **3**:5/33-39.

14. Crippen GM: **A novel approach to calculation of conformation: Distance Geometry.** *J Comp Phys* 1977, **24**:96-107.

PART II

Analog-Based Pharmacophores

- **Manual Pharmacophore Generation**

- **Pharmacophore Definition**

- **Automated Pharmacophore Development Systems**

- **Predictive Model Development: 3D QSAR**

- **Application in Drug Design**

2

Manual Pharmacophore Generation: Visual Pattern Recognition

Osman F. Güner

Abstract

In this chapter, the practical concept of pharmacophore perception is explored. The readers are provided an opportunity to examine a small number of biologically active compounds and to identify common features. Following several straightforward procedural steps, we develop a simple, yet very effective pharmacophore model for Cardiotonic drugs (phosphodiesterase inhibitors). Through such visual pattern recognition, one can develop the basis of a pharmacophore model that can be used to screen 3D databases. This basic understanding is the essence of pharmacophore modeling. Computers are handy when the pattern among the active compounds is not apparent. Consideration of the relative activities in pharmacophore development provides predictive pharmacophore models. Evolution of pharmacophore development tools now enables us perception of a pharmacophore within a receptor active site. Nevertheless, the very first step in developing a pharmacophore model is recognition of a pattern that exists among the active compounds but missing in inactive ones.

2

Manual Pharmacophore Generation: Visual Pattern Recognition

Osman F. Güner

Molecular Simulations Inc., San Diego, California

How does one go about identifying a pharmacophore model from a series of active compounds? How does one go about obtaining it from an active site of a receptor, or from a complex of receptor with ligand? All of these topics are covered within this and the later chapters. Before we go into the details of any particular approach, let's go through the process of identification of a possible pharmacophore model. As a good learning exercise, we will develop our first pharmacophore model manually. The process involves the following steps:

1. Visual identification of common structural and chemical features among the active molecules and those that are missing in the inactive ones.

2. Measurement of the 3D aspects of the common features with each other.

3. Development of a draft pharmacophore.

4. Validation that the pharmacophore fits the active compounds and fails to fit the inactive ones.

5. Refinement of the model by applying it to a database of compounds with known activity, until the desired result is obtained.

Now let us apply this procedure to the four cardiotonic compounds displayed in Plate 2.1.

Step 1. Visual pattern recognition:

i.   One can tell from a quick glance at the structures that all four compounds contain an aromatic ring that can be either phenyl or pyridyl.

ii. They all contain a second ring system that can be a 5- or 6-membered ring.

iii. The second ring system contains either a ureic group or an amide functionality (the last two points can be summarized as 5- or 6-membered lactam being present).

iv. The two ring systems are side-by-side (not necessarily co-planar but also not perpendicular to each other).

Step 2. Measurements:

i.   From the amide nitrogen to the center of the aromatic ring is about 5-6 Å

ii. The aromatic ring and the amide group are within 0.5 Å RMS deviation from planarity.

Step 3. Development of pharmacophore model:

i.   The model displayed in Plate 2.2 defines the aromatic ring as either phenyl or pyridyl, depending on whether the distinguishing atom is nitrogen or carbon.

ii. The five- or six-membered ring is defined with the link option of having one or two methylene units.

iii. The presence of an additional nitrogen is allowed next to the carbonyl carbon, and double bonds are allowed in various parts of the ring with "any" bond types.

iv. Finally, the observed measurements of the distance and planarity constraints are placed.

This model is displayed in Plate 2.2.

What does one do with such a model? There are several important uses for pharmacophore models.

The most obvious next step is 3D database searching with the objective of identifying potential leads. At this point, several different types of databases can be screened with the pharmacophore model:

1.   Corporate databases: to identify lead candidates from a company's own existing compounds.

2. Commercially available chemicals databases (e.g., Maybridge, ACD): to identify compounds available for purchase that already contain the desired pharmacophore. They can be sent for testing directly or can be used as synthetic precursors for potential new compounds.

3. Databases of structures with known biological activities (e.g., MDDR, CMC, WDI): for validating that the pharmacophore model retrieves compounds with correct activities, or securing patent coverage or evaluating other companies' patent coverage.

4. Other 3D structural databases or virtual libraries may be useful for identifying compounds for screening or those that can be synthesized.

Figure 2.1 displays one of the cardiotonic hits obtained from MDDR-3D database with the query we have developed above. This query retrieves a very large number of the known cardiotonic drugs following a 3D database search.

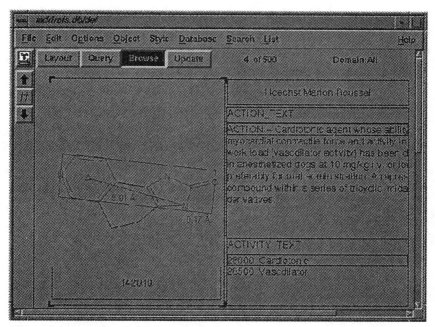

Figure 2.1. A cardiotonic hit from 3D search of MDDR-3D is displayed. Highlighted is the exact way the compound in the database fits onto the query. The search was performed with ISIS/3D.

Another use of a pharmacophore model is in the area of activity/property prediction. This in a sense resembles a QSAR approach that is applied to 3D pharmacophoric features. Several examples are provided in this chapter. The objective with this approach is to develop a predictive model based on how well particular compounds fit to a particular model in such a way that the activity distribution of the compounds in a training set is well correlated. Once a good model is obtained, one can use this model to predict activities for other relevant compounds.

The above are the two primary uses of a pharmacophore model. However, other potential uses of pharmacophore models include library focusing, evaluation and prioritization of virtual high throughput screening (vHTS) results, and *de novo* design.

The procedure we discussed above is loosely called "analog-based design." The following chapters will go through several technologies and programs that have been developed in this area and provide some examples of successful application of these techniques in drug design. Starting with the "active analog approach" in Chapter 3, various automated pharmacophore development programs are discussed in Chapters 4-7 and programs that develop predictive pharmacophore models are discussed in Chapters 8-10. The applications of these methods in drug design are presented in Chapters 11-17.

3

Pharmacophore Definition Using the Active Analog Approach

Denise D. Beusen and Garland R. Marshall

Abstract

The Active Analog Approach enables determination of the common three-dimensional arrangement of key interaction sites in a receptor-ligand complex from the sets of conformations accessible to a series of high affinity, flexible ligands. Systematic search is used to enumerate all possible conformations of each ligand and from them derive all possible shared orientations of the key functional groups. In this review, we discuss enhancements in sampling and speed that have removed some of the historical limitations in using systematic search. Parameters that impact the speed and sampling properties of systematic search are reviewed. In addition, general approaches to applying the Active Analog Approach and analyzing the results are presented.

3

Pharmacophore Definition Using the Active Analog Approach

Denise D. Beusen and Garland R. Marshall

St. Louis, Missouri
Washington University, St. Louis, Missouri

3.1. Introduction

Although modern methods in molecular biology and biophysics have enhanced the likelihood that a drug discovery effort will be based on a detailed atomic structure of the target, the fact is that pharmacology generally precedes receptor structural data. In most cases, the medicinal chemist is forced to offer novel compounds to the target and hope for consistent responses which enable inference of its three-dimensional structure. Ideally, the resulting operational model provides predictive value when considering new compounds for synthesis and biological testing.

The intellectual framework for utilizing structure-activity data to extrapolate information regarding the receptor is the pharmacophore. A concept introduced by Ehrlich at the turn of the century, the pharmacophore is the critical three-dimensional arrangement of molecular fragments (or distribution of electron density) that is recognized by the receptor and, in the case of agonists, causes subsequent activation of the receptor upon binding. In other words, some parts of the molecule are essential for interaction, and they must be capable of assuming a particular three-dimensional pattern that is complementary to the receptor in order to interact favorably. The pharmacophore construct leads to a problem statement composed of two processes. First is the determination, by chemical modification and biological testing, of the relative importance of different functional groups in the drug to receptor recognition. This can give some indication of the nature of the functional groups in the receptor responsible for binding to the set of drugs. Second, a hypothesis is proposed concerning correspondence between functional groups in different congeneric series of the drug.

3.2. The Active Analog Approach

If one assumes that a common binding mode exists for two or more compounds, then one can use computational methods to verify its geometric feasibility. The aim of the Active Analog Approach[1] is to deduce the common three-dimensional arrangement of key interaction sites in a receptor-ligand complex from the sets of conformations accessible to a series of high affinity, flexible ligands. One approach is to generate the set of minimum energy conformations for each ligand and then to align them in an effort to identify a conformation of each ligand that superimposes the designated functional groups. A successful alignment demonstrates the geometrical plausibility of the current pharmacophore hypothesis. This geometrical arrangement may be only one of many arrangements possible, however, due to the inherent flexibility of most ligands. The second approach attempts to enumerate systematically all possible conformations of each ligand and from them derive all possible shared orientations of the key functional groups. The latter approach can directly address the question of whether or not the common pattern is unique.

We have employed systematic search[2,3] in our applications of the Active Analog Approach[4,5] to generate the set of sterically allowed conformations based on a grid search of the torsional variables at a given angle increment. In contrast to stochastic methods such as distance geometry and molecular dynamics, systematic search methods are algorithmic. Each and every grid point is evaluated in a systematic fashion to determine its validity. The path through the grid points is regular and defined. In principle, systematic search can, within the resolution of the grid, identify all sterically allowed conformations of a molecule. Consequently, systematic search is an ideal tool for conformational analysis because it is not path dependent and cannot become entrapped in local minima.

For each sterically allowed conformation, the distances between the postulated pharmacophoric groups are measured (Figure 3.1). This set of distances, each of which represents a unique pharmacophoric pattern, constitutes an IMAP (information map, also referred to as an OMAP, or orientation map). The binding site geometries are represented as points in distance space (Figure 3.1), where each dimension represents an internuclear distance between points in different pharmacophoric groups. Each point of the IMAP is simply a submatrix of the distance matrix and, as such, is invariant to global translation and rotation of the molecule. Assuming that the same mode of interaction is common to the set of molecules under consideration, the IMAP for each active molecule must contain the pharmacophore pattern encrypted in its set of distances. The Active Analog Approach sequentially determines all the sterically allowed conformations for each molecule under consideration, generates an IMAP from those conformations, and computes the logical intersection of the IMAPs. This simple manipulation of IMAPs enables determination of patterns that are common to all of them. In essence, the distances found between pharmacophore elements in one molecule are used to constrain the conformational search of the next molecule in the series.

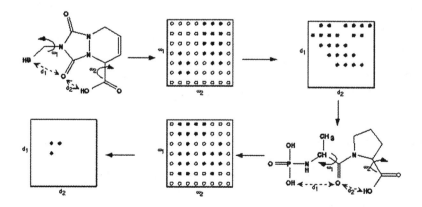

Figure 3.1. The flow of information in the Active Analog Approach. Sterically allowed conformations (represented by filled circles on the ω_1, ω_2 torsional grid) of a molecule are determined and the distances (d_1, d_2, etc.) between pharmacophore elements are recorded for each. The resulting OMAP (or IMAP) is used to constrain the next molecule in the series. Ideally, once all of the molecules have been evaluated, only a single point or cluster of points remains in the OMAP.

3.3. Systematic Search and the Rigid Geometry Approximation

The starting point for systematic search is a rigid geometry, in which bond lengths and bond angles are fixed at reasonable values. Atoms are represented by hard spheres, and bonds by lines connecting the atoms. The use of a rigid geometry eliminates variables and reduces the computational complexity of conformational analysis. There is experimental justification for this simplification in that the energetics of torsional deformation are significantly less than for bond length and bond angle distortion. Bond angle deformations from the ideal can be accommodated by appropriate adjustment of van der Waals radii.[6] Using this rigid starting geometry, torsion angles are varied in regular increments. At each resulting conformation, every atom pair in the molecule is examined to determine if they are in steric contact. In terms of energy, only the cost of forcing atoms to occupy the same space is considered. High-energy (sterically disallowed) conformations are eliminated from the list of conformers. While interaction with a receptor will certainly perturb the conformational energy surface of a flexible ligand, high affinity would suggest that the ligand binds in a conformation that is not exceptionally different from one of its low-energy minima. In these calculations, we do not consider solvation *per se* because our goal is to screen out only those conformations whose energy is high enough that they would be unlikely under any solvent conditions, including interaction with the receptor.

3.4. Combinatorial Nature of Systematic Search

The conceptual simplicity of systematic search stands in sharp contrast to the combinatorial complexity of its calculation. If T is the number of rotatable bonds in the molecule and A is the torsion angle increment, then the total number of possible conformers to be examined for steric conflict is $(360/A)^T$. If N is the number of atoms in a molecule, $N(N-1)/2$ pairwise van der Waals evaluations must be done for each conformation. Consequently, the number of pairwise van der Waals evaluations, V, required for a molecule during the course of a systematic search is given by $(360/A)^T \times N(N-1)/2$. Simply because of their sheer number, these van der Waals comparisons are the rate-limiting step in systematic search, and any algorithmic improvement, which reduces the number of van der Waals checks or enhances the efficiency of performing such checks, increases the feasibility of systematic search as a tool.

3.5. Strategies for Defeating the Combinatorial Explosion

In the simple analysis outlined above, the staggering growth of van der Waals checks places demands on computational resources that severely limit the size and number of molecules that can be analyzed. In reality, a brute force approach is not necessary, as there are strategies that truncate the combinatorial explosion. These enhancements extend the use of systematic search to much larger problems.

3.5.1. Rigid Body Rotations and Building Molecules from Aggregates

As shown in Figure 3.2, the possible conformations to be evaluated can be represented in a "search tree." "Once an "anchor" atom—the fixed reference point for all subsequent rotations—is selected, the structure of the search tree is defined. The termini of the branches represent all of the possible torsional settings for the molecule. A significant reduction in computational complexity can be realized by "pruning" the search tree—determining at an early fork that a branch or branches can be eliminated from further consideration.

In our approach to systematic search, molecule construction occurs simultaneously with the determination of angle ranges that may contain sterically allowed conformers, through the use of aggregates. These are sets of atoms whose relative positions are fixed (independent of torsional rotations) because of the rigid geometry approximation. In other

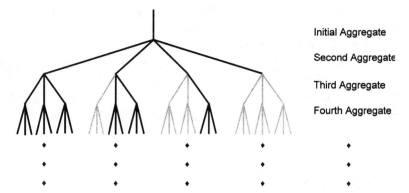

Initial Aggregate

Second Aggregate

Third Aggregate

Fourth Aggregate

Figure 3.2. The tree structure of systematic search. At each branch point, the possible addition of a new aggregate to the existing partial conformation is evaluated for steric contacts. Gray lines represent "pruning" of the search tree by eliminating from further consideration those branches in which the addition of an aggregate is not sterically allowed at any torsion setting. The process continues until the addition of all aggregates along every branch has been considered. Reprinted with permission from[2]. © 1996 Elsevier Science.

words, aggregates consist of atoms that are bonded to each other or share bonding to a third atom (a 1,3 relationship). In Figure 3.3, *n*-butane is divided into aggregates. Once identified, the pairwise distances within aggregates are eliminated from further van der Waals evaluations.

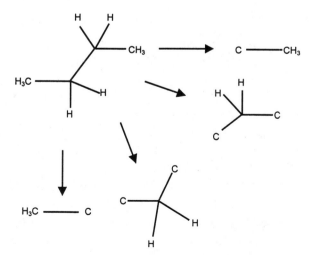

Figure 3.3. Decomposition of n-butane into aggregates.

We employ a "build-up" procedure which involves the stepwise addition of aggregates and evaluation of inter-aggregate van der Waals contacts at each point in the search tree (for a more detailed explanation, see prior published reports).[7,8] Partial conformations are sterically allowed combinations of aggregates representing branch points in the search tree. When there is no torsion setting that allows an aggregate to be added to the existing partial conformation such that it is sterically allowed, construction of that branch terminates. This process continues in every branch until the entire set of sterically allowed conformations is determined. In Figure 3.2, the gray portions of the search tree represent branches that were never considered in the build-up procedure because addition of an aggregate at an upstream branch point was not sterically allowed. It should be evident from Figure 3.2 that systematic search could involve many redundant calculations because the same adjacent aggregate contacts are evaluated in all branches of the tree. Whenever possible, these evaluations are done once and the information is stored in the form of angle tuples for recall instead of recalculating them.

We use distance constraint equations to analytically determine the possible angle ranges in which a new aggregate can be added such that there is no overlap of atoms in the new aggregate with those in the sterically allowed partial conformation. Assuming a rigid body rotation, the locus of possible positions of any atom in the new aggregate can be described as a circle (Figure 3.4) whose center lies on the axis of rotation (the bond connecting the partial conformation and the new aggregate). Equations which describe the variable distance between two atoms (for example, atom c and atom i in Figure 3.4) as a function of a single torsional variable between them have been described elsewhere.[7,8] These equations can be used to determine if the two atoms will:

1) be in contact regardless of the torsional rotation of the aggregate. This implies that the current partial conformation has to be discarded because there is no sterically allowed way to add the aggregate, and the search branch is truncated.

2) never come in contact for any value of the torsional rotation so that this pair of atoms does not need to be considered.

3) come in contact for some values of the torsional rotation that can be calculated for that pair. These segments of the torsional circle

are removed from consideration for other atom pairs in the aggregate and the existing partial conformation. If, when these disallowed ranges are unioned over all atom pairs, no segment of the torsional circle remains, then the new partial conformation of the molecule is disallowed since further construction is not feasible.

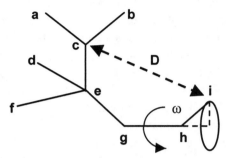

Figure 3.4. The distance between any two atoms that span a torsion (ω) can be described as a function of the torsion separating them. In this diagram, atoms *a, b, c, d, e, f,* and *g* represent a partial conformation, and atoms *g, h,* and *i* represent a new aggregate whose addition is being evaluated.

The distance equations minimize the number of pairwise distances that must be evaluated in a systematic search. They prune the search tree by analytically determining torsion angle ranges that may contain sterically allowed conformers. The intersection of the allowed angle ranges for every atom pair spanning a torsion defines the torsion ranges in which conformers must actually be built and evaluated to determine if they are sterically valid. Based on these angle ranges, trigonometric tables are constructed to guide the rotation matrices that govern the construction of conformations. Entries in the trigonometric table represent points on the sampling grid which lie within potentially sterically valid torsion ranges as determined by the distance equations.

As it turns out, the analytical determination of allowed ranges is so effective that it is "chained" before actual execution of the search in order to find possible valid torsion ranges for atoms separated by *two* torsions. Every allowed torsion of each entry in the trigonometric table is considered fixed, and the ranges accessible to the next torsion angle downstream are calculated. Sample points for which the subsequent torsion has no allowed ranges are eliminated from the table, thereby further reducing the number of conformations that must be evaluated by brute force.

3.5.2. Look-Ahead

"Look-ahead"[2,3] is a process by which pharmacophore or experimental distance constraints are used to further edit the trigonometric table prior to and during execution of the search. Look-ahead uses the projection of constraint atoms onto rotational axes to approximate new ranges for the constraints that can be used in the distance equations described earlier. With the exception of cyclic structures, look-aheads extending beyond three rotatable bonds down the search tree do not significantly refine the allowed ranges for the initial rotatable bond. Our experience is that the look-ahead feature contributes speed enhancements of 20- to 100-fold. Look-aheads are used at many points in the search process to filter entries from the existing trigonometric table.

3.5.3. Energy Filtering

The local energy of partial conformations can be evaluated in concert with the search, thereby further pruning the search tree. At every rotatable bond, the steric (Leonard-Jones) and torsional energies across that bond are evaluated for each grid point. The average energy over all torsion settings is calculated, and grid points at which the energy exceeds a user-specified percentage of the average are dropped from further consideration. This energy filter must be used judiciously so that it does not screen out conformers that might be feasible in the context of long-range interactions. Our experience is that this results in a speed-up of 3- to 10-fold in the search.

3.5.4. Ring Closures

The distance equations discussed earlier can be readily applied to closing cyclic structures and in the process speed a systematic search. This is represented for cyclooctane in Figure 3.5. Closure bond angle distances (d_{ac}, d_{bd}) and bond length (d_{bc}) are determined from the starting structure (I), which can be a closed cycle or an open chain having the closure bond atoms duplicated at each end. At the start of the calculation, the user defines the margin of error that will be tolerated in both of these distances for a structure to be considered closed. The solid-headed arrows in step II represent torsion angles that are evaluated in a conventional grid-based fashion. For each partial conformation defined by these torsions, the distance equations described earlier are used to solve for ranges of ω_1 and ω_2 that satisfies the bond angle distances within the specified epsilon (II & III). In a final step (IV), combinations of ω_1 and ω_2 are evaluated against the bond length $d_{bc}\pm\varepsilon$. When a small value of epsilon is used ($\varepsilon=0.05$ Å), the result is nearly exact closures. This hybrid approach, in which five torsions are solved analytically, is much more efficient than systematically searching all of the torsion variables in the ring.

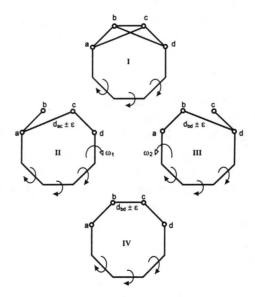

Figure 3.5. Analysis of cyclic structures during systematic search. Closure bond length and bond angle distances are determined from the starting structure I and used in subsequent steps to constrain the conformational analysis, which is a hybrid of grid-based searching and an analytical approach (see text fod detailed explanation.)

An early version of the Active Analog Approach is available in SYBYL®.[9] Recent improvements described above are available in

RECEPTOR®[10] with the result that the analysis is 10^7-10^{12} times faster. The newer version includes:

- heuristics for ensuring that the most constrained molecules are searched first and thereby pruning search trees early in the analysis;

- early termination of the search of a given molecule when all of the previously known points in distance space have been found; and

- eliminating exhaustive evaluation of all conformational possibilities for pendant groups which are not on the path of torsions directly connecting the pharmacophoric groups.

Improvements in the speed and accuracy of systematic search have made the Active Analog Approach a nearly interactive tool for the computational chemist. The reduced runtime means numerous analyses can be done using different sets of adjustable parameters. In fact, the speed is such that one can readily test different hypotheses regarding the correspondence of functional groups in different ligands. Historically, it has been necessary to use both large grid sizes and simplifying assumptions that decrease the number of degrees of freedom in order to reduce the size of the overall calculation. Algorithmic improvements have removed these limitations, with the result that the Active Analog Approach can now be applied to a much broader range of problems.

3.6. Systematic Search Parameters Which Impact Sampling Completeness

While in principle systematic search should be a straightforward means of generating all of the possible conformations of a molecule, in practice there are a number of parameters which have a significant impact on the completeness of the results. The optimal values of these parameters can only be determined empirically, as the effect of changing them cannot be expressed analytically. Another complication is the fact that the error function in systematic search is discontinuous. In other words, conformations are either allowed or not allowed. In other methods of conformational analysis based on optimization protocols, such as molecular dynamics and distance geometry, the continuous error function results in acceptance of conformations having a broad energy range. Localized regions of poor energy are compensated by other areas in which the energy is favorable, with the result that information is homogenized. In systematic search, discreet interatomic distances determine whether or not a conformation is allowed. Slight changes in any of the adjustable parameters discussed below can have a profound impact on whether or not experimental distance restraints or van der Waals distances are valid.

Because perturbations in bond lengths and angles can propagate as slight differences in interatomic distances, the **starting geometry** can dramatically impact the conformational sampling of a search. Torsional settings valid for one starting geometry may not be valid for another. Extensively minimized structures may not be optimal for systematic search, because terms in the force field are balanced against each other to optimize the overall energy. Calculation of a minimum energy for a given conformation effectively couples all the terms in the force field, yielding structures that may have bond angles and bond lengths which are not at equilibrium values but are compensated by favorable van der Waals or charge interactions. If used in systematic search, these structures may effectively sample the conformational space in their local minimum. However, when set to the torsions for another minimum, these structures may have steric contacts which cause that conformation to be discarded. In our studies of peptides and proteins, we have used averaged geometries of amino acids derived from crystallographic observations in the Protein Databank.[11] In unconstrained searches, these geometries yield ϕ,ψ plots which are consistent with statistically allowed regions seen in X-ray structures of proteins. However, this is not always true when these geometries are minimized in a variety of force fields and then subjected to search analysis.

The **anchor atom** of each molecule determines the shape of the search tree. A search tree structured to require extensive explicit van der Waals evaluations at late points in one or more branches will require extended run time.

The **reference torsion angle** determines the starting torsion setting—in other words, this is the value from which the torsion angles are incremented. In absolute mode, all torsions in the starting geometry are set to zero and rotations proceed from this point. In relative mode, the original conformation of the molecule is used as the starting point. A search run in absolute mode at 5° increments will sample points at 0°, 5°, 10°, etc., whereas the same search run in relative mode from a starting torsion of 2° will sample points at 2°, 7°, 12°, etc. In the context of earlier comments about the discontinuous error function of search and the fact that even very slight distance violations can result in a conformation being discarded, it is clear that these two searches sample different regions of conformational space.

As noted earlier, appropriate handling of the **van der Waals radii** can accommodate slight deformations from bond angle equilibrium values. There are two means of dealing with the radii: calibrating a set appropriate for systematic search, and using blanket-scaling factors, which reduce all of the radii. Our studies have shown that radii calibrated for standard force fields may not be suitable for systematic search,[6] and we instead use radii generated specifically for search. There are typically three distinct scaling factors: a general scaling factor applied to all atoms; a 1,4 scaling factor, which accounts for the anisotropic pear-shaped character of electron clouds and their overlap for atoms in a 1-4 relationship; and a hydrogen bonding scaling factor which allows close approach of atom pairs that are possible H-bond donors or acceptors (default values of 0.95, 0.87, and 0.65, respectively). A reduction in the general scaling factor may compensate for an improperly balanced set of radii, but in the extreme case results in retention of conformations that otherwise lie in disallowed regions of torsional space. Thus one runs the risk of generating larger datasets which contain erroneous information.

By defining the resolution of the grid, the **torsion angle increment** dictates the fineness of the conformational search and therefore the completeness of the results. A large angle increment results in a coarse grid that may fail to sample regions corresponding to local minima. In other cases, these sparse samples may have a very small overlap in van der Waals volume (0.01 Å or less) that disallows conformers, which in reality are valid. By reducing the angle increment, the search stringency is relaxed, and the chance of finding valid conformers among the increased number of sample points around a local minimum increases. Unfortunately, the combinatorial explosion created by decreasing the torsion angle increment may impose practical limits on how small an increment can be used.

Radial Sampling is a means of dealing with the over- or undersampling of Cartesian and distance space that can occur when there are large variations in the number of fixed (non-rotatable) bonds that separate atom pairs. In Figure 3.6, rotation of a methyl group and a phenyl group are compared. The length of the rotating arm in these cases is quite different, and with a uniform angle increment of 10° the much larger three-dimensional space swept by the hydrogens of the phenyl group would be undersampled relative to that of the methyl group. In these cases, a sampling grid in distance space compensates for differences in arm length and provides more uniform sampling. The distance grid is determined by identifying a key atom in each aggregate and dividing the circumference of the key atom's rotation circle into arcs of an equal length. Torsion angle values, which move the key atom by the user-specified uniform arc length, are then calculated. With radial sampling, each torsion has a unique floating-point angle increment. Selection of a key atom in an aggregate is always a compromise, since optimal sampling for one atom is likely to produce over- or undersampling for other atoms. In practice the choice of key atom has minimal impact on the search, since the improvement in sampling realized by changing from a torsion to a distance grid is so great.

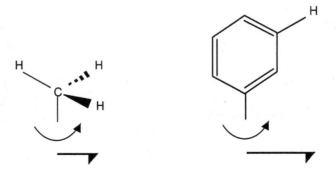

Figure 3.6. Comparison of the rotor arm length for hydrogens bonded to a methyl group (left) and a phenyl group (right). When uniform torsional grid sampling is used, the difference in arm length results in different sampling in distance space and in Cartesian space for the hydrogens bonded to each group. Reprinted with permission from[2]. © 1996 Elsevier Science.

Adaptive Sampling is a means of addressing the "tyranny" of the systematic search grid. For a given torsion, the ranges that possibly contain valid conformations may be fragmented (disjoint) and constricted as they are the intersection of the allowed angle ranges for all non-bonded atom pairs across that torsion. Consequently, they may not be well sampled by a fixed search grid. In Figure 3.7, the horizontal arrows represent the 0-359° range of torsional space. The shaded boxes represent angle ranges, which may possibly contain sterically allowed conformations. In the top diagram, the leftmost box represents a range, which is not sampled at all using conventional grid-based sampling; the rightmost box is an allowed range, which is inadequately sampled.

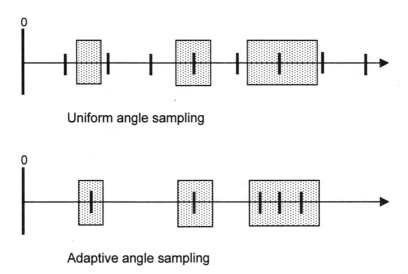

Uniform angle sampling

Adaptive angle sampling

Figure 3.7. Schematic representation of adaptive sampling. The horizontal arrows represents the entire range of torsion angles from 0 to 360°; ranges that may contain sterically allowed conformations are represented by gray boxes. The vertical bars represent search grid points. **Top)** Possible allowed angle ranges are determined by the distance constraint equations for every atom pair across a given torsion. Intersection of these ranges yields fragments of torsional space that may not be sampled at all (leftmost box) or are inadequately sampled (rightmost box). **Bottom)** Adaptive sampling repositions the search grid points to improve sampling. Reprinted with permission from[2]. © 1996 Elsevier Science.

Adaptive sampling is shown in the bottom half of Figure 3.7, where grid points are moved to ensure that all allowed ranges are adequately sampled. By determining the sample points dynamically, adaptive sampling

abandons the concept of a fixed grid. This can be done in several ways:
The new sample points can be positioned at the midpoint of the allowed
range; they can be positioned a fraction of an increment inside the
boundary of each range; or the grid can be adjusted to maximize the
number of sample points in the range. Our experience, in results discussed later, is that adaptive sampling produces more complete results
than the fixed grid approach. Note that the concept of adaptive sampling
can be applied not only to torsional grids, but to distance (radial) grids
as well. The distance equations discussed earlier enable determination
of allowed distance ranges that can be subjected to the same treatment.

3.7. Analysis of Datasets

Ideally, the Active Analog Approach produces a single pharmacophore
geometry, that is a single point or a single cluster of closely related
points in distance space. Generally, there are several solutions, and a
cluster analysis followed by selection of representative points is
required. Once representative points have been selected, the conformers
corresponding to those points are generated. Because of the many-to-
one mapping of distance space to torsional space, resulting in a multitude of conformers for each IMAP point, the selection of conformers
generally also requires a cluster analysis and selection of representative
conformers.

Both IMAP points and conformations can be sorted into families
based on the proximity of valid grid points. A family has no path of sterically allowed conformations on the torsional grid or the distance grid
that connects it to any other family. This is represented in simplified
form in Figure 3.1, where the results for two 2-rotatable bonds (ω_1 and
ω_2) are represented. Torsional grid points are represented by circles, and
sterically allowed conformers are represented as filled black circles.
Both plots indicate two families. These families can be sampled in several ways: points with the greatest number of nearest neighbors, the
point which is most highly favored when the results are projected onto
a selected single dimension, the first point, etc. In the case of conformer
families, energetic or RMS criteria can also be used for sampling.[3]

3.8. Considerations in Using the Active Analog Approach

3.8.1. Pharmacophore vs. Active-Site Models

In simplest terms, the pharmacophore model assumes overlap of functional groups in the set of compounds under analysis. For example, the carboxyl group from one compound physically overlaps with the corresponding carboxyl group in another. While it is true that two or more molecules can have corresponding functional groups that interact with the same site on a receptor, it is also true that these functional groups are capable of assuming a variety of orientations with that receptor site while maintaining equal affinity for the receptor. The simplest example is the cone of nearly equal energetic arrangements of a hydrogen-bond donor and acceptor. The pharmacophore requirement for superimposable functional groups is a stringent limitation, since the observed binding mode represents the optimal position of a ligand in an asymmetric force field created by the receptor subject to perturbation by solvation and entropic factors. Less restrictive is the assumption that the receptor-binding site remains relatively fixed in geometry when binding the series of compounds under study. Experimental support for such a hypothesis can be found in crystal structures of enzyme-inhibitor complexes where the enzyme presents essentially the same conformation despite large variations in inhibitor structures.[12]

Active-site models address limitations in the conventional pharmacophore assumption, by focusing on the groups of the receptor that interact with ligands as the common features needed for recognition of a set of analogs. The ligands are augmented with appropriate molecular extensions (Figure 3.8) that represent the binding site, and the set of possible geometrical orientations of site points is determined to see if there is at least one that shared by all ligands. The number of degrees of freedom in an active-site hypotheses is greater, due to the addition of virtual bonds between groups on ligands and active-site elements. While the use of active-site models allows multiple binding modes of the ligands to a rigidly determined receptor model, the additional degrees of freedom increase the size of the computation and may decrease the likelihood of a single unique solution.

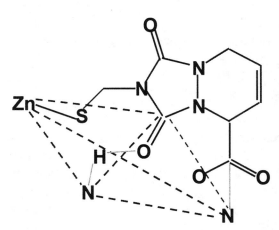

Figure 3.8. The use of active-site models in the Active Analog Approach. The structure shown is one of a series of ACE inhibitors analyzed. The thick gray lines are noncovalent interactions between the inhibitor and active-site points in the enzyme. The dashed lines correspond to the six interatomic distances monitored for each of the inhi-bitors analyzed. Reprinted with permission from[3]. © 1996 Elsevier Science.

3.8.2. Selection of Molecules for Analysis

We have already noted that the correspondence between functional groups in different molecules must be known or hypothesized before the Active Analog Approach is applied. Another consideration is the conformational diversity of the molecules. Ideally, each ligand should eliminate some pharmacophore geometries for the other molecules. For ligands having a large number of degrees of freedom, this requirement becomes even more important if one is to converge on a single solution or single family of solutions. Common methods for enhancing the conformational diversity of a set of molecules include adding ligands which incorporate cyclic structures or have a reduced number of atoms between functional groups.

3.8.3. Interpreting the Results

One caveat, which must be remembered, is the probability of alternate, or multiple, binding modes. The interaction of a ligand with a binding site depends on the free energy of binding, a complex interaction with both entropic and enthalpic components. Simple modifications in structure may favor one of several nearly energetically equivalent modes of interaction with the receptor, and change the correspondence between functional groups that has previously been assumed and supported by experimental data. Changes in binding mode of an antibody FAB fragment to progesterone and its analogs[13,14] has been shown by crystallography of the complexes. Compounds which clearly are inconsistent with models derived from large amounts of structure-activity data may be indicative of such changes in binding mode, and may require a separate structure-activity study to characterize their interaction.

Because for many problems there is not enough experimental data to distinguish between several self-consistent active site models on a geometric basis, development of models which utilize binding data to distinguish between alternatives is of considerable value. In other words, one needs to utilize all the information in the experimental data. Three-dimensional, quantitative structure-activity relationships (3D QSAR) offer a solution to this problem. Comparative molecular field analysis (CoMFA)[15] is a good example of a tool that can discriminate between alternative binding geometries determined using the Active Analog Approach.

An alternative to additional analyses of a set of data to distinguish between hypotheses is to gather more experimental data on different compounds. The greatest amount of new information is generated from compounds dissimilar to those already assayed.

3.9. Examples of the Application of the Active Analog Approach

3.9.1. Morphiceptin Analogs

Based on structure-activity data, the tyramine portion and phenyl ring of residue three of morphiceptin (Tyr-Pro-Phe-Pro-NH2) were postulated to be the pharmacophoric groups responsible for recognition and activation of the opioid μ-receptor.[16] It was assumed further that the aromatic rings bound to the receptor in the different analogs were coincident and coplanar. A series of active analogs with a variety of conformationally constrained amino acid analogs in positions two and three were analyzed. A unique conformation was found for the two most constrained analogs which allowed overlap of the Phe and Tyr portions of the molecules (Figure 3.9). In this case, a five-dimensional orientation map with distances between the nitrogen and normals to the two aromatic rings was used in the analysis.

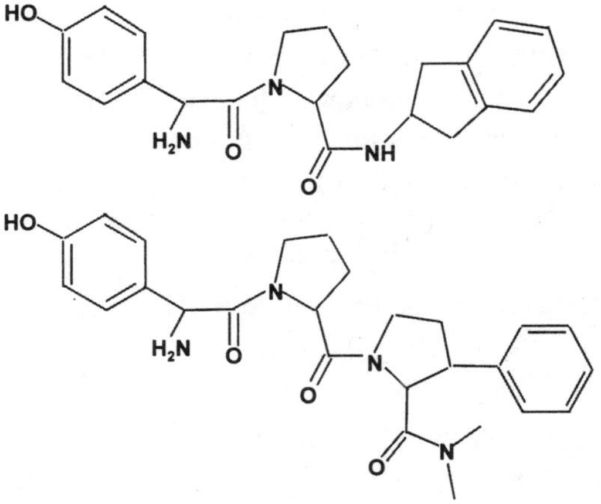

Figure 3.9. Two constrained analogs of morphiceptin used to determine the bound operations of Tyr1 and Phe3 aromatic rings. Reprinted with permission from[5]. © 1995 John Wiley & Sons, Inc.

3.9.2. ACE Inhibitors

In a study of the angiotensin-converting enzyme (ACE),[17] an active-site model was used that incorporated the active-site components as parts of each ligand undergoing analysis. As an example, the sulfhydryl portion of captopril was extended to include a zinc atom bound at the experimentally optimal bond length and bond angle for zinc-sulfur complexes (Figure 3.8). The OMAP was based on the distances between active-site points such as the zinc atom. Despite the increased number of degrees of freedom due to the use of site points, the analyses of nearly thirty different chemical classes of ACE inhibitors led to a unique arrangement of the components of the active site postulated to be responsible for binding of the inhibitors. In a subsequent study,[18] a CoMFA analysis was used to distinguish between two alternatives for aligning the ACE inhibitors in an active site model, based on significant differences in the predictive power of the resulting models derived from the two alternative geometries.

The ACE set of inhibitors was subsequently reinvestigated using the algorithmic improvements described above.[19] Searches using uniform angle, uniform radial, adaptive angle, and adaptive radial sampling at several different increments were compared directly. The results revealed that radial sampling is more comprehensive than torsion angle sampling, and that adaptive sampling is more complete than simple grid-based sampling. Radial adaptive sampling combines both of these enhancements and is the most efficient approach of all. The results also suggested that the IMAP partition size must be suitably matched to the torsion or radial increment to achieve proper sampling.

3.9.3. Substance P Antagonists

The Active Analog Approach was used to analyze a set of high affinity Substance P (SP) antagonists[20] representing all known classes of SP antagonists. Initial studies revealed that all elements of the pharmacophore could not adopt a common geometry, requiring that the molecules be split into two subsets. By expanding and contracting the dimensionality of the IMAP, information about the geometry of the shared pharmacophore elements from each subset could be used to constrain the other subset. The results revealed that only an edge-to-face orientation of the two phenyl rings common to all of the classes of antagonists was allowed. These analyses, done with all of the cyclic structures completely flexible and using a radial increment of 0.0625 Å (equivalent to an average torsional increment of 2.66°) required 1 CPU day on a DEC alpha 3000/300. An overlay of four members of the piperidine class of antagonists is shown in Figure 3.10.

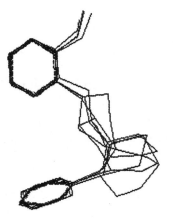

Figure 3.10. The alignment of four substance P piperidine antagonists determined using the Active Analog Approach. Reprinted with permission from[3]. © 1996 Elsevier Science.

Acknowledgements

The authors acknowledge support from the National Institutes of Health (GM24483) which has made the development of our systematic search software possible. We thank the many researchers whose efforts through the years have been essential to the progress described in this report and whose contributions are cited in the references. In particular, the recent improvements in systematic search reflect significant intellectual contributions by Richard A. Dammkoehler, Steve F. Karasek, and E.F. Berkley Shands.

References

1. Marshall GR, Barry CD, Bosshard HE, Dammkoehler RA, Dunn DA: **The conformational parameter in drug design: The active analog approach.** In: *Computer-Assisted Drug Design*, Vol. 112, Olson EC, Christoffersen RE, eds., Washington, DC: American Chemical Society, 1979:205-226.

2. Beusen DD, Shands EFB: **Systematic search strategies in conformational analysis.** *Drug Discovery Today* 1996, **1**(10): 429-437.

3. Beusen DD, Shands EFB, Karasek SF, Marshall GR, Dammkoehler RA: **Systematic search in conformational analysis.** *J Mol Struct (Theochem)* 1996, **370**:157-171.

4. Marshall GR: **Binding-site modeling of unknown receptor.** In: *3D QSAR in Drug Design: Theory, Methods and Applications*. Kubinyi H, ed. Leiden: ESCOM Scientific Publishers, 1993:80-116.

5. Marshall GR: **Molecular modeling in drug design.** In: *Burger's Medicinal Chemistry and Drug Discovery*, Vol. 1, 5th ed. Wolff ME, ed. New York: John Wiley & Sons, Inc., 1995:573-659.

6. Iijima HI, Dunbar JB, Jr., Marshall GR: **The calibration of effective van der Waals atomic contact radii for proteins and peptides.** *Proteins: Struct Func Gen* 1987, **2**:330-339.

7. Dammkoehler RA, Karasek SF, Shands EFB, Marshall GR: **Constrained search of conformational hyperspace.** *J Comput-Aided Mol Des* 1989, **3**: 3-21.

8. Motoc I, Dammkoehler RA, Mayer D, Labanowski J: **Three-dimensional quantitative strucure-activity relationships. I. General approach to the pharmacophore model validation.** *Quant Struct-Act Relat* 1986, **5**:99-105.

9. *SYBYL 6.5.* Tripos, Inc., 1699 S. Hanley Road, St. Louis, MO 63144.

10. *RECEPTOR 3.2.* Tripos, Inc., 1699 S. Hanley Road, St. Louis, MO 63144.

11. *Protein Data Bank.* http://www.rcsb.org/pdb/.

12. Appelt K: **Crystal structures of HIV-1 protease-inhibitor complexes.** *J Comput-Aided Mol Des*, PD3 1993, **1**(1): 23-48.

13. Arevalo JH, Stura EA, Taussig MJ, Wilson IA: **3-dimensional structure of an anti-steroid FAB' and progesterone FAB' complex.** *J Mol Biol* 1993, **231**:103-118.

14. Arevalo JH, Taussig MJ, Wilson IA: **Molecular basis of crossreactivity and the limits of antibody-antigen complementarity.** *Nature* 1993, **365**:859-863.

15. Cramer RD, III, Patterson DE, Bunce JD: **Comparative Molecular Field Analysis (CoMFA). 1. Effect of shape on binding of steroids to carrier proteins.** *J Am Chem Soc* 1988, **110**(18):5959-5967.

16. Nelson RD, Gottlieb DI, Balasubramanian TM, Marshall GR: **Opioid peptides: Analysis of specificity and multiple binding modes through computer-aided drug design and structure-activity studies.** In: *Opioid Peptides: Medicinal Chemistry*, Vol. 69. Rapaka RS, Barnett G, Hawks RL, eds., Rockville: NIDA Office of Science, 1986:204-230.

17. Mayer D, Naylor CB, Motoc I, Marshall GR: **A unique geometry of the active site of angiotensin-converting enzyme consistent with structure-activity studies.** *J Comput-Aided Mol Des* 1987, **1**(1):3-16.

18. DePriest SA, Mayer D, Naylor CB, Marshall GR: **3D-QSAR of angiotensin-converting enzyme and thermolysin inhibitors: A comparison of CoMFA models based on deduced and experimentally determined active site geometries.** *J Am Chem Soc* 1993, **115**:5372-5384.

19. Dammkoehler RA, Karasek SF, Shands EFB, Marshall GR: **Sampling conformational hyperspace: Techniques for improving completeness.** *J Comput-Aided Mol Des* 1996, **9**:491-499.

20. Takeuchi Y, Shands EFB, Beusen DD, Marshall GR: **Derivation of a three-dimensional pharmacophore model of Substance P antagonists bound to the nerokinin-1 receptor.** *J Med Chem* 1998, **19**:3609-3623.

Automated Pharmacophore Development Systems

4

DISCO: What We Did Right and What We Missed

Yvonne Connolly Martin

Abstract

DISCO (**DIS**tance **CO**mparisons) is a fast, automated, systematic analysis used to discover (1) how many pharmacophores, using which conformations and superposition rules, explain the data; (2) the trade-off between a low RMS for superposition and including more points in the model; and (3) the trade-off between having a low RMS and including higher-energy conformations in the model. DISCO searches over the input conformations of a set of structures to find pharmacophores by default identifying positive, negative, hydrogen-bond donor, hydrogen bond acceptor, and hydrophobic points in common within the set. The points are located at atom centers or at projections from the heavy atoms of the ligand to the hypothetical location of complementary macromolecular atoms. DISCO considers only active compounds; experienced users eliminate redundant information within this set. Frequently DISCO produces one pharmacophore with several possible bioactive conformations for some compounds. Sometimes DISCO produces more than one distinct pharmacophore map, indicating that there was not enough information to distinguish between the possibilities. On one occasion DISCO could find no suitable pharmacophore, thus ending our search for one. The distance matrix for enantiomers is identical; hence an additional step is needed to be certain that the bioactive enantiomers are selected for the pharmacophore. DISCO is not suited to datasets for which all of the molecules are extremely flexible. DISCO is intended to support interactive molecular modeling. Its optimal use requires judicious selection of the compounds to be included; careful conformational searching and structure optimization of the compounds considered; and thoughtful examination of the possible pharmacophores produced.

4

DISCO: What We Did Right and What We Missed

Yvonne Connolly Martin

Abbott Laboratories, Abbott Park, Illinois

4.1. Overview of DISCO

DISCO arose in the late 1980s as an automation of a molecular model-ing operation that was extremely time-consuming and frustrating.[1] By that time we had wonderful molecular graphics display devices; con-venient interactive molecular graphics computer programs; methods to search conformational space, optimize structures, and calculate their energy; methods to search for matching conformations given a proposed atom correspondence; 3D QSAR to explain the differences between molecules tested in the same assay; and 3D searching to identify new compounds to test or design new molecules to synthesize. We needed a systematic method to recognize the 3D features that a set of molecules has in common. We wanted to automate the process that determine sev-eral properties of a dataset:

1) How many pharmacophores explain the data? Zero, one, or many?

2) Which conformations match each pharmacophore found?

3) How does the increasing the number of points included in each pharmacophore affect root mean square (RMS) difference between the superpositions?

4) How much could the RMS for a pharmacophore be lowered by including successively higher-energy conformers in the analysis? Does adding these conformers result in the identification of other possible pharmacophores?

DISCO is a fast, automated, systematic analysis that provides answers to many of these questions and frees the scientist to weigh the various resulting hypotheses. While dramatically automating the process of comparing conformations of different molecules, DISCO does not automatically select the best pharmacophore hypothesis: This task remains with the user.

DISCO (**DIS**tance **CO**mparisons) searches over the input conformations of a set of structures to find pharmacophores, matching points in common within the set.[1] Hence, it proposes a superposition rule and bioactive conformation of each molecule. Instead of considering a conformation to be a three-dimensional object in space, DISCO considers a conformation to be a set of interpoint distances. This is a concept familiar to those who use distance geometry for conformational searching of single molecules or ensembles of molecules, particularly the work of Blaney, Dixon, Crippen, and Sheridan.[2,3]

In contrast to distance geometry, however, for DISCO the points are not labeled by atom symbol or type, but rather by their character with respect to intermolecular interactions. The default set of point characters is positive charge, negative charge, hydrogen-bond donor, hydrogen-bond acceptor, and hydrophobic atom. A point can have more than one label; for example, a hydroxyl oxygen is labeled as both a hydrogen-bond acceptor and donor. Furthermore, the distances are calculated not only between the locations of atoms, but also between points located at the hypothetical position of the complementary atoms of a macromolecule. The importance of considering such site points in pharmacophore evaluation was emphasized by the Marshall group in their detailed study of ACE inhibitors.[4]

DISCO uses the Bron-Kerbosh clique-detection algorithm[5,6] for the distance comparisons. Brint and Willett had earlier shown this algorithm to be the fastest available method for discovering the maximum common substructure in a set of 3D structures.[7] DISCO thus represents a synthesis of the concepts central to distance geometry and the active analogue approach with techniques for maximum common substructure perception. Somewhat earlier than our work, but unknown to us, Takahashi and colleagues had proposed a similar strategy.[8] Because DISCO was the first automated pharmacophore matching program it is instructive to examine, several years later, how well the concepts used in its design meet today's needs. Most of this discussion applies specifically to the method as originally developed; however, the commercial version provided by Tripos remains true to the original but incorporates many features that enhance its ease of use and the interpretation of results.[9] This discussion will not include a detailed comparison of the DISCO strategy with others available, since this has been covered elsewhere.[10]

The first of several design decisions that are central to DISCO is whether or not conformational searching will be a part of the program. We decided that it would not. We chose this strategy because in our experience we could (and should) use existing technology to do a comprehensive conformational search and energy minimization. Furthermore, no one program was suitable for the energy minimization of the various types of molecules that we considered in our work. For example, we typically used MM2 for small molecules,[11] particularly those that contain alicyclic rings; Discover for peptides;[12] and AM1 for heteroaromatic compounds.[13]

The second design criterion was that we would concentrate on the set of active compounds for the analysis. This not only speeds up the analysis, but also isolates pharmacophore mapping from a subsequent QSAR. It follows from concepts promoted by Kier[14] and Marshall,[15] that while there are many reasons why a compound may be inactive, commonality within the set of actives can provide a powerful hypothesis against which inactives can be measured. For example, a particular compound can be inactive because:

1) It does not contain the groups in the geometry required for recognition by the biomolecular target, that is, it does not match the required pharmacophore;

2) Although it contains the pharmacophore, it also contains groups that interfere with recognition and that can be detected by a subsequent QSAR;

3) It is less soluble than its bioactive concentration;

4) It contains groups that sterically prevent interaction with the target biomolecule, another potency-decreasing property that can be detected by QSAR.

The third design criterion was that we did not expect the computer program to provide an automated answer, but considered the output to be similar to an all-possible regression program: All answers that are consistent with the input criteria were to be output. The user would be responsible for evaluating the output and using it to design further computational or laboratory experiments.

One DISCO input is the set of conformations for each molecule. As discussed later in this chapter, these conformations are pre-calculated and user-selected to be unique. The user also specifies the relative energy of each conformation. DISCO outputs this with the pharmacophores found to help the user evaluate the solutions. DISCO uses a default set of definitions of potential pharmacophore points,[16] but the user may choose to override these. The user also specifies the compound that DISCO will use as the reference for the conformational comparisons.

4.2. The Problem of Searching for Correspondences

Why did we need a computer program to search for potential superposition rules? Consider the simple case of five molecules, each of which has five low-energy conformations and ten possible points for superposition. Each conformation of one molecule will be compared with a total of 20 structures of the other molecules; doing this for the five conformations of the reference molecule results in 100 comparisons of conformations. If one uses only three points in the comparison, then for every pair there are six ways to select the points from each conformation, or 36 correspondences to examine. Thus, in the worst case, the modeler would have to examine 3600 potential pharmacophore maps just to look for three-point pharmacophores! Although the real number of comparisons might be lower because some comparisons would not be necessary, the number nevertheless explodes if one considers larger pharmacophores. It is easy to see that the human tendency would be to stop when one found a "good" pharmacophore even though a better one might be waiting to be discovered.

A simple example is our search for a pharmacophore for D1 agonists. It would require 5800 comparisons to examine the low-energy conformations of compounds *1-5*. DISCO accomplished these comparisons at several tolerance levels, including making the output, in one minute on a slow VAX.

4.3. The Importance of Conformational Searching

Although we certainly did not believe that the various energy minimization programs are completely accurate, we also assumed that a pharmacophore based on quite active compounds should not require any of them to be in a high-energy conformation that results from a steric clash between atoms in the structure. Consider the example of cyclic renin inhibitors for which Sham and colleagues experimentally demonstrated that the IC_{50} decreases from >100 nM for the analogue that has zero percent trans in the NMR to 27nM for the analogue that has 50% trans.[17] We hypothesized that it is more realistic to propose a pharmacophore with less-than-perfect superposition of points using relatively low-energy conformations than it is to select a pharmacophore with a lower RMS that includes high-energy conformations. This is consistent with crystallographic observations that show small but observable structural shifts in the structure of the ame protein in complexes of closely related ligands.

On the other hand, we also believed that the search for correspondences must include all low-energy conformations. We did not trust any computer program to identify the global minimum energy conformation, nor did we believe the energy calculated was necessarily relevant to the environment experienced by the molecules in the biological test system. Generally we use DISCO on systems for which we have developed a good feeling for the conformations available and the reliability of the energy calculations. We also do supplementary DISCO runs varying the energy cutoffs to see if we would find a "better" pharmacophore by including higher-energy conformations. A particular issue was the conformational search of peptides for which the extended conformation is not stable in any of the programs tested; even turning off electrostatics results in folded conformations.

4.4. Selecting the Conformational Ensemble

We typically examine the conformational possibilities of a molecule by generating the conformations with distance geometry[2] and minimizing them with the most appropriate method. We use distance geometry because it handles alicyclic ring conformations automatically and includes no user bias as to the fineness of the conformational sampling. In our hands it required fewer energy minimizations to identify the relevant minima than did high-temperature molecular dynamics. The problem with conformational searching using distance geometry is that there is no clear protocol as to how many original conformations to generate. Coupled with this is the issue of when one conformation is different "enough" from another to be useful.

In the early 1980s we developed the program Reject.[18] It also considers conformations as a matrix of interpoint distances. The user tells the program which atoms to consider in the comparison-for example, the hydrogens of a CH^2 group are equivalent and one would typically not consider as different those conformations that differ only in the distances between these atoms and the rest of the structure. We typically consider only the heavy atoms of the structure and usually also do not consider atoms of a symmetric pair, such as the methyls of a t-butyl group. We use 0.3 Å as the tolerance because this distinguishes the boat from the chair conformation of cyclohexane. Reject first compares all required interpoint distances of the lowest-energy conformation (the reference conformation) with the corresponding distances in all other conformations. Reject considers those conformations for which all distances are within the tolerance to be the "same" conformation as the reference. The process then moves to the unassigned conformation with the lowest energy and uses it as the reference for the remaining unassigned conformations. Reject repeats the process until it assigns all conformations. This procedure results in the smallest number of low-energy structures that describe all of the conformations found in the search. We have found this method to be both faster and more accurate at identifying unique conformations than clustering. If there are many repeats of the conformations, then we decide empirically that the conformational search is complete: If Reject finds most of the conformations only once, then we need to do more distance geometry searches.

Figure 4.1 shows the low-energy conformations of compounds *1-5*. They were generated with DGEOM, optimized with MMP2, and processed by Reject.

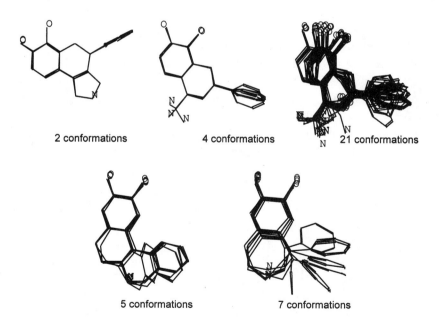

2 conformations   4 conformations   21 conformations

5 conformations   7 conformations

Figure 4.1. The low-energy conformations of compounds *1-5*. Structures are discussed in reference.[1]

4.5. Selecting Compounds for the DISCO Analysis

Although we decided that DISCO would emphasize active compounds, we realized that inactive compounds also provide important information. Hence, we added a provision to DISCO directing it to provide solutions that did not include certain specified molecules. As a result, we could manually evaluate whether the pharmacophores that include the inactive compound(s) were more or less reasonable than those that exclude them.

The more information one provides to DISCO, the more reliable the results will be. More information does not mean more data; rather, it means more information about the possible bioactive conformation and about the points recognized by the biomolecule. As a consequence, conformationally restricted compounds and those with few recognition sites contain the most relevant information. These considerations mean that the user should include unique compounds with high information content even if they are not the most potent compounds. For example, we were not able to choose the bioactive conformation of the catechol OH groups in dopaminergic compounds such as apomorphine, compound *6*, without considering ergolines such as compound *7*.[19] This compound also restricts the pharmacophore to contain a hydrogen-bond donor on the aromatic ring; that is, the catecholic OH groups are not acting as a hydrogen-bond acceptor.

6   7

A more subtle decision involves the active compounds to exclude from the analysis: The more compounds included in the analysis, the more work it is to evaluate the output. Redundant information does not add to the quality of the output. Remembering that we would typically use the same conformation of all analogues for a 3D QSAR, we would not need to perform the DISCO analysis on all conformations of all of the analogues. Rather, the appropriate conformation of one could be selected using DISCO, and this conformation used for the others. Consider the pair of compounds **8** and **9**. Because we would require any conformation of **8** to mimic one of the more constrained analogue, **9**, we need to include only **9** (which has fewer conformations) in the analysis.

8   9

Since we expect all analogues to match the pharmacophore in the same way, the representative compound of a series to be used for DISCO should be the one that has the fewest features. Sometimes this may be a virtual compound, selected to limit the search to the relevant information. For example, although we would use **9** for a DISCO run, we would remove from consideration the points corresponding to the para hydroxyl group because this is not present in the active analog **8**. In a similar fashion, we would include only those conformations of any "representative compound" that have 3D features in common with all other active members of the series. Sometimes one can make these decisions by making a DISCO run with tight distance tolerance on just the series.

The DISCO algorithm uses one conformation on the reference compound to compare with each conformation of every other compound. It intersects the cliques identified to tabulate the clique, if any, contained in all pairs of molecules, at least one conformation per molecule. It repeats this process for every conformation of the reference compound. We use the compound with the fewest conformations or that with the fewest potential pharmacophore points as the reference. The exact choice does not affect the results substantially; however, since DISCO presents the results as potential pharmacophores that match a particular reference conformation, the results are easier to interpret if fewer reference conformations are examined—more conformations are automatically matched to one pharmacophore.

4.6. What DISCO Uses as Points to Match

Since we view a pharmacophore as a model of the binding site of a macromolecule, the character of the points in DISCO models reflects the character of the point with respect to intermolecular interactions. Early in our experience with molecular modeling we realized that the minima and maxima in electrostatic potential surfaces essentially always fall very close to projections of lone pairs or the H-O or H-N bond axis. We expected that DISCO would account for any deviations from this idealized behavior with the superposition tolerance. We programmed a series of Daylight SMARTS targets for Aladdin[20] to define groups that can be positively charged, be negatively charged, act as a hydrogen-bond donor, or act as a hydrogen-bond acceptor. Each of these descriptions could apply to a point located at an atom or a point, of complementary character, located at the hypothetical position of the interacting atom of a macromolecule. Any location in space can correspond to several points of different character. For example, the oxygen of an alcoholic OH group is labeled as both a hydrogen-bond donor and acceptor. The positions of the site points are calculated from extensions of idealized lone pairs or hydrogen-bonding hydrogens. Generally this agrees with observed positions of complementary atoms in the Cambridge Structural Database.[21] In the original version we used our Daylight-based 3D searching program Aladdin[20] to process the structures and prepare the input for DISCO, but the commercial version is integrated in SYBYL.[9]

The calculations to locate the positions of site points are based on the positions of the heavy atoms in the ligand structure, with the result that one conformation can result in many possible locations of site points. For example, one conformation of an alcohol will result in three locations of the complementary hydrogen-bond donor and three locations of the complementary hydrogen-bond acceptor. In effect, basing the site points on the location of the heavy atoms produces many virtual conformations from one conformation. Figure 4.2 shows the points selected for one conformation of Structure 1. This calculation of site points is an advantage over field-based structure comparisons for which each rotation of a group containing a polar hydrogen results in a different structure to compare. If there is more than one polar hydrogen in the molecule, a combinatorial explosion of the positions of minima and maxima in the electrostatic potential surface can result. For example, field-based comparison of another molecule with Structure 1 would require four conformations that result from the combination of the two relative catechol OH orientations with two orientations of the NH. This contrasts with the one conformation used in DISCO.

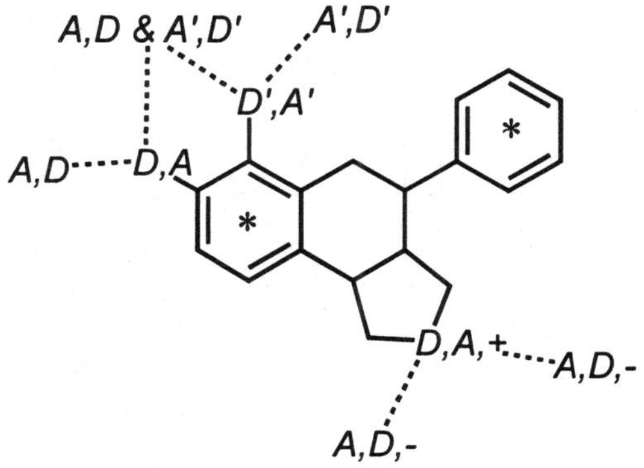

Figure 4.2. The potential pharmacophore points selected by DISCO for compound *1*.

Early in our investigations we discovered that if we included every hydrophobic atom in a structure, DISCO would produce pharma-cophores that overlay hydrophobic groups but no polar atoms. Empirically, we now limit the number of hydrophobic points by, for example, taking only the first atom of a hydrophobic chain. We also programmed DISCO so that one could require that a certain number of points of a certain type were part of any pharmacophore. We would also compare runs where we labeled the centers of aromatic and aliphatic rings the same and runs where we distinguished them.

4.7. Tolerance: The Trade-Off between a Close Match and Including More Points

DISCO considers two distances to be the same if they are within some specified tolerance of each other. It looks for sets of points in two conformations such that all distances between those points are the same in the two conformations. We found that the tolerance is usually approximately double the RMS for superposition of the two objects.[1] In a DISCO run one specifies the lowest tolerance to consider, an increment, and the highest tolerance. We typically start at 1.0 Å and increment by 0.2 Å up to 4.0 Å tolerance.

Our analysis of the D1 dopaminergics *1-5* produced the results shown in Table 4.1.[1] The pharmacophore that results from increasing the tolerance from 0.8 Å to 1.0 Å not only includes the center of mass of the catechol ring but also uses minimum-energy conformations for all of the molecules. The tolerance must be increased to 1.8 Å for the pharmacophore to include the center of mass of the pendant phenyl ring, but even setting 2 Å tolerance and including conformations up to 3 kcal/mole above the global minimum did not result in a pharmacophore that includes the site point for the para-OH group. Plate 4.1 shows the pharmacophore identified at 1.0 Å tolerance. Notice that the centers of the right aromatic ring do not superimpose well and that the projection of the p-OH hydrogen bond would not overlap either.

Table 4.1. The Effect of Varying the Tolerance on the Pharmacophore Maps Produced by DISCO for Structures 1-5 1

Tolerance (Å)	Largest minimum ΔE (kcal/mole)	Points Included	
		Ligand Atoms	**Site Points**
0.8	0.85	N, m-O	N, m-O
1.0	0.02	N, m-O, cm-catechol ring	N, m-O
1.8	0.02	N, m-O, p-O, cm-catechol ring, cm-pendant phenyl	N, m-O
>2.0	>3.00	N, m-O, p-O, cm-catechol ring, cm-pendant phenyl	N, m-O, p-O

4.8. Typical Outcomes and Strategies for Follow-Up

It is natural to expect that a DISCO analysis will produce one compelling pharmacophore. When this is the case, the user moves on to investigating the validity of the result with a 3D QSAR analysis based on the proposed superposition, and then investigating if all inactive compounds are explained by the pharmacophore and 3D QSAR results.

Frequently DISCO produces one pharmacophore, with several possible bioactive conformations for some compounds. The basis for the selection is a matter of balancing the relative energy of the conformation, the match of the pharmacophore points to other compounds in the dataset, and the volume overlap with other compounds.

When DISCO produces more than one distinct pharmacophore map, it indicates that there was not enough information provided to DISCO to distinguish between the possibilities. It may be that one or more pharmacophores can be ruled out because they provide no basis, when coupled with 3D QSAR, to explain inactive compounds. On the other hand, there may be compounds that were not included in the initial analysis that could provide the information to help one decide. Of course, the best course may be to test compounds whose activity or inactivity will distinguish between the possibilities. The D1 novel dopaminergic agonists *1-3* resulted from just such an exercise designed to derive the bioactive conformation of *4*.[22]

For one dataset DISCO could find no pharmacophore that includes more than one site point. We did find subsets of the molecules that match two distinct pharmacophores. We hypothesized that this result suggests either that the molecules are recognized by two different subtypes of the receptor or that some part of the binding site of the receptor is flexible. The value of DISCO is that we felt confident that no over-arching pharmacophore existed: Previously we had spent days hunting for one.

4.9 Shortcomings in DISCO

Whether one considers it a shortcoming or not, the above discussion emphasizes the fact that DISCO is intended to support interactive molecular modeling. Its optimal use requires judicious selection of the compounds to be included; careful conformational searching and structure optimization of the compounds considered; and thoughtful examination of the possible pharmacophores produced.

The distance matrix for enantiomers is identical. As a result, the strategy of using distances to search for pharmacophores must include a post-processing step to identify those pharmacophores for which the molecules superimpose in 3D. This can be either a report of the RMS for each molecule with the reference if the pharmacophore points do not lie in a plane, or a report of the union volume of all compounds.

DISCO bases its pharmacophores only on the distances between the points identified in the input. Hence it does not warn the user that certain of the reported pharmacophores are unattractive because the general shapes of the various molecules do not overlap well. The Tripos version does provide this information to the user, but it is up to the user to decide the relevance of the information.

DISCO is not well suited to deriving pharmacophores when all of the molecules are extremely flexible. Although one could envision strategies to overcome this problem, it is likely that with only flexible molecules in the dataset there is not enough information to derive a pharmacophore.

DISCO is qualitative. Because it considers all points with the same label type to be equivalent, it does not take into account the differences in the tendency of the particular groups to participate in the interaction of interest. For example, many phenols are labeled as potentially being anionic. Given such a phenolate in a structure that also contains a carboxylate, should preference be given to matching the carboxylate to carboxylate in another molecule? If both superpositions meet the distance criteria, then DISCO will report both to the user. The separation between QSAR and pharmacophore mapping is deliberate-specifically, it allows one to base a pharmacophore hypothesis on data from different laboratories without being concerned if the potency measurements are quantitatively comparable. It also allows one to rapidly examine the data for possible pharmacophores and then perform the 3D QSAR once the proposed bioactive conformations and superposition rules have been established.

4.10. DISCO in the Age of HTS and Molecular Diversity

The techniques used in drug discovery have changed dramatically since DISCO was first written. Is it still relevant in the era of high-throughput screening (HTS) and combinatorial chemistry? Pharmacophore mapping has two uses in a drug discovery program: First, to form the basis for the 3D design of a novel structural series, perhaps with the aid of 3D searching; second, to devise a superposition rule for use in 3D QSAR analyses. To the extent to which HTS can identify novel leads, the first use of pharmacophore mapping is not needed. Our experience suggests that a screen's hits in a company compound collection do not contain enough 3D information to provide a basis for a robust pharmacophore model. The compounds frequently have many potential pharmacophore interaction points, are conformationally flexible, or are all close analogues.

Our experience with DISCO prompted us to take a 3D view of molecular diversity. Although we found that atom-based 3D descriptors did not perform as well as substructure-based ones,[23,24] we have indications that for some purposes site-point descriptors outperform substructures.[25] When we select compounds for purchase or combinatorial library design we consider 3D pharmacophore diversity and coverage as well as the substructure diversity.[26-29]

In summary, although we designed DISCO to save modeler time, it is not an automated pharmacophore recognition program. Rather, it is a complement to traditional molecular modeling. Using DISCO can provide answers to a number of questions with the result that the interactive modeling is more efficient.

References

1. Martin YC: **Distance comparisons (DISCO): A new strategy for examining 3D structure-activity relationships.** In: *Classical and 3D QSAR in Agrochemistry.* Hansch C, Fujita T, eds. Washington, DC: American Chemical Society, 1995:318-329.

2. Blaney JM, Crippen GM, Dearing A, Dixon JS: *DGEOM. Distance Geometry; QCPE 590 Quantum Chemistry Program Exchange.* Bloomington IN 47405: Indiana University, 1990.

3. Sheridan RP, Nilakantan R, Dixon JS, Venkataraghavan R: **The ensemble approach to distance geometry: Application to the nicotinic pharmacophore.** *J Med Chem* 1986, 29:899-906.

4. Mayer D, Naylor C. B, Motoc I, Marshall GR: **A unique geometry of the active site of angiotensin-converting enzyme consistent with structure-activity studies.** *J Comput-Aided Mol Des* 1987, **1**:3-16.

5. Bron C, Kerbosch J: Algorithm 457. **Finding all cliques of an undirected graph.** *Communications of the ACM* 1973, **16**:575-577.

6. Kuhl FS, Crippen GM, Friesen DK: **A combinatorial algorithm for calculating ligand binding.** *J Comp Chem* 1984, **5**:24-34.

7. Brint AT, Willett P: **Algorithms for the identification of three-dimensional maximal common substructures.** *J Chem Inf Comput Sci* 1987, 27:152-158.

8. Takahashi Y, Maeda S, Sasaki S-I: **Automated recognition of common geometrical patterns among a variety of three-dimensional molecular structures.** *Analytica Chimica Acta* 1987, **200**:363-377.

9. *SYBYL, Molecular Modeling Software.* TRIPOS, Inc.: 1699 S. Hanley Road, St. Louis, MO 63944.

10. Martin YC: **Pharmacophore mapping.** In: *Designing Bioactive Molecules: Three-Dimensional Techniques and Application.* Martin YC, Willett P, eds. Washington, DC: American Chemical Society, 1998:121-148.

11. Burkert U, Allinger NL: *Molecular Mechanics.* Washington, DC: American Chemical Society 1982.

12. *DISCOVER.* Molecular Simulations: San Diego, CA, 1992.

13. Dewar MJS, Zoebish EG, Healy EF, Stewart JJP: **AM1: A new general purpose quantum mechanical molecular model.** *J Am Chem Soc* 1985, **07**:3902-3909.

14. Kier LB: *Molecular Orbital Theory in Drug Research.* New York: Academic Press, 1971.

15. Marshall GR, Barry CD, Bosshard HE, Dammkoehler RA, Dunn DA: **The conformation parameter in drug design: The active analog approach.** In: *Computer-Assisted Drug Design.* Olson EC, Christoffersen RE, eds. Washington, DC: American Chemical Society, 1979:205-226.

16. Martin YC, Bures MG, Danaher EA, DeLazzer J, Lico I, Pavlik PA: **A fast new approach to pharmacophore mapping and its application to dopaminergic and benzodiazepine agonists.** *J Comput-Aided Mol Des* 1993, **7**:83-102.

17. Sham H, Bolis G, Stein H, Fesik S, Marcotte P, Plattner J, Remple C, Greer J: **Renin inhibitors: Design and synthesis of a new class of conformationally restricted analogs of angiotensinogen.** *J Med Chem* 1988, 31:284-295.

18. Martin YC, Danaher E, Rys J: REJECT, Private communication.

19. Martin YC, Lin CT: **Three-dimensional quantitative structure-activity relationships: D2 dopamine agonists as an example.** In: *The Practice of Medicinal Chemistry.* Wermuth CG, ed. London: Academic Press, 1996:459-483.

20. Van Drie JH, Weininger D, Martin YC: **ALADDIN: An integrated tool for computer-assisted molecular design and pharmacophore recognition from geometric, steric, and substructure searching of three-dimensional molecular structures.** *J Comput-Aided Mol Des* 1989, 3:225-251.

21. *Cambridge Structural Database System User's Manual.* Parts 1 and 2. Cambridge, England: Cambridge Crystallographic Data Centre, 1989.

22. Martin YC, Kebabian JW, MacKenzie R, Schoenleber R: **Molecular modeling-based design of novel, selective, potent D1 dopamine agonists.** In: *QSAR: Rational Approaches On The Design Of Bioactive Compounds.* Silipo C, Vittoria A, eds. Amsterdam: Elsevier, 1991:469-482.

23. Brown RD, Bures MG, Martin YC: **A comparison of some commercially available structural descriptors and clustering algorithms.** In: *Proceedings of the First Electronic Computational Chemistry Conference.* Bachrach SM, Boyd DB, Gray SK, Hase W, Rzepa HS, eds. Landover, MD: ARInternet, 1995.

24. Brown RD, Martin YC: **Use of structure-activity data to compare structure-based clustering methods and descriptors for use in compound selection.** *J Chem Inf Comput Sci* 1996, 36:572-584.

25. Martin YC, Brown RD, Danaher EA, DeLazzer J, Lico I: **3D descriptors that outperform substructures in diversity analysis.** In: *Abstracts of Papers of the American Chemical Society,* 1997, 214:46-CINF.

26. Bures MG, Brown R, Martin YC: **Analyzing larger databases to increase the diversity of the Abbott corporate compound collection.** In: *Abstracts of Papers of the American Chemical Society,* 1995, 210:60-CINF.

27. Brown RD, Bures MG, Martin YC: **Similarity and cluster-analysis applied to molecular diversity.** In: *Abstracts of Papers of the American Chemical Society,* 1995, 209:3-COMP.

28. Martin Y, Brown R, Bures M, Pavlik P: **Strategies and concerns in applying diversity or similarity measures to large databases.** In: *Abstracts of Papers of the American Chemical Society,* 1995, **210**:126-MEDI.

29. Martin YC, Brown RD, Bures MG: **Quantifying diversity.** In: *Combinatorial Chemistry and Molecular Diversity.* Kerwin JF, Gordon EM, eds. New York: Wiley, 1998:369-385.

5

HipHop: Pharmacophores Based on Multiple Common-Feature Alignments

Omoshile O. Clement and Adrea Trope Mehl

Abstract

A daunting task for the researcher today is to decipher how structurally diverse molecules can bind at a common receptor site. When considering a receptor of unknown structure, an analysis of the ligand set will be highly dependent on both the choice of active conformation and the proposed alignment of these molecules with respect to one another. Although the molecules belong to different structural classes of compounds, they may contain a common three-dimensional arrangement of features. The Catalyst program HipHop generates a set of common feature pharmacophore models from a set of compounds known to be active at a specific therapeutic area. The features consist of generalized chemical functions that simulate those characteristics necessary for receptor binding. The resulting three-dimensional configuration can be used as a search query for mining a 3D database in order to identify other possible lead candidates. The compounds retrieved from a database search using this generalized query are often more structurally varied than if the query is based solely on topology. HipHop can also be used to suggest possible alignments of the active molecules. This is a key step in field-based 3D QSAR methods. Finally, using HipHop, one can generate a pharmacophore in the early stages of a project from only a small set of compounds of known or unknown activities. The generated pharmacophore model, or hypothesis, can be further optimized in an iterative manner in the quest for new lead candidates.

5

HipHop: Pharmacophores Based on Multiple Common-Feature Alignments

Omoshile O. Clement and Adrea Trope Mehl

Molecular Simulations Inc., San Diego, California

5.1. Background

Different tools and strategies can be applied to the drug discovery process depending on the available information of ligand or receptor structures and activities. Traditional drug discovery processes often involve taking a lead molecule, iteratively synthesizing a large number of its analogs, and carrying out biological testing of these compounds. These steps help to derive a structure-activity relationship which relates structural property to some measure of therapeutic efficacy.[1]

In the absence of a crystallographic structure of a protein for which the active site for receptor binding is clearly identified, the chemist must rely on the structure activity data for a given set of ligands. If these ligands are known to bind to the same receptor, then one can attempt to define the commonality between them. MSI's Catalyst®[2] can generate two types of chemical feature-based models or hypotheses, depending on whether or not activity data is used. If activity data is included, then Catalyst/HypoGen®[2] is employed. Feature-based models derived by Catalyst/HypoGen have been successfully used to suggest new directions in lead generation/lead discovery[3-6] and for searching a database to identify new structural classes of potential lead candidates.[7,8] Alternatively, when no activity data is considered during hypothesis building, and only common chemical features are requested, the Catalyst/HipHop program[9] can be used for this purpose.

A pharmacophore model, or hypothesis, consists of a three-dimensional configuration of chemical functions[10] surrounded by tolerance spheres. A tolerance sphere defines that area in space that should be occupied by a specific type of chemical functionality. Each chemical function is assigned a weight, which describes its relative importance within the hypothesis. A larger weight indicates that the feature is more important in conferring activity than the other composite parts of the hypothesis.

In this chapter, we describe the generalized methodology employed in automated pharmacophore model generation using the Catalyst/HipHop program.[9] The terms "pharmacophore" and "hypothesis" will be used interchangeably to refer to these three-dimensional objects. In addition, we shall outline some important factors that we hope the reader will find helpful in obtaining a useful feature-based pharmacophore model. Finally, we will highlight recent examples of the utility of this approach in the design/discovery and evaluation of new drug candidates.

5.2. Methodology

5.2.1. General Considerations

The alignment of a group of training set molecules plays a key role in 3D QSAR techniques.[11,12] Selecting the proper relative orientation of molecules will have a profound impact on the pharmacophore model. Numerous combined approaches have been reported in the literature using Catalyst/HipHop or Catalyst/HypoGen® as the alignment tool, followed by field analysis[12] or generation of receptor surface models.[11] In cases where the biological activities are known, and cover a range of 4 to 5 orders of magnitude, Catalyst/HypoGen can include the dependent property—biological activity—in the alignment phase. Langer and Hoffmann used this approach to align a set of structurally diverse squalene epoxidase inhibitors, followed by PLS analysis of the steric and electrostatic matrices as 3D descriptors, to produce predictive 3D QSAR models.[13] Similar applications of this approach in the generation of 3D-QSAR models for ergosterol biosynthesis inhibitors,[14] GABA receptor blockers,[14] and LTD$_4$ receptor antagonists,[15] have also been reported.

When the ligand set is small (less than 15 compounds), and sufficient biological data is absent, one can build a model based on common feature alignments using Catalyst/HipHop.[9] This is a first step approximation of the orientation of ligands at the receptor site. HipHop has been used to align a set of molecules based on their common chemical features.[7,8,16,17] In one such study, the aligned molecules generated by HipHop were used to build a Receptor Surface Model[11] for ETA endothelin antagonists.[16] The molecular properties (descriptors) of these antagonists were derived from the interaction energies of the molecules with points distributed over the surface of the pseudo receptor model. These descriptors/independent variables were then used to generate a 3D QSAR model.

5.2.2. Algorithm

HipHop identifies configurations or three-dimensional spatial arrangements of chemical features that are common to molecules in a training set.[9] The configurations are identified by a pruned exhaustive search, starting with small sets of features and extending them until no larger common configuration is found. Training set members are evaluated on the basis of the types of chemical features they contain, along with the ability to adopt a conformation that allows those features to be superimposed on a particular configuration. The user defines how many molecules must map completely or partially to the hypothesis. This user-defined option allows broader and more diverse hypotheses to be generated. The resultant pharmacophores are ranked as they are built. The ranking is a measure of how well the molecules map onto the proposed pharmacophores, as well as the rarity of the pharmacophore model.[9] If a pharmacophore model is less likely to map to an inactive compound, then it will be given a higher rank; the reverse is also true.

5.2.3. Choosing Relevant Conformations

HipHop uses conformational models that are not limited to a specific reference conformer. Rather, each training set member is comprised of a collection of low energy conformers that covers the conformational space available to that molecule.[18,19] Catalyst selects conformers using a Poling technique[20] to ensure broad coverage of the available conformational space. Poling explicitly promotes conformational variation within the accessible space. Alternatively, any set of conformations generated outside Catalyst can also be imported into the program and used as HipHop input. The program recognizes a variety of multi-conformer input file formats such as sd [MDL], mol2 [SYBYL], and mmod [MACROMODEL]. All conformers are treated equally; each is considered as a possible configuration of functional groups or features.

5.2.4. Feature Definitions

Rather than limiting descriptions of molecular features to simple topological features such as a phenyl, carbonyl group, or nitrogen, feature definitions are general chemical functions that describe the kinds of interactions important for ligand-receptor binding. HipHop contains, by default, definitions for hydrogen-bond donors and acceptors, negative and positive charge centers, and surface accessible hydrophobic regions.[10] The hydrophobe definition can be specific for aliphatic and aromatic, or nonspecific to include both. Hydrogen-bond acceptors and donors are comprised of two parts: the heavy atom and the projected point of complementary site atoms. The projected points must reside outside the ligand surface. The resulting vector gives the hydrogen-bonding features directionality, and provides further discrimination in a search query. In addition, feature definitions can be customized using the CHM query language.[21] For example, the positive ionizable feature can be expanded to include an imidazole ring, since the latter would be protonated at physiological pH.[22]

5.2.5. Generating Common Feature Hypotheses Using HipHop

HipHop generates feature-based 3D pharmacophoric alignments in a three-step procedure: (a) A conformational model for each molecule in the training set is generated, (b) each conformer is examined for the presence of chemical features, and (c) a three-dimensional configuration of chemical features common to the input molecules is determined. These steps are described below.

5.2.6. Input Conformers

One can create a common feature hypothesis using HipHop with as few as two or as many as 32 compounds in a training set. No activity data is required because only chemical features common to all training set molecules are taken into account in the model generation. Each training set compound must have conformational models. This can either be a set of conformers which describes the conformational space available to that compound, or a single set of coordinates which represents the active conformer. In the latter case, this information is usually extracted from the X-ray structure of the enzyme-bound ligand.

Where the X-ray structure has not been determined, representative conformational models can be generated using Catalyst/ConFirm®.[2] This method aims to cover the available conformational space using distance-based geometry optimization of each conformer. A poling function is added to the minimization equation,[20] which penalizes a newly generated conformer if it is too close to any other conformer in the set. This ensures a representative conformational model.

5.2.7. Parameter Settings

(a) *Feature types*: The user selects the feature types that the program should consider during hypothesis generation. The available features in the Catalyst program are: hydrogen-bond donors and acceptors, hydrophobes (aliphatic and aromatic), and ionizable groups (negative and positive). Any knowledge of criteria for ligand-receptor binding should be included in the feature selection. If hypothesis generation is biased towards specific feature types, then HipHop can focus on hypotheses which are more biologically relevant. For example, if it is known that an ionized carboxylic acid is crucial for receptor binding, then the HipHop set-up should include a **negative ionizable** feature. The minimum and maximum number of any one feature can also be specified. Similarly, one would not include any feature type that is not present in training set members.

HipHop can accommodate hypotheses with up to 10 different features or a maximum of 20 points per hypothesis. The user can specify the minimum number of features in each generated hypotheses. Some of the features (i.e., HBA, HBD, RING AROMATIC) are represented by a vector, and hence are comprised of two points. Other features such as hydrophobes and ionizable functions are made up of a single point. A pharmacophore model with three **hydrophobes**, two **hydrogen-bond acceptors**, and a **positive ionizable** is described as a six-feature model with a total of eight points. The default value for the minimum number of feature points in any hypothesis is four—the smallest number of points which will return a hypothesis that is enantio-selective. Small molecules with few chemical features may require setting the minimum number of total points to a value of three.

(b) *Inter-feature distance:* This is the minimum distance between any two features to be considered by the program during the iterative generation of a pharmacophore model. The training set will often dictate how this parameter should be set. In the Catalyst/HipHop program, the default inter-feature spacing of 3 Å may not be suitable for all training set members. This default setting of 3 Å is often applicable to larger, more flexible molecules, while small, rigid molecules will often require a value lower than 3 Å. Hoffmann and Kitson[17] showed that small, highly flexible piperazino compounds can be mapped simultaneously to both a hydrophobe and a positive ionizable feature if the inter-feature spacing is set to 1 Å. In small molecules with relatively few features, the ability to adjust this parameter allows for more hypotheses to be generated. However, in cases where molecules are feature-rich, the user may want to adjust the inter-feature spacing to allow the return of fewer and more meaningful hypotheses.

Other strategies for dealing with small, rigid training sets have been employed. For instance, vectored features place very stringent constraints on small molecules. Not only does the molecule need to contain the feature type, but all training set members must also map to the heavy atom and the projected point along a single vector. To relax this requirement, custom features which contain only the projected points for the HBA and HBD can be used in hypothesis generation.

(c) *Partial mappings:* HipHop allows for partial mappings of compounds to the pharmacophores. This will accomodate more diverse pharmacophore models in which not all compounds map to every feature. It also allows for cases where a training set member completely misses mapping to the pharmacophore. This is an important consideration, since a compound can show activity in a given assay, but may actually bind at a different site or act through a different mechanism.

(d) *HipHop output:* The user can define the maximum number of hypotheses that will be generated. All hypotheses that meet the user specified criteria will be returned in order of rank. Hypotheses are ranked based on the portion of training set members that fit the proposed pharmacophore, and the rarity of the pharmacophore. The higher the ranking, the less likely it is that the molecules fit the hypothesis by a chance correlation. The geometrical fit of the pharmacophore to the molecules considers partial mappings, as specified by the user during the hypothesis generation setup.

5.3. Applications

Two previous reviews published since 1995[7,8] have covered in some detail feature-based pharmacophore modeling of known inhibitors of (a) angiotensin converting enzyme (ACE), (b) the protein farnesyl transferase (PFT), (c) HIV-1 protease (PHIV), and (d) HIV reverse transcriptase (RTHIV). In these studies, activity-based Catalyst/HypoGen hypotheses were generated and evaluated as search queries to mine 3D databases in the quest for new leads. Here we describe the application of the Catalyst/HipHop program[9] for generating chemical feature-based models for arylpiperazine-based serotonin 5-HT3 antagonists,[17] ETA endothelin antagonists,[16] and HIV-1 protease inhibitors.

5.3.1. 5-HT3 Antagonists

A common feature-based pharmacophore modeling study of arylpiperazine-based serotonin 5-HT3 receptor antagonists has been reported.[17] The training set for the study had 12 structurally homologous compounds (Chart 1) which, combined with the small range in measured binding affinities, made this suitable for a HipHop hypothesis generation. Using Catalyst/HipHop, a set of four 5-feature pharmacophore models were generated consisting of two hydrophobes, a hydrogen-bond acceptor (with a point feature projected from the heavy atom of the antagonists), a positive ionizable feature, and a ring aromatic feature.

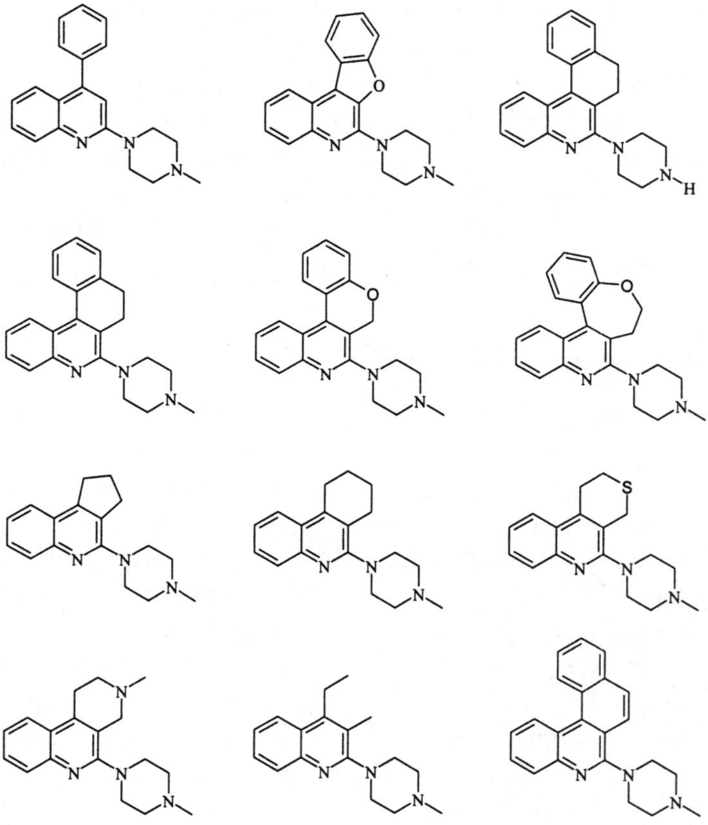

Chart 5.1.

The 12 arylpiperazines in the training set were mapped onto all four HipHop models. Two of the models mapped the hydrophobic features in the piperazine moieties, while two others mapped the 4-phenyl and 3-alkyl substituents on the quinoline ring. By merging two of these hypotheses, a 6-feature model was derived (Plate 5.1). The merged model was further refined by manually adjusting the weights and tolerances of the hydrophobic features.

The model was validated by mapping it onto two well known non-arylpiperazine-based 5-HT3 antagonists—MDL72222[23] and Ondansetron.[24] Finally, the model in Plate 5.1 was used as a search query to mine the Derwent WDI database[25] for new leads. Cilansetron, a well known 5-HT3 antagonist, was retrieved from the database search with a high geometric fit value to the search query.

5.3.2. ET$_A$ Endothelin Antagonists

A set of four highly active arylsulfonamide-based ETA inhibitors (Chart 5.2)[16] were used as training molecules to generate common feature-based alignments (Plate 5.2). Using Catalyst/HipHop, all four training molecules were constrained to map to all the chemical features in the pharmacophore models. Feature-based alignment of a set of 36 molecules (including the four training set members) with the statistically most relevant pharmacophore model was then carried out. The aligned molecules were exported into MSI's Cerius^2 (see reference[26]) as input for generating a 3D QSAR receptor surface model (RSM).

5.3.3. HIV-1 Protease Inhibitors

In a previous study, Sprague[8] identified 12 chemical functionalities for an HIV-1 protease inhibitor (SB-203386), using an enzyme bound conformation as the template molecule. A subset model of these features containing three hydrogen-bond acceptors and four hydrophobic groups was derived and used as a search query to mine the Derwent Drug Database.[25] Although preliminary in nature, this model was useful in suggesting a biologically relevant, and synthetically accessible motif based on a sulfonamide-sulfone backbone.

With the significant increase in reported crystal structures of HIV-1 protease-inhibitor bound complexes deposited in the Brookhaven Protein Databank, a common feature-based pharmacophore alignment of the enzyme-bound ligands can be determined using HipHop. In the present study, six of these structures (Chart 5.3) were used to generate a chemical feature-based pharmacophore model. A set of 10 models were generated. The highest ranking was a 6-feature model containing three hydrogen-bond acceptors, one hydrogen-bond donor, one ring aro-

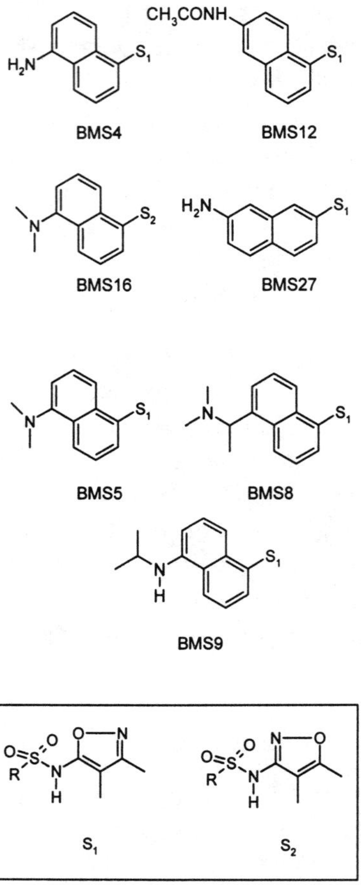

Chart 5.2.

matic and one hydrophobic group (Plate 5.3, a). The model was evaluated against two HIV-1 protease inhibitors—JE2147[27] and L-700,417.[28] Alignment of the model onto these compounds is shown in Plate 5.3, b. For these molecules, the HipHop model consistently mapped one or more hydrogen-bond acceptors, the ring aromatic feature and the aliphatic hydrophobic group, while missing the hydrogen-bond donor and one hydrogen-bond acceptor. This may indicate that some features in the pharmacophore model are more important than others.

This model was then used as a search query to mine the Derwent Drug Database. A flexible (BEST) search retrieved 294 compounds (<1%) in the database, indicating its high selectivity. The model retrieved two known HIV-1 protease inhibitors—U76088 and CGP-57813. A feature-based alignment of one of these compounds with the HipHop model is shown in Plate 5.4.

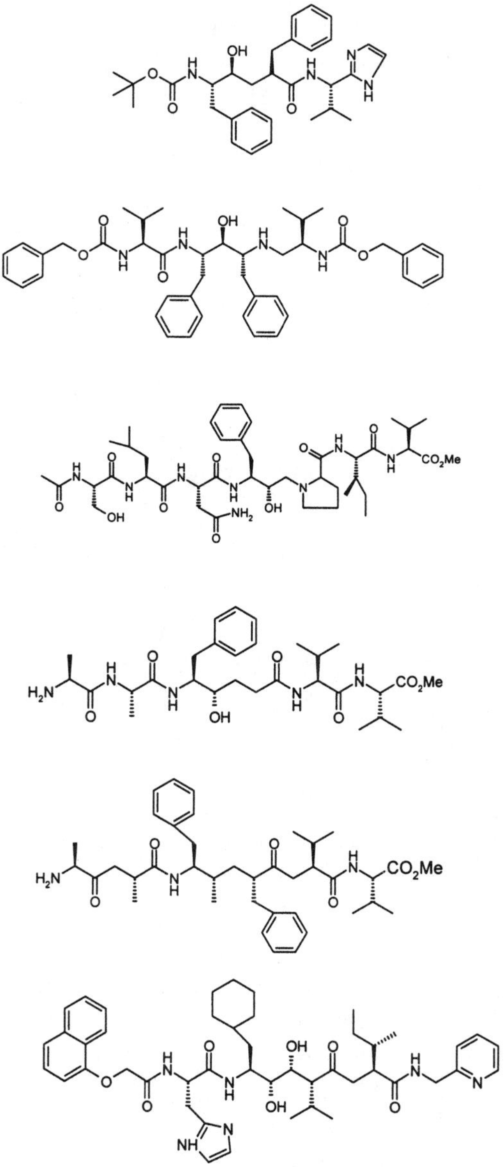

Chart 5.3.

5.4. Conclusion

We have shown that the Catalyst/HipHop program can be used to generate three-dimensional pharmacophore hypotheses based on common features for a set of molecules. Regardless of the structural diversity or similarity of the training set, HipHop hypotheses that describe these configurations are useful as starting alignments for further 3D QSAR studies, database queries, and/or lead generation.

References

1. Greer J, Erickson JW, Baldwin JJ, Varney MD: **Application of the three-dimensional structures of protein target molecules in structure-based drug design.** *J Med Chem 1994*, **37**:1035-1042.

2. *Catalyst* is distributed by Molecular Simulations Inc., 9685 Scranton Road, San Diego, CA 92121, USA.

3. Duffy JC, Dearden JC, Green DSV: **Use of Catalyst in the design of novel non-steroidal anti-inflammatory analgesic drugs.** In: *QSAR and Molecular Modelling: Concepts, Computational Tools and Biological Applications.* Sanz F, Giraldo J, Manaut J, eds. Barcelona: Prous Science Publishers, 1995:289-291.

4. Daveu C, Bureau R, Baglin I, Prunier H, Lancelot J, Rault S: **Definition of a pharmacophore for partial agonists of serotonin 5-HT3 receptors.** *J Chem Inf Comput Sci* 1999, **39**:362-369.

5. Quintana J, Contijoch M, Cuberes R, Frigola J: **Structure-Activity relationships and molecular modeling studies of a series of H1 antihistamines.** In: *QSAR and Molecular Modelling: Concepts, Computational Tools and Biological Applications.* Sanz F, Giraldo J, Manaut F, eds. Barcelona: Prous Science Publishers, 1995:282-288.

6. Grigorov M, Weber J, Tronchet JMJ, Jefford CW, Milhous WK, Maric D: **A QSAR study of the antimalarial activity of some 1,2,4-trioxanes.** *J Chem Inf Comput Sci* 1997, **37**:124-130.

7. Sprague PW, Hoffmann R: **Catalyst pharmacophore models and their utility as queries for searching 3D databases.** In: *Computer Assisted Lead Finding and Optimization-Current Tools for Medicinal Chemistry.* Van de Waterbeemd H, Testa B, Folkers G, eds. Basel: VHCA, 1997:230-240.

8. Sprague PW: **Automated chemical hypothesis generation and database searching with Catalyst.** In: *Perspectives in Drug Discovery and Design,* Vol. 3. Müller K, ed. ESCOM Science Publishers B. V., 1995:1-20.

9. Barnum D, Greene J, Smellie A, Sprague P: **Identification of common functional configurations among molecules.** *J Chem Inf Comput Sci* 1996, **36**:563-571.

10. Greene J, Kahn S, Savoj H, Sprague P, Teig S: **Chemical function queries for 3D database search.** *J Chem Inf Comput Sci* 1994, **34**:1297-1308.

11. **(a)** Hahn MA: **Receptor surface models. 1. Definition and construction.** *J Med Chem* 1995, **38**:2080-2090; **(b)** Hahn M, Rogers D: **Receptor surface models. 2. Application to quantitative structure-activity relationships studies.** *J Med Chem* 1995, **38**:2091-2102.

12. Cramer RD III, Patterson DE, Bunce JD: **Comparative Molecular Field Analysis (CoMFA). 1. Effect of shape on binding of steroids to carrier proteins.** *J Am Chem Soc* 1988, **110**:5959-5967.

13. Langer T, Hoffmann RD: **On the use of chemical function-based alignments as input for 3D-QSAR.** *J Chem Inf Comput Sci* 1998, **38**:325-330.

14. Norinder U: **The alignment problem in 3D-QSAR: A combined approach using Catalyst and a 3D-QSAR technique.** In: *QSAR and Molecular Modelling: Concepts, Computational Tools and Biological Applications.* Sanz F, Giraldo J, Manaut, F, eds. Barcelona: Prous Science Publishers, 1995:433-438.

15. Palomer A, Giolitti A, Garcia ML, Cabre F, Mauleon D, Carganico G: **Molecular modeling and CoMFA investigations on LTD4 receptor antagonists.** In: *QSAR and Molecular Modelling: Concepts, Computational Tools and Biological Applications.* Sanz F, Giraldo J, Manaut F, eds. Barcelona: Prous Science Publishers, 1995:444-450.

16. Hoffmann R, Kitson D: **3D-QSAR Models for ETA endothelin antagonists using Catalyst and Cerius². RDD Application Note.** (http://www.msi.com/solutions/cases/notes/endothelin_full.html) Molecular Simulations, Inc., 9685 Scranton Road, San Diego, CA 92121, USA.

17. Hoffmann R, Kitson D: **Building a common feature hypothesis for arylpiperazine based 5-HT3 antagonists. Application Note.** (http://www.msi.com/solutions/cases/notes/5HT3.html) Molecular Simulations, Inc., 9685 Scranton Road, San Diego, CA 92121. USA.

18. Smellie A, Kahn SD, Teig S: **An analysis of conformational coverage 1. Validation and estimation of coverage.** *J Chem Inf Comput Sci* 1995, **35**:285-294.

19. Smellie A, Kahn SD, Teig S: **An analysis of conformational coverage 2. Applications of conformational models.** *J Chem Inf Comput Sci* 1995, **35**:295-304.

20. Smellie A, Teig SL, Towbin P: **Poling: Promoting conformational coverage.** *J Comp Chem* 1995, **16**:171-187.

21. Berezin S, Greene J, Kahn S, Ku S, Teig S: CHM: **A chemically expressive database query language.** *Noordwijkerhout Camerino Medicinal Chemistry Symposium.* Noordwijkerhout, Netherlands, 1993.

22. *Catalyst Tutorials*, Release 4.0, Exercise 11, Molecular Simulations, Inc., San Diego, CA. 92121, USA.

23. Martin Y, Burs M, Danaher E, DeLazzer J: **New strategies that improve the efficiency of the 3D design of bioactive molecules.** In: *Trends in QSAR and Molecular Modelling 92.* Wermuth CG, ed. Leiden: ESCOM, 1993:20-27.

24. **(a)** Hibert M, Hoffmann R, Miller RC, Carr AA: **Conformation-Activity relationship study of 5-HT3 receptor antagonists and a definition of a model for this receptor site.** *J Med Chem* 1990, 33:1594-1600; **(b)** Swain CJ, Baker R, Kneen C, Moseley J, Saunders J, Seward EM, Stevenson G, Beer M, Stanton J, Watlin K: **Novel 5-HT3 antagonists: Indole-oxadiazoles.** *J Med Chem* 1991, **34**:140-151.

25. *Derwent Drug Database* is distributed by Derwent, 1725 Duke Street, Suite 250, Alexandria, VA 22314. USA.

26. *Cerius²* is distributed by Molecular Simulations Inc., 9685 Scranton Road, San Diego, CA 92121, USA.

27. Mimoto T, Kato R, Takahu H, Nojima S, Terashima K, Misawa S, Fukazawa T, Ueno T, Sato H, Shintani M, Kiso Y, Hayashi H: **Structure-Activity relationship of small-sized HIV protease inhibitors containing allophenylnorstatine.** *J Med Chem* 1999, **42**:1789-802.

28. Bone R, Vacca JP, Anderson PS, Holloway MK: **X-ray crystal structure of the HIV protease complex with L-700,417, an inhibitor with pseudo C2 symmetry.** *J Am Chem Soc* 1991, **113**:9382-9384.

6

GASP: Genetic Algorithm Superimposition Program

**Gareth Jones, Peter Willett,
and Robert C. Glen**

Abstract

GASP is a program that uses a genetic algorithm to superimpose sets of flexible molecules. A chromosome in this algorithm encodes angles of rotation about flexible bonds and mappings between hydrogen-bond donor proton, acceptor lone-pair and ring-center features in pairs of molecules. The molecule with the smallest number of features in the dataset is used as a template onto which the remaining molecules are fitted with the objective of maximizing structural equivalences. The fitness function in this algorithm is a weighted combination of: the number and the similarity of the features that have been overlaid in this way; the volume integral of the overlay; and the van der Waals energy of the molecular conformations defined by the torsion angles encoded in the chromosomes. The algorithm has been applied to a number of pharmacophore elucidation problems with satisfactory results.

6

GASP: Genetic Algorithm Superimposition Program

Gareth Jones[†], Peter Willett[†], and Robert C. Glen[‡]

[†]Arena Pharmaceuticals Inc., San Diego, California
[‡]University of Cambridge, Cambridge, U.K.

6.1. Introduction

As this book shows, there is much interest in computer methods to assist in the discovery of pharmacophoric patterns, thus helping to rationalize the wealth of structural and biological data now available from combinatorial chemistry and high-throughput screening programs in the pharmaceutical and agrochemical industries. In this chapter we describe a program, called GASP (for Genetic Algorithm Superimposition Program),[1] that can be used for this purpose. GASP was developed as part of a research project to evaluate the utility of genetic algorithms (hereafter GAs) for tackling combinatorial problems in molecular recognition. The project also considered procedures for matching large chemical graphs,[2] for 3D database searching[3] and for flexible ligand docking;[4,5] indeed, GASP exploits some of the methods that were developed in the docking program, GOLD.

GAs first attracted widespread attention as a general method for combinatorial optimization with the publication of Goldberg's book at the in 1989,[6] but there had been very few reports of their use for applications in molecular recognition when we commenced work in 1991 (since then, of course, they have been used extensively, as detailed in the comprehensive bibliography maintained by Clark).[7] Our interest in the use of GAs for pharmacophore identification arose from the fact that the pharmacophore-detection procedures then available suffered from one or more of the following characteristics: They required manual intervention to specify at least some points of commonality, thus biasing the resulting overlays; they encompassed conformational flexibility by considering some low-energy conformations, rather than by considering the full conformational space of the molecules that were to be overlaid; or they were extremely time-consuming in operation. GASP was designed to align sets of molecules, and thus to identify the patterns common to them, without suffering from these limitations.

A GA is a computer program that mimics the process of evolution by manipulating a *population* of data-structures called *chromosomes*. A *steady-state-with-no-duplicates* GA[6,8,9] was used in the experiments reported here, as summarized in Figure 6.1. Starting from an initial randomly generated population of chromosomes, the GA repeatedly applies two genetic operators, *crossover* and *mutation*. These result in chromosomes that replace the least-fit members of the population, where the fitness measures how good a solution to the problem under investigation is encoded in that chromosome. Crossover combines chromosomes while mutation introduces random perturbations. Both operators require *parent* chromosomes that are randomly selected from the existing population with a bias towards the fittest, thus introducing an evolutionary pressure into the algorithm. This selection is known as *roulette-wheel selection,* as the procedure is analogous to spinning a roulette wheel with each member of the population having a slice of the wheel that is proportional to its fitness. The emphasis on the survival of the fittest ensures that, over time, the population should move towards the optimum solution: In the present context this corresponds to the best possible structural overlay of a series of active molecules that are presumed to bind to a biological receptor in a similar fashion.

Given a set of active molecules, GASP selects one of them as a *base molecule,* to which the other molecules are fitted. A chromosome in GASP encodes a range of information that is necessary to ensure an appropriate overlay of a molecule onto the base molecule. Specifically, each chromosome contains binary strings that encode angles of rotation about the rotatable bonds in all of the molecules, and integer strings that map hydrogen-bond donor protons, acceptor lone pairs and ring centers in the base molecule to corresponding sites in each of the other molecules. A least-squares fitting process is used to overlay molecules onto

---

1. A set of reproduction operators (crossover, mutation, etc.) is chosen. Each operator is assigned a weight.

2. An initial population is randomly created and the fitnesses of its members determined.

3. An operator is chosen using roulette-wheel selection based on operator weights.

4. The parents required by the operator are chosen using roulette-wheel selection based on scaled fitness.

5. The operator is applied and child chromosomes produced. Their fitness is evaluated.

6. The children replace the least fit members of the population.

7. If an acceptable solution has been found stop; otherwise go to Step 3.

Figure 6.1. Operator-Based GA.

the base molecule in such a way that as many as possible of the structural equivalences suggested by the mapping are formed. The fitness of a decoded chromosome is then a combination of the number and similarity of overlaid features, the volume integral of the overlay, and the van der Waals energy of the molecular conformations. The genetic operators are used to drive the algorithm to the molecular superimposition that maximizes the value of this fitness function.

Having given a brief introduction to GAs and the overall structure of GASP, we now present the principal components of the program before illustrating its performance on several typical datasets: A more detailed account is provided by Jones et al.[1] GASP is available as a commercial product from Tripos Inc., as an additional module to the SYBYL molecular modeling package.[10]

6.2. The Chromosome Representation and the Genetic Operators

6.2.1. Input of 3D Structures

In the absence of refined crystallographic coordinates, an input structure is created using the SYBYL BUILD module, with hydrogen atoms added to all atoms with free valences. Groups within the input structure are ionized if this is appropriate at physiological pH (e.g., alkyl amines or carboxylic acids), and specific atoms are protonated if this is indicated by pK_a or NMR data. A low-energy conformation is generated using the SYBYL MAXIMIN energy minimizer with Gasteiger-Marsilli charges, and the resulting conformation written out as a MOL2 file. It should be noted that while we have used SYBYL routines to prepare input files, GASP merely requires low energy starting structures in MOL2 format which may be generated by alternative packages.

The conformations are used as input to the GASP program. Initially, all rings are identified using a smallest-set-of-smallest-rings algorithm,[11] and each structure is then analyzed to determine the *features* that are present, where a feature is a hydrogen-bond donor proton, a lone pair or a ring. The *base molecule* is defined to be that molecule with the smallest number of features. Hydrogen-bond donor and acceptor atoms are identified in each of the input structures using the SYBYL atom-type characterization in Table 6.1 (with the restriction that each donor must be bonded to at least one hydrogen). Donor hydrogens can then be identified, and lone pairs are added to acceptors at a distance of 1.0 Å from the acceptor. All freely rotatable single bonds that are not connected to terminating atoms are selected as rotatable. Prior to superimposition, a random translation is applied to each input structure (including the base molecule) and random rotations are applied to each of the rotatable bonds.

Table 6.1. Allowed donors and acceptors based on SYBYL atom types.

SYBYL Atom Types	Donor	Acceptor
N.3, N.2, O.3	Y	Y
N.1, N.ar, O.2, O.co2, F, Br, Cl	N	Y
N.am, N.pl3, N.4	Y	N

6.2.2. Chromosome Representation

Assume that a set of N molecules, processed as described above, is to be analyzed to find the pharmacophoric patterns that are common to them. Then a chromosome in GASP contains a total of $2N$-1 strings, these comprising:

- N Gray-coded[6] binary strings, each encoding conformational information for one structure with each byte encoding an angle of rotation about a rotatable bond;

- N-1 integer strings, each encoding a mapping between features in a molecule (other than the base molecule) to features, of the same type, in the base molecule.

On decoding a chromosome, GASP's fitness function tries to satisfy the specified mappings by using a least-squares fitting technique. In order to make the mapping chemically sensible, the mapping is one-to-one between similar features: For example, it would not make sense if a lone pair is mapped to two different lone pairs in the base molecule, or if a lone pair is mapped onto a hydrogen-bond donor proton. Each of the N-1 integer strings is of length L, where L is the number of features in the base molecule. Because the mappings are one-to-one the integer string is constrained to have no duplicate values. Each feature in each molecule is assigned a unique label, and the labels of the base-molecule features are then arranged in a list of length L. If V is the integer value at position P on the integer string and if B is the Pth element in the list of base-molecule labels, then the feature with label V is mapped onto the base-molecule feature with label B. By associating features in each molecule to base-molecule features, these mappings suggest possible pharmacophoric points: On decoding the chromosome GASP uses a least-squares fitting routine to attempt to form as many points as possible. Note that it is possible for the base molecule to have a larger count of a particular feature than another molecule; This problem is solved by assigning dummy labels that are ignored by the fitness function.[1]

6.2.3. Genetic Operators

GASP uses two genetic operators: The crossover operator requires two parents and produces two children, while the mutation operator requires one parent and produces one. Both operators are given the same weight (see Step 1 of Figure 6.1) and chromosomes are selected for processing using roulette-wheel selection on linear normalized fitness values,[6] these fitness values having been calculated as detailed in the following chapter. A *selection pressure* of 1.1 is used, where the selection pressure represents the relative probability that the best individual will be chosen as a parent compared to the average individual. This low selection pressure reduces the likelihood of GASP converging to suboptimal solutions.

The crossover operator performs two-point crossover on the integer strings, using the PMX crossover operator (including the duplicate removal stage) that is described by Goldberg,[6] and traditional one-point crossover on the binary strings. A random number, r, between 1 and $2N$-1 (the number of strings in each chromosome) is generated, crossover is applied to the rth string in the parents' chromosomes (using the appropriate integer or binary operator), and the remainder of the parents' chromosomes are then copied to the children unchanged.

The mutation operator performs binary-string mutation on binary strings and integer-string mutation on integer strings, using the mutation operators described by Davis[8] and by Brown et al.,[2] respectively. A random number, r, between 1 and $2N$-1 is generated, mutation is applied to the rth string in the parent's chromosome (using the appropriate integer or binary operator) and the remainder of the parent's chromosome is then copied to the child unchanged.

6.3. The Fitness Function

The fitness function lies at the heart of any GA, and the evaluation of the one developed for GASP involves six distinct stages:

t· A separate conformation is generated for each molecule by applying the bond rotations encoded in the appropriate binary string.

· Each molecule is superimposed on top of the base molecule using a transformation obtained from a least-squares procedure that fits to the mapping encoded in the appropriate integer string.

- A van der Waals energy is obtained for the internal steric energy of each molecule.

- A volume integral is obtained for the common volume between each molecule and the base molecule.

- A similarity score is generated by determining which features were common to all molecules in the current overlay.
- A final fitness score is generated by performing a weighted sum on the terms calculated in the three previous stages.

These stages are detailed below.

6.3.1. Generation of Conformations and Least-Squares Fitting

Each Gray-coded byte in the binary string is decoded to give an integer value between 0 and 255. This integer value is linearly rescaled to give a real number between 0 and 2π, which is used as an angle of rotation, in radians, for the appropriate rotatable bond. The randomized 3D coordinates for the molecule are used as a starting configuration, and bond rotations are successively applied around the rotatable bonds to generate a new set of co-ordinates for the molecule. The resulting conformations are then passed to the least-squares fitting procedure.

A *virtual point,* representing a donor or acceptor atom in the receptor with which the molecules interact, is created for each hydrogen-bond donor proton and acceptor lone pair in a molecule at a distance of 2.9 Å from the donor or acceptor, in the direction of the hydrogen or lone pair. Virtual points are also created at the center of each ring.

Consider the superimposition of one molecule, *A,* onto the base molecule. As before, let L be the number of base molecule features (minus any dummy labels that are required by molecule A), so that decoding a chromosome gives rise to L pairs containing a virtual point in the base molecule and a virtual point in A. A Procrustes rotation,[12] with a correction to remove inversion, yields a geometric transformation that, when applied to all the virtual points from molecule A in the L pairs, minimizes the least-squared distance between all of the virtual points from molecule A and the corresponding base-molecule virtual points. Because not all possible features in the base molecule will necessarily be included in a pharmacophore, a second least-squares fit is applied to minimize the distance between those pairs of points that are less than 3 Å apart. Note that the least-squares fit will fail if the second pass contains fewer than three pairs of points: In this case, the fitness function returns an error and the chromosome is excluded from the population.[1]

6.3.2. Calculation of the van der Waals Energy

The internal steric energy for each molecule is calculated using a Lennard-Jones 6-12 potential with parameters taken from the SYBYL force field[13] and with an energy lookup table and an inter-atomic cutoff distance being employed to maximize the efficiency of the calculation.

The steric energy of a molecular conformation is expressed as the difference between the 6-12 energy of the conformation and the 6-12 energy of the original input molecular conformation, prior to the randomization of molecular coordinates. If this difference is negative (indicating that the conformation was of lower energy than the input structure), then the steric energy for that molecule is set to zero (to ensure that the GA does not optimize on van der Waals energy rather than the similarity, as discussed below). To insure that the van der Waals energy term in the final fitness score is independent of the number of molecules in the overlay, the mean 6-12 energy *per* molecule is determined. Let this energy be *vdw_energy*.

6.3.3. Calculation of the Volume Integral

In order to predict which portions of the molecules are in contact with the active site, GASP should ideally determine common molecular surface areas as a measure of similarity. However, such a calculation is extremely time-consuming. Instead, pairwise common volumes are determined between the base molecule and each of the other molecules. In order to speed up the determination of common molecular volume, the calculation is approximated by treating atoms as spheres and summing the overlay between spheres in the two different molecules.

To determine the volume integral between two molecules, A and B, each atom, i, in A is compared with every atom, j, in B. Let d_{ij} be the inter-atomic distance between the two atoms, let R_i be the van der Waals radius of the atom in A, and let R_j be the van der Waals radius of the atom in B. The values of the van der Waals radius are dependent on atom type and are the same as those used in the SYBYL force field.[13] There are four possible results when determining the volume integral between the two atoms:

- The distance d_{ij} is greater than either R_i or R_j. Here, the common volume between the two atoms is 0.

- $R_i > R_j$ and $d_{ij} < R_i - R_j$. Here, atom j is completely enclosed in atom i, and the common volume is given by $\frac{4}{3}\pi R_j^3$.

- $R_j > R_i$ and $d_{ij} < R_j - R_i$. Here, atom i is completely enclosed in atom j, and the common volume is given by $\frac{4}{3}\pi R_i^3$.

- Otherwise the two atomic spheres partially overlap. Here, the common volume is defined by the equation for the intersection of two spheres. Let

$$x = \frac{R_i^2 - R_j^2 - d_{ij}^2}{2d_{ij}} \, ;$$

then the common volume is given by

$$\frac{\pi}{3}(2\,R_i^2 + 2\,R_j^2 + d_{ij}^2) - \pi(x\,R_i^2 + (R_j^2 + x\,d_{ij})(d_{ij} - x)) \, .$$

The total volume integral between molecules A and B is determined by summing all the individual terms from atomic common volumes. In order that the volume integral term in the final fitness score is independent of the number of molecules in the overlay, the mean volume integral *per* molecule with the base molecule is determined. Let this term be *volume_integral*.

6.3.4. Calculation of the Similarity Score

A similarity score, *similarity_score,* is determined for the overlaid molecules. This score is the sum of three terms:

- A score for the degree of similarity in position, orientation, and type between hydrogen-bond donors in the base molecule and hydrogen-bond donors in the other molecules
- A score derived from comparing hydrogen-bond acceptors
- A score that results from comparing the positions and the orientations of aromatic rings.

Thus

$$similarity\_score = donor\_score + acceptor\_score + ring\_score.$$

In order to assign similarity scores GASP requires the use of a function that determines how similar two hydrogen-bond donor or acceptor types are. Let *type_sim[a, b]* be a weight between 0 and 1 that measures the similarity between hydrogen-bond types *a* and *b*, where *a* and *b* are either both donor types or both acceptor types. Donor and acceptor types are labeled by the fragment types used by Jones et al.[4] to model their bonding strengths (the labels NPLCG and NPLCA refer to the guandine and arginine donor types). Let ACCEPTORS and DONORS be the sets of acceptor and donor atom types, respectively:

DONORS	=	{ N4, NPL3, N3DA, NAM, O3DA, N2DA , NPLCG, NPLCA}
	=	{ d_1, d_2 ...... d_8 }
ACCEPTORS	=	{ BR, N2DA, O2, OCO2, CL, N1, N3A, O3A, F, N2A, N3DA, O3DA, NACID}
	=	{ a_1, a_2 .... a_{13} }

Let *bond_strength[d_i, a_j]* be the strength of the hydrogen-bond between donor d_i and acceptor a_j experimental determination of these values being detailed by Jones et al.[4] Then for donors, *type_sim[d_1, d_2]* is defined as follows:

$$ratio\_sim[d_1, d_2] = \sqrt[13]{\prod_{i=1}^{13} \frac{bond\_strength[d_1, a_i]}{bond\_strength[d_1, a_i]}} \ ;$$

if   *ratio_sim[d_1, d_2]* > 1,

then $type\_sim[d_1, d_2] = \dfrac{1}{ratio\_sim[d_1, d_2]}$,

else   *type_sim[d_1, d_2]* = *ratio_sim[d_1, d_2]*.

For acceptors, *type_sim[a_1, a_2]* is defined analogously, as follows:

$$ratio\_sim[a_1, a_2] = \sqrt[8]{\prod_{i=1}^{8} \frac{bond\_strength[d_i, a_1]}{bond\_strength[d_i, a_2]}} \ ;$$

if $ratio\_sim[a_1, a_2] > 1,$

then $type\_sim[a_1, a_2] = \dfrac{1}{ratio\_sim[a_1, a_2]},$

else $type\_sim[a_1, a_2] = ratio\_sim[a_1, a_2].$

A correction is made to these calculations if the bonding energy is positive, that is, if the bond is unattractive.[1]

The calculated values of *ratio_sim* are shown in Table 6.2: This lists the geometric means rather than the atom type similarities, so that it is clear which of the two donors or acceptors in the ratio is the stronger. The rationale behind this approach of measuring similarity is that the GA should overlay donor or acceptor groups of similar strength. While the method described here is intuitively acceptable, the main justification for the adoption of this similarity index is GASP's success in superimposing sets of known actives (as discussed later in this chapter).

Table 6.2. Donor and acceptor atom-type similarities. These atom-types are defined by Jones et al.[4] in the GOLD program for docking flexible ligands.

d_1 \ d_2	N4	NPL3	N3DA	NAM	O3DA	N2DA	NPLCG	NPLCA
N.4	1.00	4.05	3.20	7.68	2.88	4.17	1.93	2.84
NPL3	0.25	1.00	2.27	0.88	0.44	1.84	0.39	0.48
N3DA	0.31	0.44	1.00	0.55	0.80	0.00	0.68	1.13
NAM	0.13	1.13	1.80	1.00	0.36	2.22	0.24	0.33
O3DA	0.35	2.25	1.25	2.77	1.00	4.02	0.66	0.96
N2DA	0.24	0.54	0.00	0.45	0.25	1.00	0.33	0.38
NPLCG	0.52	2.60	1.47	4.25	1.52	3.00	1.00	1.48
NPLCA	0.35	2.09	0.89	3.04	1.04	2.61	0.68	1.00

ratio_sim[d_1, d_2]

a_1 \ a_2	BR	N2DA	O2	OCO2	CL	N1	N3A	O3A	F	N2A	N3DA	O3DA	NACID
Br	1.00	0.18	0.29	0.12	0.68	0.37	0.19	0.95	2.11	0.20	0.61	0.38	0.31
N2DA	5.58	1.00	1.21	0.22	2.41	2.05	1.30	1.26	0.00	1.12	0.98	1.17	0.39
O2	3.47	0.83	1.00	0.27	1.99	0.95	0.51	2.76	6.94	0.71	0.58	1.11	0.65
OCO2	8.11	4.54	3.72	1.00	8.73	9.77	6.25	10.3	13.1	7.85	5.63	4.55	2.35
CL	1.46	0.42	0.50	0.11	1.00	0.85	0.45	0.52	1.74	0.47	0.89	0.44	0.19
N1	2.73	0.49	1.05	0.10	1.18	1.00	0.54	1.25	0.00	0.74	0.61	0.74	0.18
N3A	5.14	0.77	1.96	0.16	2.22	1.87	1.00	2.34	0.00	1.39	0.90	1.16	0.30
O3A	1.05	0.79	0.36	0.10	1.91	0.80	0.43	1.00	1.44	0.60	0.49	0.40	0.23
F	0.47	0.00	0.14	0.08	0.57	0.00	0.00	0.70	1.00	0.00	0.22	0.22	0.22
N2A	4.96	0.89	1.41	0.13	2.14	1.34	0.72	1.68	0.00	1.00	0.82	0.99	0.25
N3DA	1.64	1.02	1.71	0.18	1.12	1.63	1.11	2.04	1.00	1.22	1.00	1.29	0.33
O3DA	2.65	0.86	0.90	0.22	2.29	1.35	0.86	2.49	4.61	1.01	0.77	1.00	0.51
NACID	3.20	2.56	1.54	0.43	5.40	5.45	3.39	4.26	4.47	3.29	3.05	1.95	1.00

ratio_sim[a_1, a_2]

Donor similarity score

Each virtual point corresponding to a hydrogen-bond donor proton in the base molecule is used to define a *hydrogen-bonding center,* with the potential to interact with acceptors within a receptor molecule. A virtual point from every other molecule, corresponding to the hydrogen-bond donor proton that is geometrically closest to the base-molecule virtual point, is added to each of these hydrogen-bonding centers. A score, *vec_wt* × *sim_wt*, is then assigned to the hydrogen bonding center, where vec_wt is a measure of closeness of virtual point positions and hydrogen-bond vectors in the hydrogen-bond centers, and where *sim_wt* is a measure of the similarity of the donors involved in the hydrogen-bond center.

The centroid of the virtual point positions is determined in order to estimate the similarity of virtual point positions within the hydrogen-bond center. Let *vp_distance_wt* be a measure of how close the centroid is to the base-molecule virtual point in the center and let *vp_d* be the distance between this virtual point and the centroid of the virtual point positions. If *vp_d* is less than 0.5 Å then *vp_distance_wt* is 1 or if *vp_d* is greater than 1.75 Å then *vp_distance_wt* is 0. Otherwise, *vp_d* lies in the interval [0.5, 1.75]: It is linearly rescaled to the interval [1, 0] and then squared to give *vp_distance_wt*. Note that a slight correction to this method must be applied to ensure that the possible points of interaction with the receptor, represented by the hydrogen-bonding center, do not lie within the van der Waals volume of the overlaid molecules.[1]

An indication of the similarity of hydrogen-bonding vectors can be obtained by considering the closeness in positions of the hydrogen-bond donors associated with the virtual points in the hydrogen-bonding center. Let such a measure be *donor_distance_wt* and let *donor_d* be the distance between the donor associated with the base molecule virtual point and the centroid of all hydrogen-bond donors that are connected to the virtual points in the hydrogen-bonding center. As before, if *donor_d* is less than 0.5 Å then *donor_distance_wt* is 1 or if d is greater than 1.75 Å then *donor_distance_wt* is 0. Otherwise, *donor_d* lies in the interval [0.5, 1.75]: It is linearly rescaled to the interval [1, 0] and then squared to give *donor_distance_wt*.

The value of *vec_wt* can now be determined.

If either *donor_distance_wt* or *vp_distance_wt* is zero then *vec_wt* is set to zero. If both are non-zero, then if *donor_distance_wt* is less than *vp_distance_wt* then *vec_wt* is set to (*donor_distance_wt* + *vp_distance_wt*)/2, otherwise it is set to *vp_distance_wt*/2. This combination is chosen so that GASP does not superimpose donors in preference to virtual points, since it is the virtual points that represent the points of interaction with the receptor.

The donor similarity term, *sim_wt*, is then determined for the hydrogen-bond center. The similarity index *type_sim* (defined above) determines the similarity between two donor types. However, if the overlay involves three or more molecules, we require a similarity term that determines the similarity between many donor types. Let *d_b* be the type of the donor atom, in the base molecule, that is connected to the virtual point at *p_b*. Let *d_m* be the donor type of a donor (in another molecule) that is associated with another virtual point in the hydrogen-bond center and let *mol_sim_wt* = *type_sim*[*d_b*, *d_m*]. Different values of *mol_sim_wt* are determined for all d_m donor types, in the hydrogen-bond center, and *sim_wt* is then set to the smallest such value found.

Once *vec_wt* and *sim_wt* have been determined for a given hydrogen-bonding center the contribution *vec_wt* × *sim_wt* is determined, and *donor_score* is then the sum of all such contributions from all hydrogen-bonding centers containing donor hydrogens. Jones et al.[1] describe the modifications that are required to ensure that the measure is not biased towards matching those donors that contained a larger number of donor hydrogens, and to ensure that a hydrogen-bond donor proton from a non-base molecule cannot appear in more than one hydrogen bonding center.

Acceptor similarity score

Each acceptor lone pair in the base molecule is used to define a hydrogen-bonding center with the potential to interact with donors within a receptor macromolecule. The process used to generate the score *acceptor_score* is entirely analogous to that used when determining *donor_score*.

Aromatic ring similarity score

The third term in the similarity score, *ring_score*, requires the use of normals to aromatic rings. Given an aromatic ring (determined using the atom types of its constituent atoms) of n atoms with position vectors p_1, p_2 .... p_n and a center

$$c = \frac{1}{n}\sum_{i=1}^{n} p_i.$$

then a mean normal direction, m, is determined:

$$m = (p_n - c) \otimes (p_i - c) + \sum_{i=1}^{n-1}(p_i - c) \otimes (p_{i+1} - c).$$

where m is scaled to a magnitude of size 2.9Å, so that similarity scores calculated on ring normals will be comparable to those calculated on virtual points.[1]

A third type of hydrogen-bonding center is created for aromatic rings. Each aromatic ring in the base molecule is used to define a hydrogen-bonding acceptor center by choosing the ring center normal that is geometrically closest to the base-molecule ring center normal.

In order to estimate the similarity of ring positions within a hydrogen-bond center the centroid of ring centers is determined. Let d be the distance between the centroid and the base-molecule ring center. As before, if d is less than 0.5 Å then *ring_distance_wt* is 1 and if d is greater than 1.75Å then *ring_distance_wt* is 0. Otherwise, d lies in the interval [0.5, 1.75]: It is linearly rescaled to the interval [1, 0] and then squared to give *ring_distance_wt*.

In order to measure the similarity of ring orientation, the centroid of the normals to the rings that comprised the hydrogen-bonding center is computed. Let *normal_distance_wt* be a measure of how close the base-molecule normal is to the centroid, where *normal_distance_wt* is determined using the same method described in the previous paragraph. If either *normal_distance_wt* or *ring_distance_wt* is zero then *ring_score* is set to zero. Otherwise, it is set to (*normal_distance_wt* + *ring_distance_wt*)/2.

As mentioned previously when discussing the donor similarity scores, a correction is made if any aromatic ring normal appears in two hydrogen-bonding centers.

Calculation of the final fitness score

The final fitness score is a weighted sum of the common volume, similarity score and steric energy, specifically

volume_integral + 750 × *similarity_score* - 0.05 × *vdw_energy.*

The weights of 750 and 0.05 were determined by empirical adjustment to give reasonable overlays (where the algorithm is driven to generate good pharmacophores without producing high-energy structures) over a wide range of examples.[1]

6.4. Identification of Pharmacophores Using GASP

Having described the principal components of GASP, we now illustrate its use when applied to several sets of compounds for which a pharmacophore is required. Further examples may be found in Jones at al.[1] All CPU times are for a Silicon Graphics R4000 Indigo II Workstation.

6.4.1. Leu-Enkephalin and a Hybrid Morphine

The first superimposition problem to be considered here involved two very different structures, specifically the hybrid morphine molecule EH-NAL,14 and leu-enkephalin shown in Figure 6.2. Although only two molecules are involved, this is an extremely demanding problem as leu-enkephalin is highly flexible, containing 20 rotatable bonds. EH-NAL, conversely, has just six rotatable bonds in sidechains. The GA was run ten times to generate ten possible overlays. The mean run time was 9 minutes and 13 seconds.

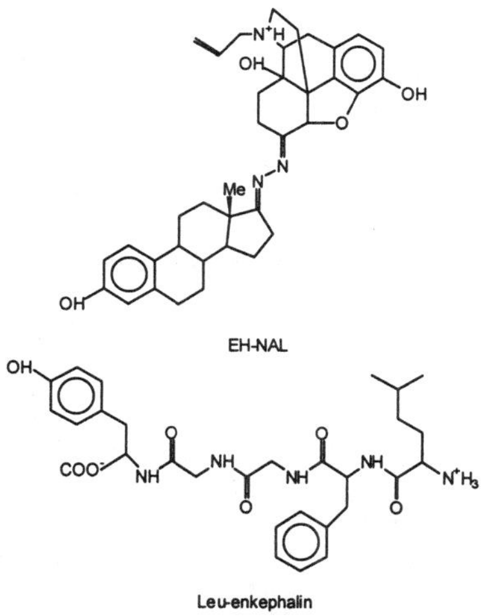

Figure 6.2. Hybrid morphine and Leu-enkephalin.

Plate 6.1 shows the best solution (ranked by GASP fitness score) that was obtained. The pharmacophore identified by the GA contains the features indicated by the circles: two aromatic rings; one phenol group; the protonated nitrogen (for which the connected hydrogens are shown in the Plate to illustrate their common directionality). Six of the ten runs identified this pharmacophore

6.4.2. Overlay of Four 5-HT3 Antagonists

Clark et al. have synthesized several series of N-(quinuclidin-3-yl)aryl and heteroaryl-fused pyridones and tested them for 5-HT3 receptor affinity.15 An overlay was attempted of the four antagonists shown in Figure 6.3, with the mean runtime being 6 minutes and 9 seconds.

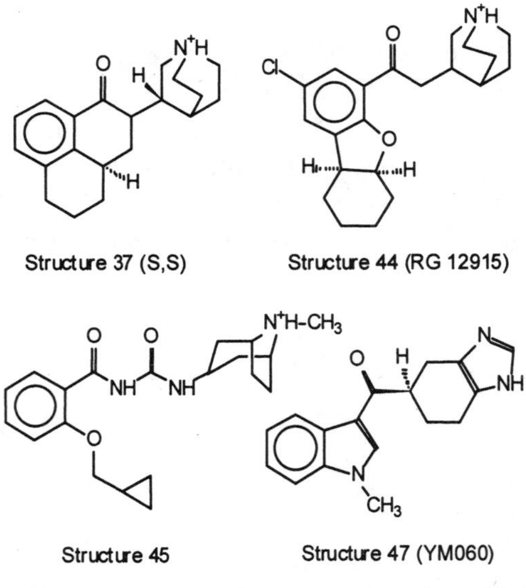

Structure 37 (S,S)   Structure 44 (RG 12915)

Structure 45   Structure 47 (YM060)

Figure 6.3. 5-HT3 Receptor antagonists (We used numbers classification described in reference.)[13]

GASP elucidated a pharmacophore consisting of a nitrogen donor, a sp^2 oxygen acceptor and an aromatic ring in all but the least-fit run. Plate 6.2 shows the superimposition obtained by the GA run that generated the highest fitness score. The circles in this Plate indicate the three pharmacophore points: the normals of the aromatic ring, the lone pairs of the sp^2 oxygen, and the donor hydrogens bonded to the nitrogens. Although the nitrogens are not overlaid, their donor hydrogens are clearly in a position to interact with the same point in the receptor. The pharmacophoric features are the same as that identified by Clark et al.[15]

6.4.3. Overlay of Six Angiotensin II Receptor Antagonists

Perkins and Dean have described a novel strategy for the superimposition of a set of flexible molecules, using a combination of simulated annealing and cluster analysis.[16] Their algorithm was tested on the six angiotensin II antagonists shown in Figure 6.4, and we have also used these structures to evaluate the GASP. The average run time was 7 minutes and 56 seconds.

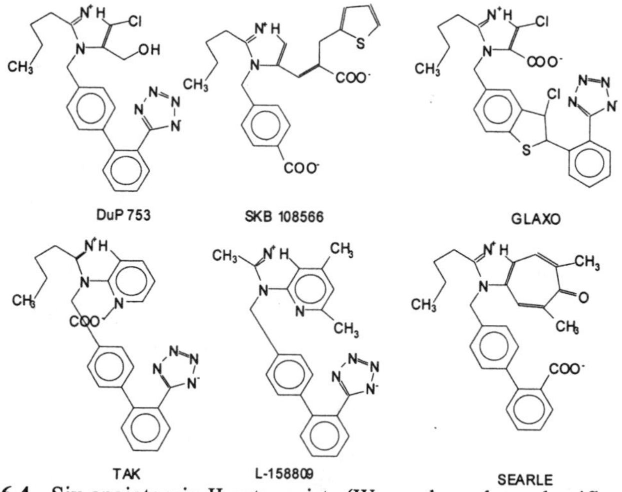

Figure 6.4. Six angiotensin II antagonists (We used numbers classification described in reference.)[16]

Six of the ten overlays (including the three fittest solutions) generated a pharmacophore comprising an aromatic ring and a protonated nitrogen. The best overlay is shown in Plate 6.3. The circles indicate: 1) the two pharmacophore points that were common to all structures, and 2) an acidic group that was overlaid in five of the six compounds (the acidic group was not found in the compound SKB 108566, which is the structure most dissimilar from the base molecule, L-158809).

The superposition obtained by Perkins and Dean16 has some similarity with the GASP result in that the imidazole group and benzene rings are also successfully superimposed (due to their structural similarity). However, their procedure is far more time-consuming.

6.5. Conclusion

The design and implementation of a GA for the superimposition of flexible molecules and the use of the resulting overlays to suggest possible pharmacophoric patterns has been described. The experiments reported here demonstrate the effectiveness and versatility of the algorithm, in that it has been possible to superimpose molecular structures on structurally diverse test systems with results that are both intuitively acceptable and often in agreement with overlays suggested by alternative means; that said, there are several additions and improvements that could be made to the program. Inactive compounds that are similar to known actives are often incorporated in a structure-activity analysis. One possible improvement is to extend GASP to incorporate inactives or to include biological activity. As the algorithm attempts to find pharmacophore points that are common to all input structures, a current limitation of the fitness function is that GASP will have difficulty incorporating molecules that do not fit the pharmacophore for some reason. Further simple improvements that could be made to the algorithm include encoding the chromosome for molecules of unknown chirality and the addition of internal hydrogen bonding. Even without these modifications, however, GASP provides a simple and direct way of exploiting the structural relationships between sets of bioactive 3D molecules.

Acknowledgements

This work was funded by the Science and Engineering Research Council and the Wellcome Foundation, with Tripos Inc. providing hardware and software support. This publication is a contribution from the Krebs Institute for Biomolecular Research, which is a designated Centre for Biomolecular Sciences of the Biotechnology and Biological Sciences Research Council.

References

1. Jones G, Willett P, Glen RC: **A genetic algorithm for flexible molecular overlay and pharmacophore elucidation.** *J Comput-Aided Mol Des* 1995, **9**:532-549.

2. Brown RD, Jones GJ, Willett P, Glen RC: **Matching two-dimensional chemical graphs using genetic algorithms.** *J Chem Inf Comput Sci* 1994, **34**:63-70.

3. Clark DE, Jones G, Willett P, Kenny PW, Glen R.C: **Pharmacophoric pattern matching in files of three dimensional chemical structures: Comparison of conformational-searching algorithms for flexible searching.** *J Chem Inf Comput Sci* 1994, **34**:197-206.

4. Jones G, Willett P, Glen RC: **Molecular recognition of receptor sites using a genetic algorithm with a description of desolvation.** *J Mol Biol* 1995, **245**:43-53.

5. Jones G, Willett P, Glen RC, Leach AR, Taylor R: **Development and validation of a genetic algorithm for flexible docking.** *J Mol Biol* 1997, **267**:727-748.

6. Goldberg DE: *Genetic Algorithms in Search, Optimization and Machine Learning.* Wokingham: Addison-Wesley, 1989.

7. Clark DE: Evolutionary Algorithms in Computer-Aided Molecular Design. http://panizzi.shef.ac.uk/cisrg/links/ea_bib.html.

8. *Handbook of Genetic Algorithms.* Davis L, ed. New York: Van Nostrand Reinhold, 1991.

9. *Handbook of Evolutionary Computing.* Back T, Fogel D, Michalewicz Z, eds. New York: Oxford University Press USA, 1997.

10. *SYBYL* is distributed by Tripos Inc. http://www.tripos.com.

11. Zamora A: **An algorithm for fining the smallest set of smallest rings.** *J Chem Inf Comput Sci* 1976, **16**:40-43.

12. Digby PGN, Kempton RA: *Multivariate Analysis of Ecological Communities.* London: Chapman and Hall, 1987.

13. Clark M, Cramer RD. III, Van Opdenbosch N: **Validation of the general purpose tripos 5.2 force field.** *J Comp Chem* 1989, **10**:982-1021.

14. Kolb VM: **Opiate receptors: Search for new drugs.** *Progress in Drug Research* 1991, **36**:49-70.

15. Clark RD, Miller AB, Berger J, Repke DB, Weinhardt KK, Kowalczyk BA, Eglen RM, Bonhaus DW, Lee C, Michel AD, Smith WL, Wong **EHF: 2-(Quinuclidin-3-yl)pyrido[4,3-b]indol-1-ones and Isoquinolin-1-ones. Potent conformationally restricted 5-HT3 receptor antagonists.** *J Med Chem* 1993, **36**:2645-2657.

16. Perkins TDJ, Dean PM: **An exploration of a novel strategy for superimposing several flexible molecules.** *J Comput-Aided Mol Des* 1993, **7**:155-172.

7

Exploring Pharmacophores with Chem-X

Stephen J. Cato

Abstract

Chem-X software contains many automated techniques based upon the pharmacophore concept. The software can quickly sample all the potential 3- or 4-center pharmacophores in all low-energy conformations of the molecules in a collection, and store the results in a binary string called a pharmacophore key. This key can be used to assess the diversity of individual libraries, compare the relative diversity of libraries, and design libraries to fill voids in pharmacophore space. In cases where a receptor model exists, the pharmacophore-based "Design in Receptor" technique allows collections of real or virtual libraries to be screened to select those having the right binding interactions and the right size and shape to fit in the receptor site of interest.

7

Exploring Pharmacophores with Chem-X

Stephen J. Cato

Oxford Molecular Group Inc., Hunt Valley, Maryland

7.1. Introduction

The Chem-X package contains a wide variety of automated tools for the study of pharmacophores. These tools allow compounds, or collections of compounds, to be represented by a pharmacophore key. This key contains a representation of all the potential pharmacophores that can be exhibited by the molecule or collection of molecules in some low-energy conformation. It thus permits compounds or libraries to be chosen to either increase the diversity of collections, or allows compounds to be chosen to fit a known target receptor.

In 1983, Keith Davies started the company Chemical Design to market a molecular modeling package called ChemGraph, but the package's name was soon changed to Chem-X. In 1990, 3D database storage and searching capabilities were added to the package.[1] As with most chemical database searching systems, this one included an initial keyed search phase, designed to eliminate most of the non-matching molecules from the search quickly, before the computationally more expensive substructure and conformational matching stages. The system chosen to implement these keys was based on existing work consisting of a combination of automatic recognition of potential centers of interaction with proteins,[2] and a distance bin model,[3] used to store the intercenter distances. These bins, containing the intercenter distances for each combination of centers, form the majority of the database search key. This system still exists today with minor changes caused by the addition of 2D and reaction searching as a major component of the Chem-X database technology.

The tremendous rise in the uptake of combinatorial chemistry, which started around 1995, led to large collection of virtual compounds that could potentially be made and the need for decision tools to tell the researcher which of them were indeed worth making and testing. The designers of Chem-X were in a good position to design tools for this market by extending the concept of 2-centered distance keys to 3-centered, and soon afterward, 4-centered, pharmacophore keys. This led to tools in Chem-X that automated the analysis of virtual libraries. These tools were initially directed towards diversity. However, the potential for their use to focus libraries in situations where the protein's receptor site was known soon became apparent and led to virtual screening tools, Receptor Screening, and its successor Design in Receptor (DiR).[4]

In 1998, Chemical Design was acquired by the Oxford Molecular Group,[5] which now markets the Chem-X product.

7.2. Centers in Chem-X

When a structure is read into Chem-X, or the user has finished drawing the structure into the 2D draw editor, a 3D structure is usually generated, and at the same time the molecule is **parameterized**. This parameterization assigns **atom types** to each of the atoms in the molecule. The user can select one of several parameterization files supplied with Chem-X, make alterations to them if they desired, or even create a brand new parameterization from scratch. Each parameterization consists of a database file and a data file. The atom types are assigned to atoms in the structure by comparing them with substructures in the database. The data file contains other data for the atom type, including the atom weight and radius, and most importantly here, the **center types** that the atom type represents. The center types in Chem-X are based on potential interaction types at the protein receptor site. The program originally started with 4 center types, this was increased to 5 by the addition of a lipophilic type, and then later increased to the current 7. The centers are listed in Table 7.1. Although there are now 7 center types available, these are only used for pharmacophore keys, as explained below. The keys for databases can use either the first 4 or the first 5 types of centers depending on the database configuration. Acidic and basic centers can be automatically softened to donors and acceptors during searching to facilitate this.

Table 7.1. Chem-X Default Center Types

No	Abbreviation	Type
1	HDON	H-bond Donor
2	HACC	H-bond Acceptor
3	PLUS	Positive Charge Center
4	AROM	Aromatic Ring Centroid
5	LIP	Lipophile
6	ACID	Acidic Center
7	BASE	Basic Center

Center types 1-3, 6, and 7 all coincide with existing atoms, so their positioning is trivial. Centers of type 4 and 5 are placed using dummy atoms. The aromatic dummy atoms AR5 and AR6, which are placed at the centers of 5- and 6-membered aromatic rings, respectively, correspond to center type 4. A more complex calculation is needed to place lipophilic centers. This algorithm finds areas with little difference of electronegativity across the bonds, splitting them into groups of no less than 3 and no more than 8 atoms, depending on the branching pattern, with the corresponding lipophilic dummy atom then being placed at the centroid for each group. Acidic and basic centers are currently detected algorithmically, but users can turn off that option, should they wish to define scripts to create their own center types replacing the existing ones.

7.3. Centers in 3D Searching

The center concept is central to the 3D-searching engine in Chem-X. In fact, the purest form of query that we give the search engine is a set of centers and the distances (or distance ranges) between them. As we shall see, Chem-X reserves a special name for this kind of query— a **pharmacophore**. While the 3D query can contain many other elements, including required substructure, distance and angles (including non-centers), planes, inclusion/exclusion spheres, and maps, both the keyed search that starts the process and the conformation matching that ends it are dependent on the centers present.

As mentioned in the introduction, the first stage of a 3D search is a **keyed** search. A large part of the keys used in this search encode the intercenter distances within the molecule. If 4 centers are used in the database, then there are 10 possible combinations of intercenter distances. For 5-center keyed databases there are 15. Each of these possible intercenter combinations is represented by a 32-bit word. The binary **distance bins** in this key represent the presence or absence of a particular intercenter distance. While it is possible for the user to change these bins, the defaults work well for most users. The spread of the bins is biased towards the lower end, as shown in Table 7.2.

Table 7.2. Standard Bins

Bin Nos	No of bins	Bin Width	Range (Å)
1	1	1.7	0.0–1.7
2–14	13	0.1	1.7–3.0
15–24	10	0.5	3.0–8.0
25–31	7	1.0	8–15
32	1	~	15+

Thus database search keys contain either 320 or 480 bits of distance key information. The total key combines this distance key with 64 bits of bond pattern, 32 bits of formula and 128 bits of functional group information to encode the whole molecule. This key information amounts to approximately 80 bytes per structure, and when the database is opened in Chem-X the keys for all the structures in the database are stored in memory, usually an easy fit on a modern workstation. Holding the keys in memory allows an extremely fast comparison of the keys of each structure to those of the search target, allowing the screening process to rapidly remove the vast majority of compounds that cannot meet the search criteria. Originally the distance keys used (termed **3D keys**) were generated using a conformational analysis procedure to discover the available intercenter distances. More recently, so-called **2D keys** have become the norm. The bits in the latter keys are set by determining the minimum and maximum distances between the centers and filling in the intermediate bits. Generating the key using this method is much quicker. Note that all of the bits set in the 3D key are also set in the 2D key, so all the desired hits are indeed found using the 2D key. In theory this can lead to more false positives coming through the screening process, but in practice the use of 2D keys has been found to cause little slowing of the 3D search. The other advantage is that 2D keys can be used for both 2D and 3D searching—removing the need to generate and store two sets of keys (3D keys cannot be used for 2D searching).

Once the keyed search has been carried out, the next phase in the typical 3D search is an atom-by-atom matching that is required to find any required substructure—all structures not containing the required substructure can be dropped at this point. The search then continues with the conformational phase. While Chem-X does contain an algorithm called **flexifit** which is targeted towards the fitting of flexible molecules, the most common search still uses **conformational generation.** In this phase of the search, each significant rotatable bond is rotated in turn to generate all the possible conformers of the molecule. The user can set the number of rotations used for each type of bond, but should remember that the default rotations have been set up to match the bin sizes in the default distance keys.

It is desirable only to retrieve conformations that are of low energy, and Chem-X offers a number of ways of achieving this. A complete energy calculation for each conformer can be carried out, but this is very time-consuming. A bump check requires less time, but is less rigorous. The most common method, then, is the use of **conformational rules.** These rules are derived from previous complete energy calculations on 6 atom chains, that are now converted to a look-up table, allowing structures likely to have an energy greater than 20 kcal/mol above the minimum to be rejected. This method only takes into account fairly localized interactions (interactions within 6 bond lengths), so it is approximate, but it is extremely fast compared to the other methods and typically gives good results. The centers in the generated conformers and their spatial relationship are at this stage compared to the query, and, if they can be matched to the query within the defined 3D search tolerances, the conformer is regarded as a hit. Hits are stored both within a structure set (that can be used with the original database) and are also written into a new output database, where individual conformations are saved in the orientation that matched the query. The number of hits desired can be set, so the user can stop on the first hit (if he or she only wanted to know which structures hit), or can save all the hits to the output database, where, if desired, they can be viewed superimposed onto the original query.

7.4. Pharmacophore Keys Defined

A **pharmacophore** is usually defined so as to express the minimum requirements of a ligand molecule to interact at the receptor site of a protein. The presence of a certain group of centers in a specific geometric arrangement can cause the ligand to interact. It is a necessary but not sufficient condition, since other factors (ranging from transport properties and metabolic stability to size and the ability to fit into the receptor site) are all likely to determine whether a particular molecule can interact.

Chem-X has a special treatment of potential 3- or 4-center pharmacophores, which it can exhaustively enumerate and store in special bit-strings called **pharmacophore keys.** Such a key can represent a molecule or collection of molecules, and expresses all the potential pharmacophores that the molecule or molecules can express in some low-energy conformation. It should be emphasized that all we are considering at the point of generating the keys is the center types and distances involved, so we have a key of potential pharmacophores rather than a specific pharmacophore that would refer to a target receptor. The repeated use of the word "potential" soon becomes clumsy, however, and tends to get dropped, so we refer to the contents of the key as pharmacophores, rather than potential pharmacophores. Context, or indeed terms like "real" or "actual," will serve to clarify the true meaning in any case.

The concept behind defining a pharmacophore key is to define the pharmacophore in such as way that a finite set of pharmacophores— **a pharmacophore space**—is defined and can be enumerated. This is a form of **partitioning,** and the pharmacophore key can be regarded as a **cell-based** methodology. Most cell-based or partitioning methods examine the molecules in some sort of chemical property space (the one used here has the advantage of using real two- or three-dimensional space) of a form that can be directly recognized by the receptor. Figure 7.1 illustrates the use of centers in pharmacophores and keys.

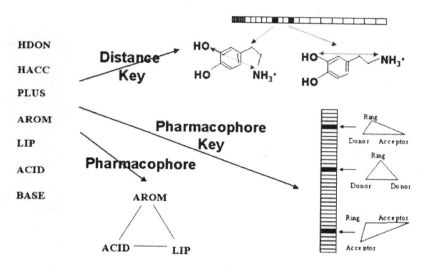

Figure 7.1. Interrelationship between centers, pharmacophores, and keys.

To look in more detail at pharmacophore space, it is useful to start by considering 3-center pharmacophores, since they are not only somewhat simpler, but also, from a historical standpoint, preceded their 4-center cousins. To begin with, it is necessary to choose 3 centers that are indistinguishably from the 7 center types allowed. There are 84 different ways to do this.* We will also partition each of the 3 sides into bins. These bins were typically the same as the ones used for distance keys, except that the indeterminate last bin (distances greater than 15 Å) was often omitted. This was the original model used for pharmacophore keys, containing 84×31^3 bits or 2,502,444 bits.

While this first version of the key was simple to generate (involving only a set of nested loops) and equally easy to interpret, it contained

---

* When choosing K centers from N center types, the number of possible combinations is:

$$\frac{(N + K - 1)!}{K! \, (N-1)!}$$

a lot of empty space. Indeed, it was calculated that approximately 65 percent of the key was actually inaccessible. There are two reasons for this. This first is the **triangle inequality.** Three-center pharmacophores are by definition planar triangles in shape, and so must obey the laws of geometry. To actually form a triangle, any side must be shorter than the sum of the other two sides. Hence although looping over the three variables will store a bit for a triangle with sides of, say, 2 Å, 2 Å, and 10 Å, such a triangle cannot physically exist and so that bit will never be set. The second reason is symmetry. If two or three of the center types in the pharmacophore were the same, there would be two or six equivalent representations of the same pharmacophore. While Chem-X would always set the same bit in these situations, it would leave either one or five bits that could never be set. A second version of the 3-center key was thus introduced that saved only the roughly 890,000 bits that are actually accessible. In theory it is computationally more expensive to save only the settable bits into the key. In reality the change is temporally imperceptible, but the resulting key is reduced from 320 kB of storage to a mere 80 kB—quite a significant reduction.

The mathematics of the 4-center keys is also interesting. The default here, for reasons that will quickly become apparent, is to use only 15 distance bins. While the 3-center pharmacophore is constrained by the rules of geometry to be planar, the 4-center pharmacophore expresses a tetrahedron in full three-dimensional glory. The 4-center pharmacophore has six sides, which must be partitioned. This leads to a sixth power in the formula, and hence the reduction in the number of bins becomes necessary. Nonetheless, there are 210 ways to choose 4 centers indistinguishably from the 7 center types, so we have potentially 210×15^6 bits (= 2,392,031,250), but fortunately only about 350 million valid geometries. The size of the resulting key is 59 MB. A number of users considered this too high and have reduced the number of bins to 10, leading to a key of approximately 3 MB. The 4-center key is much larger, and thus is more discriminating than the 3-center key. Although the requirement of a large amount of physical memory (>0.5 GB) has so far restricted its use, this is becoming less problematic with the falling price of computer memory.

Another factor that can be taken into account is chirality. For each tetrahedral 4-center pharmacophore (excepting those that have some form of symmetry) there will be a non-superposable enantiomeric form. If we take the chirality into consideration, then a molecule with a chiral center will correspond to one chiral pharmacophore and not the other, but generating a key from the enantiomeric molecule would have the opposite effect. As one might expect, turning on the chirality option doubles the size of the resulting keys.

7.5. Generating Pharmacophore Keys

The generation of a pharmacophore key is usually carried out for a set of compounds. Each compound is considered in turn, each of its low-energy conformations is generated (typically using the conformational rules discussed earlier), then every permutation of 3 or 4 centers is considered, and the corresponding bit is set in the pharmacophore key (assuming it was not already set). The user may specify cutoff points in terms of the number of rotatable bonds or the number of samplable conformations. These are precalculated so that any molecule exceeding these specifications can be immediately rejected. It is also possible to put a time limit on the calculation, but this is typically less satisfactory since it requires the time to be wasted before the compound is rejected. The resulting key, termed the **union key,** is the logical OR of the keys of the individual compounds in the set. The key may be saved to disk for later analysis as a compact binary **.pky file,** or as a human-readable **.pka file.** At this stage the pharmacophore keys are not saved in the Chem-X database. However, this feature will likely be added in future version of the software and is also available through a new product called Diamond Pharmacophores (see below).

Chem-X can also generate a common key for a set of molecules. This key is in fact the logical AND of the keys for the individual modules-that is, a bit will be set in the final key only if it is set in all the molecules in the set. This method affords an easy and rapid way to find a common pharmacophore, which is particularly useful to study a set of active compounds to create a pharmacophore hypothesis.

There are several settings that the user may choose that affect the way pharmacophore keys are calculated. Among these are restrictions that

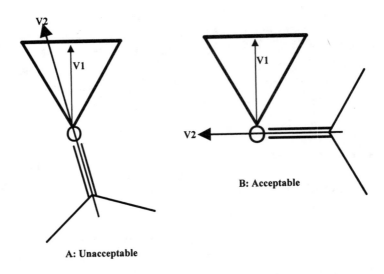

Figure 7.2. Pharmacophore Accessibility.
Vector V1 is the bisector of the pharmacophore triangle apex. V2 is the vector along the heteroatom bond. θ is the semiangle at the apex. φ is the angle between V1 and V2. If φ > θ then V2 points outside of the triangle, and the geometry is acceptable.

can be placed on pharmacophores based on their size or their direction. Pharmacophore **accessibility** checks that the general orientation of centers like donors and acceptors is outward, rather than towards the other centers comprising the pharmacophore, before a solution is accepted The accessibility test is not performed for centers considered non-directional like AROM or LIP (see Table 7.1). For each pharmacophore triangle, the apexes are considered sequentially. The test is performed by constructing two vectors from the heteroatom center, as shown in Figure 7.1, and generating the solid angle, or cone, that they define. If the solid angle between the two vectors is less than half the angle at the triangle apex, the center is considered inaccessible, because the heteroatom is oriented into the middle of the pharmacophore. A pharmacophore **volume** calculation may be used to eliminate solutions where the pharmacophore is matched by a relatively insignificant proportion of the molecule. The size of each potential solution is calculated as the area of the pharmacophore triangle, in square Ångstroms. When the number of non-hydrogen atoms in the matched molecule, multiplied by the **fractional volume factor,** *f,* is larger than the triangle area, the solution is rejected. The variable f is a user-definable parameter with a range from 0.0 to 1.0, and a default value of 0.25.

The pharmacophore keys discussed up until now have assumed only a single bit to represent the presence or absence of a pharmacophore. However, there are instances where the user wants to instead count the number of times a pharmacophore occurs. This technique is called **profiling,** and allows the user to record how many times a pharmacophore occurs within a set of molecules, either as an overall count for each conformer of each molecule or by the number of molecules in which it occurs. The size of the profile can be controlled by selecting 4, 8, 16, or 32 bits to store the count. Of course selecting the profile option will increase the size of the pharmacophore key accordingly.

7.6. Working with Pharmacophore Keys

Chem-X does include the capability of viewing pharmacophore keys, though it is really most useful in the case of 3-center keys. In such a plot, which is three-dimensional, the three axes are used to represent the distance bins along the three sides of the pharmacophore triangle. Each pharmacophore is indicated by a letter, so that reference to the legend will indicate the three center types involved. Various color schemes may be used, including user-defined ones, or two libraries may be overlaid in different colors. The plot may be rotated in 3D space for easier viewing, and any pharmacophore may be selected, in which case its details are displayed so that the user does not in practice need to read off the distances along the axes. Plots for libraries with many pharmacophores tend towards a characteristic shape: a cube with 3 corners rounded away. This shape is, of course, a result of the triangle inequality mentioned earlier. Plate 7.1 shows a typical pharmacophore key plot.

Since pharmacophore keys are bit strings, we expect to be able to manipulate them using logical operations, and this is indeed the case. The logical operation AND generates a key which contains the pharmacophores common to the keys being compared. A user might use this for analysis of a proposed virtual library, to study its pharmacophore overlap with an existing library such as a corporate database. The logical OR operation results in a key which exhibits all the pharmacophores of all the original keys—this allows larger databases of molecules to be processed as several separate sets, and their keys combined later. Using the OR operation creates the same key as if the total set had been processed in one operation. The NOT operator may be used to "subtract" a set of pharmacophores from a key, for instance, if the pharmacophore key for a set of inactives has been generated, the inactive pharmacophores can be eliminated from the key of active molecules (this, however, makes the dangerous assumption that inactive compounds do not contain the active pharmacophore).

When performing AND and NOT logical operations (but not OR operations) on pharmacophore keys, Chem-X takes the system defined tolerances into account, usually one bin width. While this is apt to confuse novices, it is useful, as the distances involved might actually be very close. For instance, the matching intercenter distances in two pharmacophores might be 4.95 and 5.05. These two values would show up in different bins, but the value of 4.95 is much closer to 5.05 than to other values in the same bin such as 4.55. If the tolerances were not taken into account then a common pharmacophore involving those two pharmacophores would not be found.

A pharmacophore key can be used as a database search query. For instance, if a molecule was found to be very active, it could be hypothesized that one of the pharmacophores exhibited by the molecule was the real pharmacophore, responsible for the activity. In this case, the key for the set containing the single molecule can be generated and then used as a search query. This technique is referred to as **lead explosion.** A corporate database, virtual library, or database of compounds that are commercially available for testing might then be searched for compounds that have one or more pharmacophores in common with the key. These could then be tested to develop common pharmacophore hypotheses. The ability to increase the match criteria from one to larger numbers is useful here too. It is quite possible that the interaction of interest involves more than three centers. For example, a 4-center pharmacophore, when searched using 3-center techniques, would show up as 4 different 3-center pharmacophores (corresponding to the faces of the tetrahedron). Allowing the minimum match criteria to be increased above one allows the user to pick up on these larger interactions, while eliminating a good proportion of the "noise."

7.7. Pharmacophore Diversity

Addressing **pharmacophore diversity** is probably the primary purpose of pharmacophore keys. If a researcher is lucky, he or she will have a well-characterized target, with a well-known receptor site. Of course, many users are not so lucky, and have no target specific information to direct their studies. Given the situation where the user is creating compounds for lead generation, trying to find the real pharmacophore for his or her receptor site, the logical thing to do is to maximize the number of different pharmacophores tried. In other words, he or she needs to maximize the pharmacophore diversity of the libraries to be tested.

Many studies have examined the different methods to assess diversity. However, none of them are really as directly applicable in the pharmaceutical arena as pharmacophore diversity. Properties such as 2D fingerprints will necessarily have some relationship to the pharmacophores present, but usually lack a spatial element. It is possible to choose a set of compounds that exhibit the same pharmacophore, yet have many other different properties. Thus if we were to use those properties to determine diversity, we could wind up testing the same pharmacophore again and again. If that does not happen, then the diversity due to mere chance, and so we might as well pick compounds at random. The pharmacophore was defined above as a necessary but insufficient condition for the ligand to interact at the receptor site, and it must be acknowledged that other factors like transport properties and size can come into play. Thus a definition of pharmaceutical diversity might include other factors, but any definition of pharmaceutical diversity that ignores pharmacophores misses the point.

Given a specific pharmacophore key, a new user might well ask how its diversity could be assessed. The diversity of a library is expressed simply by the number of different pharmacophores it can exhibit, which means that the more bits set in the pharmacophore key, the more diverse the library. Having created a pharmacophore space, it is now possible to assess diversity by looking at how well any particular library fits it. This result might seem surprising to some, but it arises naturally from the initial assumptions that all of our pharmacophores are independent. Armed with this concept, the ability to perform logical operations on pharmacophore keys gives the user a potent set of decision-making tools.

Logical comparison of keys in Chem-X allows rational decisions to be made concerning libraries of compounds, but because the keys we use typically refer to collections of compounds, special techniques are needed when the task at hand involves the selection of individual compounds. No matter whether the compounds are being made or purchased, the perennial question is which compounds should be tested. In Chem-X, the technique known as **diverse subset** selection can be used either to pick subsets from an existing or virtual library, or to find compounds that are complementary to an existing one. Very often, having designed a virtual library on the computer, the chemist will ask whether just making some subset of it would be sufficient. The answer is usually yes: In fact in many cases screening approximately 10% of the library can cover nearly all of the pharmacophore space occupied by the whole virtual library.

The process of diverse subset selection in Chem-X is order dependent, and there is no single correct answer. There are a number of criteria that the user can superimpose on the compounds at the start of the process including a minimum/maximum number of rotatable bonds and pharmacophores. These are useful for removing uninteresting and rigid compounds, as well as promiscuous ones such as peptides, which are often seen to display so many pharmacophores that they rapidly saturate the pharmacophore keys. When the diverse subset selection process starts, the first accepted compound in the set being tested automatically goes into the diverse subset. The pharmacophore key for that compound is calculated. The next compound is then considered. Its pharmacophore key is also calculated, and the overlap with the first one is determined. If this compound shows a significant number of new pharmacophores, not expressed in the first key, it will be accepted into the diverse subset; otherwise it is omitted. Note that the term "rejected" is applied to compounds that fail the initial test; those not accepted because they have insufficient novel pharmacophores are termed "omitted." If the candidate compound is accepted, then its key will be ORed with the key of the compound already accepted, so that as the process continues, each compound is compared to the running union key representing all of the compounds already selected into the diverse subset. The user can control the process by specifying the required number or percentage of novel pharmacophores a compound must exhibit to be accepted. If pharmacophore profiling is enabled, the situation becomes a little more complicated, and the overlap between two keys is actually the cosine of the angle between their profile vectors.

The above technique can also be altered slightly: Instead of starting with a blank slate, the process can be seeded with an existing pharmacophore key, usually representing compounds already tested. It can then process a database of compounds and select those that are diverse from compounds that are represented by the seed key or that it has already selected in this run. This can provide a very useful tool for those who need to purchase diverse compounds for testing, since they can use it to pick compounds that are different from the compounds that they have bought on previous occasions.

7.8. Virtual Screening

If a user is fortunate to have access to the protein structure and receptor site information for his or her target, then Chem-X allows that information to be used to drive the process of finding compounds that will interact at the receptor site. This process is called **Design in Receptor.**

Typically the starting point of such studies is the reading into Chem-X of a PDB file containing the structure of the protein. This file might also contain site records, and if these are present the program will read and make them available. The user can select or combine such site records, or can individually select a series of residues in the protein that will be regarded as the receptor site. It is important to select a set of residues that physically form the site, even if these are not necessarily involved in the ligand-protein interaction.

Once the user is satisfied with the selection of the site, Chem-X will generate **complementary centers** within the receptor cavity. These complementary centers indicate where centers of ligand molecules would need to be placed to have favorable interactions with the receptor site. Once the site has been generated, the user may edit it if desired. This allows any knowledge of medicinal chemistry to be added to the process. For instance, centers can be removed if they are known not to be involved (this may be the case of a residue added to the site for its effect on the shape of the site rather than its chemistry). The centers can also be moved, for instance to compensate for flexibility, or centers can even be added. Other constraints may be imposed, for instance requiring only one of a small collection of centers to be present in any selected pharmacophores.

Once the user has specified the database to be searched, the search process can begin. This search is termed **site-based,** since, although there are many centers present, the system is not trying to find them all at the same time, as would be the case in a query-based search. The set of pharmacophore queries is created based on the users' specifications, and a 3D search ensues. However, there is one major difference between a site and a pharmacophore key. The centers in the site still have their coordinates in relationship to the protein cavity. Thus, as molecules are fitted to the complementary centers, a determination can be made if the molecule has undesirable steric interactions with the protein. Traditionally a map of the receptor site has been included as part of the 3D query, but more recently an option was added to allow this to be replaced by bump checking against the atoms of the site, which is considerably faster. The structures in the candidate database are considered in turn and each conformer that is generated is then compared to the list of pharmacophores to determine a match.

The user has a number of options for early termination. If it is just desired to select a set for screening, the process may be ended as soon as a single match is found. Often however, it is useful to know which pharmacophores are being "hit." Here a process known as **adaptive pharmacophore searching** can be used to temporarily remove pharmacophores from further consideration once they have led to a match. The end result allows the user to find molecules from their screening database or virtual library that not only have the right chemistry to interact at the receptor site, but also have the correct size and shape to fit into it. These compounds should be prime candidates for screening. Plate 7.2 shows an example of Design in Receptor in use.

7.9. Diamond Pharmacophores

Diamond Pharmacophores is part of the **Diamond Discovery** range of decision support tools that Oxford Molecular is designing. The underlying concept is to make data available to end users, to enable them to make decisions without the need to spend time themselves or to engage experts for modeling or calculating data. The system is based on a property server that can automatically run calculations on molecules that are stored in the user's database. Diamond Pharmacophores uses Chem-X as an engine in this process to generate pharmacophore keys for each compound, which are then stored back into the database as a list of pharmacophores for each structure. A front-end process will quickly allow users to compare the pharmacophores in different structures, find common pharmacophores, and so on. The process is of course extremely fast, since the pharmacophore info needs only be retrieved from the database.

References

1. Murrall NW, Davies EK: **Conformational freedom in 3D databases. 1. Techniques.** *J Chem Inf Comput Sci* 1990, **30**:312-316.

2. Martin YC, Danaher EB, May CS, Weinenger D: **MENTHOR, a database system for the storage and retrieval of three-dimensional molecular structures and associated data searchable by substructural, biologic, physical and geometric properties.** *J Comput-Aided Mol Des* 1998, **2**:15-29.

3. Sheridan RP, Nilakantan R, Rusinko A III, Bauman N, Haraki KS, Venkataraghavan R: **3DSEARCH: A system for three-dimensional substructure searching.** *J Chem Inf Comput Sci* 1989, **29**:255-260.

4. Murray CM, Cato SJ: **Design of libraries to explore receptor sites.** *J Chem Inf Comput Sci* 1999, **39**(1):46-50.

5. Oxford Molecular Group Inc., http://www.oxmol.com

Predictive Model Development—
3D QSAR

8

Apex-3D: Activity Prediction Expert System with 3D QSAR

Erich R. Vorpagel and Valery E. Golender

Abstract

Apex-3D is an automated pharmacophore identification expert system developed to represent, elucidate, and utilize knowledge on structure-activity relationships. Activity data can be either qualitative or quantitative. Apex-3D builds 3D-SAR and 3D-QSAR models, combining the two concepts of pharmacophores and QSAR equations, which can be used for activity classification and prediction. This chapter briefly describes the philosophy and algorithms behind Apex-3D and presents the results of its application to the frequently used benchmark dataset of 21 endogenous steroids. Apex-3D's unique ability to analyze more than one biological activity at a time allows direct comparisons between pharmacophores for analyzing the preferential binding of steroids to testosterone-binding globulin and corticosteroid-binding globulin. Frequently encountered difficulties with datasets for QSAR analysis are discussed along with specific problems associated with this 3D-QSAR benchmark.

8

Apex-3D: Activity Prediction Expert System with 3D QSAR

Erich R. Vorpagel and Valery E. Golender

Pacific Northwest National Laboratory,
Richland, Washington
Mutek Solution Ltd., Or-Yehuda, Israel

8.1. Introduction

All molecular interactions are essentially electronic, changing with time, always moving toward equilibrium. This is a direct consequence of molecules being made of atoms, which are composed of electronically charged particles. Any biological activity stimulated by a molecule comes from the interaction of its electron density distribution and polarizability with that of the biological system's over time. Changes in electron density distributions cause changes in conformation bringing about modifications in the biological system.

In rational drug design one must first identify an enzyme or receptor target, which when modified by a drug molecule will cause the desired therapeutic effect. When designing active molecules, one should know the electron density distribution and polarizability requirements of the active site in the enzyme or receptor. In addition, the active molecule must be able to get to its recognition site (receptor or enzyme) by crossing membrane boundaries and eluding metabolic processes. Side effects occur when the molecule meets the electron distribution and polarizability requirements of other enzymes and receptors. Thus, a successful drug must have a reasonable therapeutic index that is, the ratio of the largest dose producing no toxic symptoms to the smallest dose routinely producing cures must be large. Modifications must often be made to improve bioavailability and reduce toxicity without significant loss of activity. The final drug molecule is a set of compromises that must then be produced in large quantities at a reasonable cost.

Unfortunately, the electron density distribution and polarizability requirements are not known, even when one has an X-ray crystal structure of the ligand-receptor complex. Though such information is very useful, still the interaction details between the biological system and the drug molecule (xenobiotic) must be surmised from sets of molecules with known activity.

Empirical screening methods have successfully identified new lead compounds for drugs and crop protection chemicals. Unfortunately, new compounds must first be synthesized, often at great expense, before they can be screened. A description of relationships between chemical structure and biological activity would provide a means to predict biological activity from chemical structures before synthesis, leading to improved efficiency and productivity. High throughput screening methods developed over the last 15 years have provided cost-effective ways of screening thousands of compounds rapidly. Active hits from such screens still need to be synthesized in larger quantities followed by more detailed screening. A xenobiotic's ability to reach the active site, how long it stays at an effective concentration, side effects, and toxicity must be considered.

Various methods have been employed to break down molecules into fragments or parts that can be used to approximate interactions between ligand and receptor and translocation to the active site. Two concepts have evolved based on the assumption that biologically active compounds have some specific structural feature, property, or shape that models the electron density distribution and polarizability requirements and provides the activity:

- Pharmacophore Model—consisting of features in a molecule having certain intramolecular distances necessary for interaction at the receptor.

- QSAR Model—consisting of a mathematical equation describing potency as a function of chemical structure and translocation to the receptor.

Pharmacophore models provide visual and qualitative information. They often capture the three-dimensional nature of the ligand-receptor interaction using distances between essential features described in three-dimensional space. Activity predictions from pharmacophore models tend to be binary: It should either be active or inactive. In some cases an estimate of the probability for activity is given. Classical QSAR models are quantitative but lack the three-dimensional aspect of the interactions. Many attempts have been made to expand and sometimes merge these two approaches as exemplified in other chapters in this book. Application of any of these approaches depends on the training set of compounds used to develop the model. Extrapolation to and prediction of molecules outside the training set will be successful only to the extent that the model includes all aspects of the biological activity being considered.

This chapter describes our attempt at combining the qualitative three-dimensional aspect of pharmacophore models with quantitative structure-activity relationships. The activity prediction expert system Apex-3D will be described in general terms and then applied to the frequently used benchmark dataset of 21 endogenous steroids[1] to analyze their preferential binding to testosterone-binding globulin and corticosteroid-binding globulin. Frequently encountered difficulties with datasets will be discussed along with specific problems associated with this dataset used by other 3D QSAR methods appearing in the literature. This includes Comparative Molecular Field Analysis (CoMFA),[2] Shape-Based Machine Learning Tool (Compass),[3] Comparative Molecular Similarity Indices Analysis (CoMSIA),[4] Molecular Similarity Matrix Analysis,[5] Receptor Surface Models (RSM),[6] and Auto-correlation of Molecular Surface Properties using Neural Networks.[7]

8.2. General Description of Apex-3D

Apex-3D is an automated pharmacophore identification expert system developed to represent, elucidate, and utilize knowledge on structure-activity relationships. Apex-3D builds 3D SAR and 3D QSAR models, combining the two concepts of pharmacophores and QSAR equations, which can be used for activity classification and prediction. The general principle of operation is based on emulating the intelligence of a scientist engaged in the analysis of structure-activity relationships. The Apex-3D methodology begins with automated identification of possible pharmacophores and active conformations involved in some biological process, the details of which could be completely unknown, using the logico-structural approach.[8-10] These pharmacophores (biophores) are composed of various atom or pseudoatom centered descriptor centers and the distances between them. Two special languages[10] for defining molecular features associated with activity were developed specifically for Apex-3D:

- SLANG—a molecular line entry language similar to SMILES[11] for describing structural patterns.
- ChemLisp—a language for defining pharmacophoric groups or pseudoatoms and associating them with physicochemical properties.

Typical features include hydrogen-bond acceptors or donors, lipophilic groups, partial atomic charge, or other quantum-mechanically calculated indexes. Bayesian statistics are used to analyze whether a particular biophore is associated with the biological activity assigned to the activity class. Significance of identified biophores is assessed using both reclassification and a leave-one-out analysis. Information is stored in the form of rules, which can be visualized as pharmacophores by browsing through the knowledge base. This approach does not require all active compounds in an activity class bind to the same receptor or even have the same mode of action. Neither do the activity data need to be quantitative. *Thus, Apex-3D can identify several pharmacophores for a heterogeneous dataset comprising compounds with different modes of actions using qualitative data.* Activity classification assumes the biological activity is sensitive to features in the molecules having certain relative distances necessary for interaction with the receptor or other chemical-biological interaction. All other aspects of biological activity are assumed negligible or equivalent for the set of molecules under consideration. Multiple biological activities can be considered at one time. When predictability is good, compounds containing identified biophores can be analyzed for possible multiple binding modes.

Built into the system is automatic selection of the best conformation and alignment of the structures on identified pharmacophores. There are two common types of molecular alignment: alignment according to pharmacophoric patterns, and alignment based on shape similarity. Apex-3D's alignment algorithm takes into account both types, producing alignments in agreement with chemical knowledge and intuition. While searching for possible pharmacophores, the combinatorial algorithm takes into account a molecule's conformational space and different properties of aligned features such as hydrogen-bond donors and acceptors, heteroatoms, and hydrophobic groups. The primary superimposition requirement is alignment of these features. The conformer selected for each molecule containing the biophore is the one maximizing the empirical shape similarity function. This alignment is used when displaying the biophore in the knowledge base and for building 3D QSAR models.

Biophores identified can be used as starting points for constructing 3D QSAR models when good quantitative biological data is available. This is a natural 3D extension of traditional QSAR for a cogeneric series (compounds having the same pharmacophore). Combination of a three-dimensional pharmacophore model with a quantitative regression equation is unique to the Apex-3D approach. Possible parameters include electronic and other physicochemical properties of pharmacophore or non-pharmacophore atoms, occupation of spacial regions relative to the pharmacophore identifying steric factors and hydrophobic regions, and whole molecule properties which may correlate with translocation and bioavailability (like octanol/water partition coefficient). It is possible to build separate 3D QSAR models for subsets of structures corresponding to different binding orientations, subtypes, or agonist/antagonist. A stepwise Multiple Linear Regression procedure (MLR) is used to generate model equations. Cross-validation (leave-one-out) and other statistics are used for model evaluation and assessment. Consistent with the MLR approach, parameters must be statistically significant (based on t-test) to be included in a model equation. Multiple regression equations are generated for a single biophore if they meet all the significance criteria. The chance that an equation is fortuitous is evaluated by randomizing assignment of activity data for each compound and repeating the MLR procedure several hundred times. If a regression equation with the same or smaller number of variables, with as good or better correlation coefficient is obtained, it is recorded. The *chance* statistic is evaluated as the ratio of recorded equivalent regression equations to the total number of randomized sets (e.g., 4/200 or 0.02, reported as 2% chance of fortuitous correlation). Activity prediction of novel compounds (those not in the training set) requires the biophore be present: Activity level is calculated from the QSAR equation. Thus, the Apex-3D QSAR method assumes the pharmacophore is essential for biological activity. Compounds lacking the pharmacophore are considered inactive.

Active conformers elucidated by Apex-3D and associated with pharmacophoric features and 3D QSAR equations have great utility in drug design. For example, stabilization of active conformation by constraining flexibility, improving bioavailability while preserving the active conformation, design of pharmacophore-based combinatorial libraries, and 3D-database searches.

8.3. Steroid Binding Data

Binding affinities for a set of 21 endogenous steroids for both testosterone-binding globulin (TeBG) and corticosteroid-binding globulin (CBG) determined by Dunn et al.[1] have been used as a benchmark for 3D QSAR methods. Cramer et al.[2] was the first to apply CoMFA to the dataset including additional 10 compounds gleaned from other sources to test CBG activity prediction. As pointed out by Wagener et al.[7] there are several errors in coding the topology and/or stereochemistry as presented in the 3D QSAR literature. Structures used in this study were taken from the original literature[1,12] and correspond to those used by Wagener et al.

Table 8.1 shows the binding affinity data for TeBG and CBG reported by Dunn et al. for the training set of 21 steroids. This data is typical of activity data used for QSAR analysis. Values for testosterone-binding globulin are a good set having a wide range of affinities (almost 4 orders of magnitude) with no bounded values. The corticosteroid-binding globulin data has a smaller range of affinities (only 2 orders of magnitude) with seven compounds measuring less than the detectable limit. Though useful for developing a qualitative pharmacophore model, such bounded data is not good for QSAR analysis. **One third of the CBG binding data is qualitative,** assigned a value less than the detectable limit of 0.1×10^6 M^{-1}. But how much less? Some compounds may be much less active than the detectable limit. Assigning activity to the minimum value, though routinely done, biases the QSAR results rendering any activity prediction dubious even though the cross-validated "predictive" r[2] value for the equation may be good. For straight QSAR analysis, bounded data should be excluded. One or more of the compounds with bounded activity can subsequently be included in the QSAR analysis followed by an evaluation of its effect. For comparison purposes, the full dataset for CBG was used as given in reference[2] and expressed in units of log K (-pK).

Table 8.1. Binding data from references[1,2] shown as association constant K and log K (-pK) for both testosterone-binding globulin (TeBG) and corticosteroid-binding globulin (CBG).

Steroid	TeBG		CBG	
	K (10^6 M^{-1})	-pK	K (10^6 M^{-1})	-pK
Aldosterone	0.21	5.322	1.9	6.279
Androstanediol	1300	9.114	< 0.1	5.0
Androstenediol	1500	9.176	< 0.1	5.0
Androstenedione	29	7.462	0.58	5.763
Androsterone	14	7.146	0.41	5.613
Corticosterone	2.2	6.342	76	7.881
Cortisol	1.6	6.204	76	7.881
Cortisone	2.7	6.431	7.8	6.892
Dehydroepiandrosterone	66	7.819	< 0.1	5.0
Deoxycorticosterone	24	7.380	45	7.653
Deoxycortisol	16	7.204	76	7.881
Dihydrotestosterone	5500	9.740	0.83	5.919
Estradiol	680	8.833	< 0.1	5.0
Estriol	4.3	6.633	< 0.1	5.0
Estrone	150	8.176	< 0.1	5.0
Etiocholanolone	1.4	6.146	0.18	5.225
Pregnenolone	14	7.146	0.18	5.225
17-Hydroxypregnenolone	2.3	6.362	< 0.1	5.0
Progesterone	8.8	6.944	24	7.380
17-Hydroxyprogesterone	9.9	6.996	55	7.740
Testosterone	1600	9.204	5.3	6.724

8.4. Conformer Generation Strategy

Since Apex-3D deals with the three-dimensional aspect of molecules, multiple conformations must be handled. Simply including the global

minimum energy conformer is not adequate since the binding conformation may be a low-energy local minimum. Steroids are relatively
rigid molecules though there is some flexibility. Conformer variation
comes from rotations of the chain attached to the C_{17} position and ring
flipping (see Chart 1 for IUPAC numbering scheme for steroids). For
this study, conformers were generated using the systematic conformational search algorithm in the Search_Compare module of Insight II
from Molecular Simulations Inc. (MSI). All single bonds were rotated
with the exception of -CH3 and -OH groups and all four rings allowed
to flip. Each conformer was optimized to a local energy minimum using
Discover and the CFF91 force field, also from MSI. Unique conformers
within 7.0 kcals/mol of the global minimum were retained yielding
between one and twelve conformations for each steroid. For more flexible molecules, the above protocol can generate hundreds or even thousands of conformers, exceeding the computational limits of the pharmacophore identification procedure. For such cases, a conformer-clus-
tering algorithm is integrated into Apex-3D[13] to reduce the number of
conformers while maintaining a good sampling of conformer space.

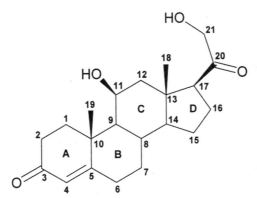

Chart 8.1. Stick structure of corticosterone with IPUAC numbering of the steroid skeleton.

8.5. Activity Classification Analysis

As discussed previously, one of the challenges of understanding structure-activity relationships is identifying certain features in a molecule

which meet the electron density and polarizability requirement of a receptor. From the data in Table 8.1, one can see there are features in this set of steroids that mediate preferential binding to either TeBG or CBG. Some steroids show a clear preference for TeBG (androstanediol and androstenediol) while others prefer CBG (cortisol and cortisone). Most pharmacophore identification methodologies work with only one binding site interaction at a time. Apex-3D can generate possible pharmacophores for binding interactions to multiple receptors in a single analysis. By setting up activity classes for each receptor interaction, Apex-3D will try to find pharmacophores specific to each activity class. From the data of Dunn et al. there are three major plasma proteins that complex with these steroids: testosterone-binding globulin, corticosteroid-binding globulin, and albumin. The first two are specific, while binding to protein albumin is fairly non-specific. These three types of binding activity become three activity classes for Apex-3D.

Activity class definitions are based on either qualitative or quantitative activity data. Bounded activity data like that for CBG is not a problem because ranges are used for activity class definitions. Activity class cutoff values can be assigned subjectively or an unbiased clustering method such as K-means clustering* can be used. In this study, steroids considered to be CBG-binding include eight compounds having K values greater than 3.8×10^6 M^{-1}. TeBG-binding steroids include six compounds having K values greater than 100×10^6 M^{-1}. The third activity class includes eight steroids without preference for CBG or TeBG. They have association constants less than 3.8×10^6 M^{-1} for CBG-binding and less than 100×10^6 M^{-1} for TeBG-binding. This class is referred to as albumin-binding compounds. The astute reader will notice this adds up to 22 compounds. That is because testosterone fits in both the CBG-binding and TeBG-binding activity classes.

Many different molecular features combining an atom center with a physicochemical property can be used by Apex-3D for possible pharmacophore interactions. It is best to include only those which are most likely to be involved in binding. In this study, three general types of interactions were considered: hydrogen-bond formation (hydrogen-donor or acceptor atoms), lipophilic (methyl groups and ring centers

---

* K-means clustering splits a set of objects into a selected number of groups by maximizing intercluster variation and minimizing intracluster variation.[14]

with various degrees of unsaturation), and electrostatic (partial atomic charge on heteroatoms and electron-donor ability based on semi-empirical MOPAC calculations). These features (descriptor centers) are identified in each conformation of each molecule, then a clique detection algorithm is used[8] to find common distances among combinations of descriptor centers in the different molecules. Thousands of possible biophores are often identified. Each biophore is statistically rated based on its occurrence in molecules in the different activity classes. These statistics are used to develop rules that are adjusted to properly classify the activities of the molecules in the training set. This includes a leave-one-out approach. Finally, the molecules containing each significant biophore are superimposed on the biophore choosing the best conformer for the fit. One or more biophores may be found to be useful in classifying the activity assigned to molecules in the training set. Each one can be viewed as a potential pharmacophore, subject to further experimental validation.

8.5.1. Pharmacophores Identified

Biophores identified by Apex-3D include features present in active molecules but absent in inactive molecules. Negative or deleterious interactions are not considered part of the pharmacophore. Inactive molecules containing the active pharmacophore are considered false positives. Frequently they have additional features that extend beyond the active molecules. Steric obstacles can be analyzed in Apex-3D using the excluded volume utility on a biophore with structures superimposed. When quantitative data is available, negative interactions can be accounted for in 3D QSAR models.

Plate 8.1 shows two pharmacophores present in molecules with testosterone-binding globulin activity. Both include all four ring centers, a hydrogen-bond donor at the 20 position and a methyl group at the 18 position. The top biophore has an additional methyl group at the 19 position. Estriol contains the lower biophore but it is not a very good TeBG binder. Estriol is a false positive because of the deleterious hydroxyl group attached to C16. Plate 8.2 shows two possible pharmacophores present in molecules with corticosteroid-binding globulin activity. Again methyl groups at the 18 and 19 position are important for binding, however, in the region where a hydrogen-bond donor was important for TeBG binding; CBG binding prefers a hydrogen-bond acceptor. The other essential feature for CBG binding is that the A-ring be an enone (3-oxo-4-ene).

8.5.2. Prediction (Classification) Results

The knowledge base of pharmacophore rules in Apex-3D can be used to predict the activity class to which other steroids belong. The ten steroid molecules from Cramer et al. were evaluated to test Apex-3D's ability to classify them as corticosteroid-binding globulin, i.e., having CBG binding association constants greater then 3.8×10^6 M^{-1}. All seven CBG binding steroids were classified correctly. Of the three steroids with smaller K values, one (19-nortestosterone) was properly classified but 11-deoxy-16α-hydroxycortisone and 2α-methyl-9-fluorocortisol were false positives. Only one molecule in the training set (estriol) had a 16α-hydroxy substitution and therefore could not pass the leave-one-out validation test for significance. None of the training set molecules had a 2α- or 9- substitution so the knowledge base would not have any information on such compounds. In the initial phases of lead discovery, false positives are more tolerable than false negatives.

8.6. 3D QSAR Models

All 3D QSAR models in Apex-3D are based on a biophore. Biophores are used to align molecules in "active" conformations, establishing a superimposition criterion and serving as a requirement for baseline activity. Thus, a one-to-one correspondence exists between biophores and QSAR equations in Apex-3D's 3D QSAR models. Multiple 3D QSAR models can be stored in a single knowledge base used for activity prediction. Independent variables based on physicochemical properties for the multiple linear regression equation can be one of three types: those associated with biophore sites, those associated with the whole molecule, and those associated with atoms or groups other than biophore sites. These secondary sites are a three-dimensional equivalent of substituents in traditional QSAR, regions of space relative to the pharmacophore which when occupied by the ligand will increase or decrease the activity. They can represent pharmacophore extensions, lipophilic pockets, or regions of space relative to the pharmacophore which bump into the receptor (steric interference). QSAR parameters can be generated by Apex-3D or assigned manually and can be continuous or indicator variables. To include all compounds in a training set, very simple (trivial, non-specific) biophores present in all molecules must be chosen to be able to include low activity molecules. Secondary sites then become extensions of the "pharmacophore." False positives found during activity classification can be correctly described in a 3D QSAR model if more than one molecule contains the deleterious feature.

Any biophore found during activity classification can be used to create a 3D QSAR model. Two such models are shown below, one for TeBG binding and one for CBG binding, each with all 21 steroids.

8.6.1. Testosterone-Binding 3D QSAR Model

A simple biophore consisting of ring centers in the A, C, and D rings was used for the TeBG 3D QSAR model so all steroids in the dataset would be included. The QSAR part of the model is shown in Table 8.2. It contains seven independent variables, including one global parameter (Total Hydrophobicity) and six secondary sites, which are indicator variables. This barely fits the rule of thumb for QSAR equations which is to have at least three compounds for each independent variable used. The reasonable statistics lend credence to the use of so many variables.

Plate 8.3 shows two views of the 3D QSAR model. Numbers for parameter type in the QSAR equation correspond to red numbers for secondary sites in Plate 8.3. The red circle has radius equal to that for the region of influence for the site. Note that secondary sites 6 and 7 are relatively large, corresponding to regions where steric interference decreases binding affinity. The parameter with the largest influence over binding is the presence of a hydrogen-bond donor on the β-side of C_{17} (sites 3 and 5) which increase binding and together account for over 70% of the variance. This feature was picked up during activity classification and appears in both pharmacophores in Plate 8.1. Two sites for the 17β-OH substituent occur in the QSAR equation because different steroids have conformations which place the substituent in different regions of space. Presence of a hydrogen-bond acceptor on the α-side of C_{17} (site 2) also increases binding, but a hydrogen-bond acceptor on the α-side of C_3 (site 4) significantly decreases activity. Chance of fortuitous correlation was tested by randomizing the binding activities and repeating the MLR analysis 500 times. Only 3% of the 500 equations had correlations as good or better. Figure 8.1 is a plot of the experimental TeBG binding values versus those values predicted by the 3D QSAR model.

Table 8.2. Testosterone-binding globulin (TeBG) 3D-QSAR equation. Numbers for parameter type correspond to red numbers for secondary sites in Plate 8.3. Column **r** is the correlation coefficient for the parameter when used alone. Probability of this being a chance correlation is 3%.

	Parameter Type	Coefficient (Std. Err)	r	Description
Log $K_{(TeBG)}$ =	1) Total Hydrophobicity	1.41 (±0.17)	0.47	(Apex logP)
	2) Presence H-Acceptor	0.67 (±0.24)	0.37	(17α-OH)
	3) Presence H-Donor	0.50 (±0.24)	0.48	(17β-OH)
	4) Presence H-Donor	-1.79 (±0.31)	0.21	(3α-OH)
	5) Presence H-Donor	1.94 (±0.21)	0.78	(17β-OH)
	6) Presence Steric	-0.82 (±0.23)	0.40	(C_6 α-side)
	7) Presence Steric	-0.87 (±0.23)	0.23	(C_{21} -Me)
	CONSTANT	2.80		
Equation Stats		$n = 21$; $r^2 = 0.95$; $s = 0.34$; $F = 34.33$; Chance$_{500}$ = 0.032		
Cross-Validated Stats		$S_{PRESS} = 0.55$; SDEP = 0.43; $q^2 = 0.87$		

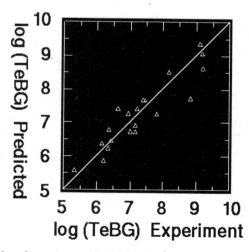

Figure 8.1. Plot of experimental TeBG binding -pK values against the -pK values predicted by the 3D QSAR model.

8.6.2. Corticosteroid 3D QSAR Model

A simple biophore consisting of ring centers in the A, B, and C rings was used for the CBG 3D QSAR model. The QSAR part of the model is shown in Table 8.3. It contains four independent variables, all secondary sites, which are indicator variables. Again, excellent statistics are obtained for the model. Plate 8.4 shows the 3D QSAR model with red numbers for secondary sites corresponding to parameters in the equation. The parameter with the largest influence over binding is the presence of a hydrogen-bond acceptor at C_3 (site 2) which increases binding and can account for over 80% of the variance. This feature was picked up during activity classification and appears in both pharmacophores in Plate 8.2. It is gratifying to see the 11β-OH substituent increases corticosteroid-binding activity since this is a distinguishing feature of cortisol. This particular feature did not show up during activity classification in many of the biophores because statistically it does not occur very frequently. Presence of a hydrogen-bond acceptor attached to C_{17} (site 1) decreases binding, as does substitution on the β-side of C_{16} (site 4). Chance of fortuitous correlation was tested by randomizing the binding activities and repeating the MLR analysis 500 times. Only 2% of the 500 equations had correlations as good or better. Figure 8.2 is a plot of the experimental CBG binding values versus those values predicted by the 3D QSAR model. Though the statistics look good, the model can still be biased because of the seven compounds with boundary values. In this model, none of the parameters are dependent on boundary valued compounds. A similar model is obtained when they are excluded.

Table 8.3. Corticosteroid-binding globulin (CBG) 3D QSAR equation. Numbers for parameter type correspond to red numbers for secondary sites in Plate 8.4. Column r is the correlation coefficient for the parameter when used alone. Probability of this being a chance correlation is 2%.

	Parameter Type	Coefficient (Std. Err)	r	Description
Log K(CBG) =	1) Presence H-Acceptor	-0.38 (±0.17)	0.51	(17-oxo)
	2) Presence H-Acceptor	1.35 (±0.19)	0.90	(3-oxo)
	3) Presence H-Donor	0.52 (±0.27)	0.49	(11β-OH)
	4) Presence Steric	-0.82 (±0.17)	0.73	(C_{16} β-side)
	CONSTANT	6.01		
Equation Stats	$n = 21$; $r^2 = 0.94$; $s = 0.33$; $F = 59.07$; Chance$_{500} = 0.018$			
Cross-Validated Stats	$S_{PRESS} = 0.42$; SDEP $= 0.37$; $q^2 = 0.90$			

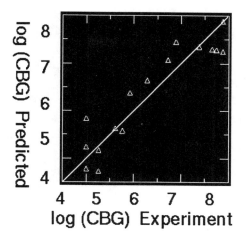

Figure 8.2. Plot of experimental CBG binding -pK values against the -pK values predicted by the 3D QSAR model.

8.7. Comparison with Other 3D QSAR Methods

Seven different types of analyses have been applied to this dataset. All but one used the set of 21 steroids for CBG binding affinity to predict the activity of a second set of 10 steroids. Others presented results for the CBG dataset but not the TeBG dataset. The Auto-Correlation of Molecular Surface Properties approach used all 31 steroids in their analysis and did not attempt to split the dataset in two for activity prediction.

QSAR models can be evaluated on two criteria: how well they reproduce the data used in the training set, and how well they predict activities of molecules not used for training. Table 8.4 compares the 3D QSAR model statistics for CBG binding affinity reported in the literature and in this study. Not all statistical data was included in each paper, sometimes because the method did not lend itself to such analysis. The models tend to cluster into two groups based on the square of their predictive correlation coefficient (q^2), the only statistic reported for all models. The first group falls in the range 0.63-0.67 while the second group is in the range 0.84-0.90. Apex-3D falls into the second group with one of the best predictive correlation coefficients. For actual prediction of test compounds, the Receptor Surface Model (RSM) method has the best score. This is primarily due to getting the low binding affinity of 2α-methyl-9-fluorocortisol correct which the other methods failed to predict. Though Apex-3D's prediction for the binding affinity of 2α-methyl-9-fluorocortisol was high by two orders of magnitude, the other nine molecules were predicted very well leading to the next best predictive standard error.

Table 8.4. Comparison of 3D QSAR model statistics for CBG binding affinity where r^2 is the square of the correlation coefficient, S the standard deviation for the equation, q^2 the cross-validated correlation coefficient ("predictive" r^2), S_{PRESS} the cross-validated standard error, and Pred. Std Err the standard error of predictions for the 10 test steroids. Models include Comparative Molecular Field Analysis (CoMFA),[2] Molecular Similarity Matrix analysis (Similarity),[5] Receptor Surface Models (RSM),[6] Comparative Molecular Similarity Indices Analysis (CoMSIA),[4] Shape-based Machine Learning Tool (Compass),[3] Auto-correlation of Molecular Surface Properties using Neural Networks (AMSP),[7] and Activity Prediction Expert System (Apex-3D).[10]

Stats	CoMFA	Similarity	RSM	CoMSIA	Compass	AMSP	Apex-3D
r^2	0.90	--	0.67	0.94	--	0.98*	0.94
S	0.40	--	--	0.33	--	0.18	0.33
q^2	0.67	0.63	0.63	0.67	0.89	0.84	0.90
S_{PRESS}	0.72	0.82	--	0.76	--	--	0.42
Pred. Std Err	0.83	0.71	0.39	0.69	0.72	*Used all 31 cmpds	0.42

Table 8.5 compares the 3D QSAR model statistics for TeBG binding affinity reported in the literature and in this study. Fewer 3D QSAR methods analyzed the TeBG dataset. Again, Apex-3D produces one of the best models, based on statistics.

As mentioned earlier, this popular steroid dataset is not an ideal benchmark for comparing 3D QSAR methods in part due to the qualitative nature of boundary data. H. Kubinyi[15] recently pointed out several other problems including the observation that a single indicator variable on a Free-Wilson type model predicts activity as reliably as the

CoMFA and CoMSIA models. The structural variables selected by Apex-3D in the 3D QSAR model of Plate 8.4 are also of the indicator type. Indeed, the qualitative biophores in Plate 8.2 include the importance of 4,5-unsaturation which corresponds to the indicator variable used by Kubinyi. A more interesting application of Apex-3D is the analysis of complex flexible peptides, peptidomimetics, and small cyclic peptides to model the somatostatin receptor recognition site.[16]

Table 8.5. Comparison of 3D QSAR model statistics for TeBG binding affinity where r^2 is the square of the correlation coefficient, S the standard deviation for the equation, q^2 the cross-validated correlation coefficient ("predictive" r^2), S_{PRESS} the cross-validated standard error. Models include Comparative Molecular Field Analysis (CoMFA),[2] Molecular Similarity Matrix analysis (Similarity),[5] Shape-based Machine Learning Tool (Compass),[3] and Activity Prediction Expert System (Apex-3D).[10]

Stats	CoMFA	Similarity	Compass	Apex-3D
r^2	0.87	--	--	0.95
S	0.45	--	--	0.34
q^2	0.55	0.74	0.88	0.87
S_{PRESS}	0.85	0.67	--	0.55

8.8. Conclusions

Many attempts have been made to apply quantitative methods to three-dimensional pharmacophore models to aid rational drug design. Some 3D QSAR models do well-correlating data used in the training set but are not easily amenable to interpretation leading to improved activity. All 3D QSAR models are limited by the good quantitative data requirement. The old adage "garbage in, garbage out" is quite applicable to QSAR models. Apex-3D provides a good balance between pharmacophore model generation from qualitative data and quantitative 3D QSAR models. A unique strength of Apex-3D is its ability to analyze more than one biological activity at a time, allowing direct comparisons between pharmacophores for different receptors. As with traditional QSAR, the 3D QSAR models generated by Apex-3D are readily interpreted making lead optimization easier. Apex-3D is a powerful tool for pharmacophore identification and 3D QSAR analysis of complex structure-activity relationships.

References

1. Dunn JF, Nisula BC, Rodbard D: **Transport of steroid hormones: Binding of 21 endogenous steroids to both testosterone-binding globulin and corticosteroid-binding globulin in human plasma.** *J Clin Endocrinol & Metab* 1981, **53**:58-69.

2. Cramer RD III, Patterson DE, Bunce JD: **Comparative Molecular Field Analysis (CoMFA). 1. Effect of shape on binding of steroids to carrier proteins.** *J Am Chem* Soc 1988, **110**:5959-5967.

3. Jain AJ, Koile K, Chapman D: Compass: **Predicting biological activities from molecular surface properties. performance comparisons on a steroid benchmark.** *J Med Chem* 1994, **37**:2315-2327.

4. Klebe G, Abraham U, Mietzner T: **Molecular Similarity Indices in a Comparative Analysis (CoMSIA) of drug molecules to correlate and predict their biological activity.** *J Med Chem* 1994, **37**:4130-4146.

5. Good AC, So SS, Richards WG: **Structure-activity relationships from molecular similarity matrices.** *J Med Chem* 1993, **36**:433-438.

6. Hahn M, Rogers D: **Receptor surface models. 2. Application to quantitative structure-activity relationships studies.** *J Med Chem* 1995, **38**:2091-2102.

7. Wagener M, Sadowski J, Gasteiger J: **Autocorrelation of Molecular surface properties for modeling corticosteroid binding globulin and cytosolic Ah receptor activity by neural networks.** *J Am Chem Soc* 1995, **117**:7769-7775.

8. Golender VE, Rozenblit AB: *Logical and Combinatorial Algorithms in Drug Design.* Letchworth, U.K: Research Studies Press, 1983.

9. Golender VE, Vorpagel ER: **Computer-assisted pharmacophore identification.** In: *3D QSAR in Drug Design: Theory, Methods and Applications.* Kubinyi H, ed. Leiden: ESCOM, 1993.

10. Golender VE, Vesterman B, Ehyahu O, Kardash A, Kletzkin M, Vorpagel ER: **Knowledge-engineering approach to drug design and its implications in the Apex-3D expert system.** In: *QSAR and Molecular Modelling: Concepts, Computational Tools and Biological Applications.* Sanz F, Giraldo, J, Manaut F, eds. Barcelona: Prous Science Publishers, 1995:246-251.

11. Weininger D: **SMILES, a chemical language and information system. 1. Introduction to methodology and encoding rules.** *J Chem Inf Comput Sci* 1988, **28**:31-36.

12. Mickelson KE, Forsthoefel J, Westphal U: **Steroid-protein interactions. human corticosteroid binding globulin: some physicochemical properties and binding specificity.** *Biochemistry* 1981, **20**:6211-6218.

13. Vesterman B, Golender V, Golender L, Fuchs B: **Conformer clustering algorithm and its application for crown-type macromolecules.** *J Mol Struct THEOCHEM* 1996, **368**:145-151.

14. Weiss SM, Indurkhya N: *Predictive Data Mining: A Practical Guide.* Morgan Kaufmann Publishers, 1997.

15. Kubinyi H: A **General view on similarity and QSAR studies.** In: *Computer-Assisted Lead Finding and Optimization. Current Tools for Medicinal Chemistry.* Van de Waterbeemd H, Testa B, Folkers G, eds. Basel: Verlag Helvetica Chimica Acta, 1997:9-28.

16. Golender L, Rosengeld R, Vorpagel ER: **Small cyclic peptide SAR study using Apex-3D system: Somatostatin receptor type 2 (SSTR2) specific pharmacophores.** In: *Molecular Modeling and Prediction of Bioactivity.* Gundertofte K, Jørgensen FS, eds. Copenhagen: Plenum Publishers, 1999, in press.

9

Pharmacophore Models and Comparative Molecular Field Analysis (CoMFA)

Robert D. Clark, Joseph M. Leonard, and Alexander Strizhev

Abstract

Comparative Molecular Field Analysis (CoMFA) is a technique for elucidating quantitative structure/activity relationships (QSARs) which uses potentials from molecular fields as descriptors. Doing so requires one or more hypotheses specifying how each molecular field relates to those of every other compound in the dataset. These alignment rules must include conformational (torsional) specifications as well as an unambiguous way of positioning each molecule in a common reference lattice. The statistical output from CoMFA can then be used to determine which alignment rule is likely to be most predictive of biological activity for compounds outside the training set. Here we describe how pharmacophore models can be used to generate good alignment rules for CoMFA and how the models obtained thereby might profitably be used in connection with flexible 3D searching for lead follow-up. A set of σ receptor antagonists recently described by A. Nakazato et al. (*J Med Chem* 1999, **42**:1076-1087) serves as a useful example.

9

Pharmacophore Models and Comparative Molecular Field Analysis (CoMFA)

Robert D. Clark, Joseph M. Leonard, and Alexander Strizhev

Tripos, Inc., St. Louis, Missouri

9.1. What Is CoMFA?

Comparative Molecular Field Analysis (CoMFA) was first described by R. D. Cramer et al. in 1988[1] and has since become the method of choice for elucidating quantitative structure/activity relationships which are dependent upon the three-dimensional structure of biologically active small molecules—i.e., 3D QSARs.[2,3] It has also become important for elucidating quantitative structure/property relationships (QSPRs).[4,5]

In CoMFA, molecular fields are used as descriptors in regression models. The seminal studies[1] involved steric fields calculated as Lennard-Jones potentials and electrostatic fields calculated as electrostatic potentials against simple probe ions. Isopotential contours from molecular fields calculated with respect to an sp^3 carbocation, for example, are shown in Plate 9.1, a and c. Other workers have extended the method to use hydrophobic fields (e.g., HINT),[6] Gaussian pseudo-potentials (CoMSIA)[7,8] and indicator fields.[9] The GRID program, which was developed contemporaneously by P. Goodford,[10] calculates a series of potentials, typically using more complex probes.

Plate 9.1 shows molecular fields calculated for compound **10g** (see Figure 9.1) plotted as contours for steric (Plate 9.1, a) and electrostatic (Plate 9.1, c) fields: Steric fields (a) are shown as Leonard-Jones steric potential contour surface at 25 kcal/mol. Plate 9.1, b shows lattice points at which the steric potential lies between 29 and 31 kcal/mol (i.e., points within the van der Waals radius). Electrostatic potential contour (b) is shown at 10 kcal/mol. Note the large positive charge surrounding the ammonium NH and the "holes" produced by the two pendant propyl groups. Plate 9.1, d shows lattice points at which the electrostatic potential lies between 9 and 11 kcal/mol.

To get a descriptor suitable for subsequent least-squares analysis, the field is sampled at discrete points, generally corresponding to points on a rectilinear lattice. The default lattice spacing in SYBYL's QSAR Module[11] is 2 Å, and that spacing was used here; indeed, default parameter settings have been used in this case study wherever possible in an effort to keep its applicability general. Fields in GRID are generally sampled at higher resolution.

Only rarely can the descriptors so obtained be used directly in "ordinary" multiple linear regression analysis (also known as OLS or MLR), in part because high correlations among potentials at adjacent lattice points often lead to unreliable models. Moreover, there are usually many more lattice points of interest (typically 1000 or more) than there are observations available—100 compounds is a large dataset. This constitutes a mathematically underdetermined system of equations not amenable to MLR.

The alternative is to use the untransformed field values as input to an alternative regression technique known as partial least-squares projection to latent structures (PLS).[12] This technique, which was developed by S. Wold et al.,[13] generates a series of mutually orthogonal linear combinations of the input descriptors which are maximally correlated with the response of interest. Generally three to five such linear combinations (components) are enough to give a predictive model without overfitting the data. For very dense fields such as those produced by GRID, even PLS is overwhelmed and a program such as GOLPE[14] must be used to select out an informative subset of lattice points used in the PLS analysis.

The mechanics of PLS virtually guarantee that the model produced will have excellent goodness-of-fit. It is more meaningful to estimate the model's predictivity—to see how accurately a model can predict responses for compounds not included in the training set. The most common way to accomplish this is cross-validation, i.e., omitting one or several compounds at a time from the training set. The actual response values are then compared with those predicted by a PLS model constructed using the remaining compounds. Summing the squares of the residuals so obtained gives the predictive sum of squares (PRESS) statistic, which in turn affords an estimate of the internally cross-validated standard error (SE_X). In some variable selection methods, it becomes necessary to use a completely external test set comprised of compounds never used in the generation of any candidate model. In that event, the corresponding predictive sum of squares statistic is sometimes referred to as the standard error of prediction (SDEP).

9.2. Alignment Rules

The above discussion glosses over the biggest practical challenge involved in carrying out CoMFA and related 3D QSAR analyses, which is to specify which part of one molecule relates to a particular part of another. Put another way, the analyst must formulate one or more hypotheses which specify how the atoms—and hence the fields—from each molecule relate to the atoms in every other molecule. The rotational and translational components are usually handled by positioning the molecules in a common coordinate system, so that each element in the descriptor vector indicates the variation in potential energy across the dataset at a particular point on the shared lattice. Simply specifying rotation and translation is not enough, however, because most molecules of interest are more or less flexible: The analyst must somehow specify which conformation is to be used for every molecule in the dataset. Taken together, the rotational, translational, and torsional heuristics constitute an alignment rule.[15] A good alignment rule is broadly applicable yet as unambiguous as possible.

It is important to remember that the diagnostic statistics obtained from CoMFA are measures of the internal consistency (model SE and r^2) and predictivity (SE_X and cross-validated correlation coefficient q^2) of the alignment rule being considered, not of the dataset itself. It is often the case that several different alignment rules are considered and one ends up being chosen as "best" on the basis of these statistics. One can easily get into trouble by testing too many closely related hypotheses: After all, given enough analyses, one is bound to look significant eventually. Fortunately, as in the σ receptor case considered here, most alignment rules are relatively independent with respect to CoMFA. So long as only a handful of distinct alignment rules are evaluated for any particular dataset this complication will not arise.

Note that alignment rules need not directly reflect the relative molecular orientations in the binding site of the receptor or enzyme of interest. X-ray structures[16,17] and docked alignments have both been used in CoMFA, but they often fail to produce models which are as predictive as alignments based on shared substructural elements.[19,20] Though the concept can be somewhat unsettling when first encountered, alignment rules based on common substructure often work well in CoMFA because they embrace a "ligand's eye view" of interaction with a protein. Superimposing common substructures tends to wash out field variations at the corresponding coordinates and focuses the analysis on those positions where structural variation is most relevant.[19] In real binding sites, ligands shift around to ease steric "bumps" with the protein, which distributes effects across the whole molecule and makes visualization less effective.

Alignment rules based on pharmacophores represent a useful generalization of this principle from groups of atoms similar in 2D structure to those which can interact similarly—for example, hydrogen bond donor or acceptor atoms and hydrophobic centers.[21-23] This similarity in interaction, of course, reflects underlying similarities in molecular fields at these centers. Note, too, that a pharmacophore model reflects an ideal geometry of its pharmacophoric elements in the absence of steric clashes and internal energy constraints and is not necessarily a configuration taken up by features in any particular ligand. Hence they, too, are "ligand's eye view" alignment rules.

9.3. The σ Receptor Dataset

Nakazato et al.[24] recently published data on the potency of 58 novel phenylalkylamine derivatives against rat brain σ receptors. The 20 struc-

---

* Taking the negative logarithm of the μM IC_{50} gives more homogeneous variances and puts the activities on a scale which is roughly in linear in free energy.

tures shown in Figure 9.1 give a general idea of the structural variability spanned by these compounds, along with their IC_{50}s; further details can be obtained from the original paper.

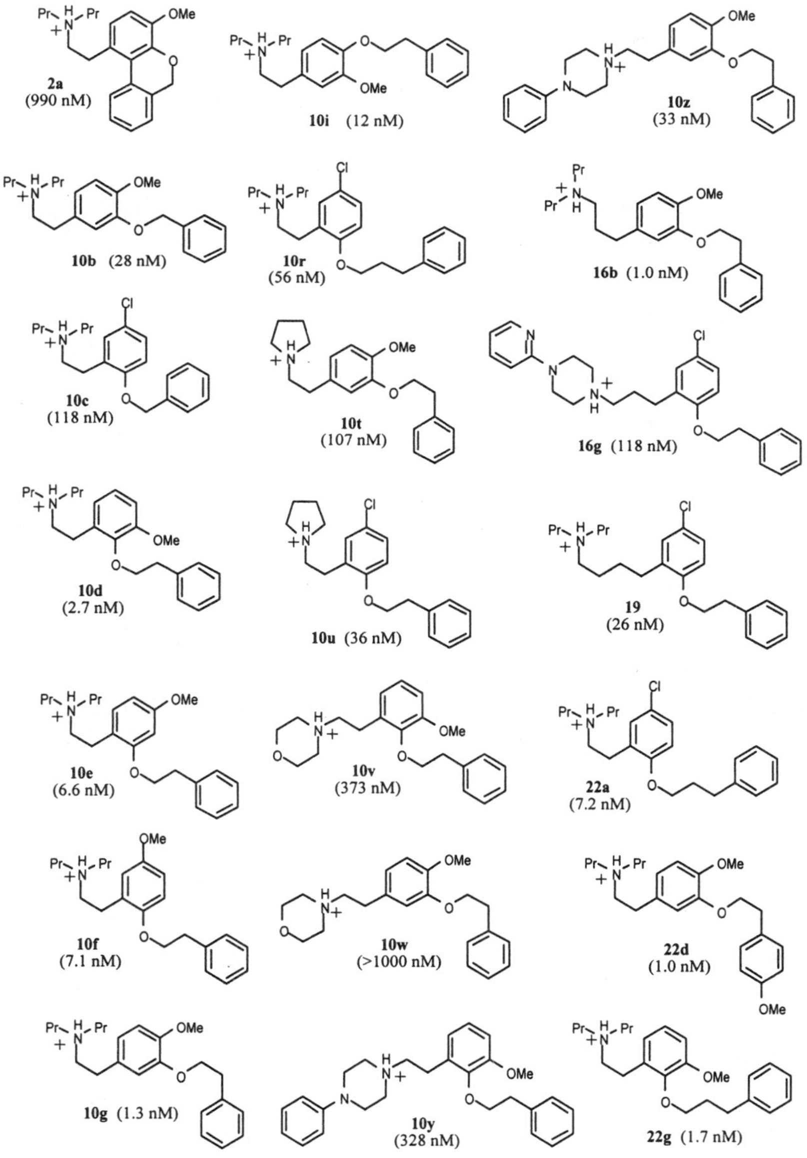

Figure 9.1. Compounds from the σ receptor antagonist dataset and their IC_{50} values.

The authors' numbering scheme has been retained for clarity. Although they discussed the SAR in broad terms, Nakazato et al. reported neither CoMFA results nor results from any other quantitative SAR analysis. The dataset includes receptor IC_{50}s for actives ranging from 0.001 to 0.99 µM, with a mean negative logarithm* (pIC_{50}) of 1.60 and a standard deviation in pIC_{50} of 0.85 (n = 53). Five examples were reported simply as having $IC_{50} > 1$ µM; these analogs were not included in model development but were used as an external test set.

This dataset is remarkably combinatorial, in that variations on relatively simple structural themes have been explored quite thoroughly:

- Most compounds are ethyleneamines, but eight are propyleneamines, including **16b**, which is one of the three 1.0 nM σ antagonists. One (**19**) is a butyleneamine.

- Most are dipropyl amines, but there are also three pyrrolidines (e.g., **10t** and **10u**), three morpholines (e.g., **10v** and **10w**), and 13 *N'*-arylpiperazines (e.g., **10y** and **10z**). The unsubstituted (primary amino) analog of **10g** was among the inactives, but the monopropyl (**25**), isoamylpropyl, hexylpropyl, and hydroxypropyl-propyl amines were fairly potent and were included in the training set. All are expected to be basic and so were treated as protonated, as indicated in Figure 9.1.

- Most (**49**) arylalkoxy substituents are phenethyl groups, but benzyl (three examples, including **10b** and **10c**) and phenylpropyl (four examples, including **10r** and **22g**) substituents are also represented, as are two relatively weak cyclized antagonists (**2a** and its 4-hydroxy congener).

- Arylalkoxy substituents off the central phenyl ring are located at the 2-, 3-, or 4-positions (33, 23 and 3 representatives of each, including exemplars **10c, 10g,** and **10i,** respectively).

- Other 2-, 3-, and 5-positions are in most cases occupied by a single methoxy, chloro, bromo, or hydroxy substituent; exceptions are the *des*-chloro analog of **10c** and a pair of 3,5-dihalo compounds (not shown).

These aspects of this dataset's composition are particularly interesting in that they convey some sense of the challenges often encountered when working with combinatorial data from high-throughput screens.

The mapping of activity to particular substituents or to their disposition around the central phenyl ring is surprisingly weak: Although the most active compounds are 3-phenethoxy-4-methoxy ethyleneamines (e.g., **10g** and **22d**), 2-phenethoxy, 4-phenethoxy, 3-phenylpropyloxy, and propyleneamine derivatives (**10d, 10i, 22g,** and **16b,** respectively) were also very active.

Moreover, the effects of non-additive interaction are clearly evident. Replacing the dipropyl amino group in 3-phenethoxy **10g** with N'-phenyl-piperazine to give **10t** reduced potency 80-fold, whereas the same substitution in 2-phenethoxy **22a** to give **10u** produced only a five-fold drop.

Taken together, these latter two observations suggest that ligand flexibility is particularly important for this dataset, which makes it a particularly attractive candidate for CoMFA using a pharmacophore-based alignment rule.

9.4. Charges and Energy Minimization

Surveying low-energy conformations of ligands is almost always an important first step in carrying out CoMFA. To this end, structure **10a** was created using the Sketcher facility in SYBYL, after which good 3D coordinates were obtained using CONCORD.[25] Structures for other compounds were obtained from that of **10a** by changing atom types or substituent groups, shifting bonds, etc., in the SYBYL Sketcher, followed by local minimization using the Tripos force field. Atomic partial charges were then calculated using the method of Gasteiger and Marsili[26] for the σ bond network; contributions from the π electron network were calculated similarly.*

At this point, one often undertakes a systematic search across fixed torsional increments in each molecule to identify low-energy conformations. Alternatively, each structure can be run through a global torsional minimizer based on a genetic algorithm. Each torsional dihedral in a molecule is treated as a separate gene, with a continuous range of values allowed. Crossover events permit an efficient survey for conformations which represent good combinations of individual genes, whereas mutations encourage incremental adaptive changes in individual torsions.

---

* SYBYL command: CHARGE <mol_area> COMPUTE GAST_HUCK.

Once torsional minimizations were complete, the entire dataset was aligned on the central phenyl ring of **10g** using the DATABASE ALIGN facility, with the INERTIAL option turned on so as to define a coordinate system along the principal axes of **10g** itself.* This would ordinarily be the first step in defining an alignment rule based on substructure as well.

As is typical of aromatic rings bearing multiple saturated substituents, the low-energy conformations identified for these compounds are positioned alternately above and below the ring. Plate 9.2 illustrates standardization of conformers by reflection through a common plane. **10b** (a) and **10i** (b) came out of the GA Torsional Minimizer with the prevailing "handedness." Analog **10g** came out in the complementary conformation (c) and was reflected through the mirror plane to give the more standard starting conformation (d). The planar nature of the central ring, however, means that there are in fact two lowest-energy conformations which are mirror images of each other (Plate 9.2, c and d,) though it is virtually certain that only one class is biochemically relevant. The starting structures used all had the alkylamine chain "up" when the more substituted side of the phenyl ring is oriented to the left (Plate 9.2, a and b.) As a result of that arbitrary choice, that "handedness" was most common among the minimized structures, and so was chosen to serve as the standard. It happened, however, that **10g** and nine other analogs came out with the alkylamine "down"; these structures were simply reflected through the plane of their central phenyl rings to get more appropriate conformations.** Enforcing such consistency is critical in alignment rules based on substructure; here it serves simply to predispose the flexible searching routines in UNITY[27] to find more homologous conformations.

9.5. Identifying an Initial Query

A set of four structurally diverse but representative active analogs (**10d, 10h, 16b,** and **22g**) were aligned with **2a** by manually manipulating

---

* This choice of coordinate system minimizes the number of lattice points going into the subsequent PLS analysis, which tends to improve the signal to noise ratio obtained.
** Note that molecules which contain chiral centers need to be inverted after reflection.

bond torsions in the alkylamine and phenylalkoxy chains in an attempt to overlap the ammonium nitrogen atom and distal aryl centers while keeping most bond configurations *trans* and avoiding intramolecular steric clashes (Plate 9.3). This produced the alignment (Plate 9.3, a), from which Query 1 was deduced; automated tools for identifying such pharmacophore models are discussed in detail elsewhere in this volume. Query 1 consists of an acceptor site/donor atom pair (**AS/DA**), a hydrophobic center corresponding to the central phenyl group (**HY-1**), and a trio (**HY-2a, HY-2b,** and **HY-2c**) of hydrophobic centers associated with one another through a partial match search constraint (only one is matched in each hit). Plate 9.3, b, shows matching conformations found by the UNITY flexible search engine. These included some similar to the expected configuration (e.g., **16b**), but **10d** and other compounds were able to adopt a conformation in which the central phenyl group mapped to a distal partial match query feature (in this case, **HY-2a**).

Query 1 includes a hydrophobic center from the central phenyl ring as well as a hydrogen-bond donor atom and its associated acceptor site. Query 1 also includes three distal hydrophobic centers linked to one another by a partial match constraint, so that only one of the three centers needs to match to qualify a molecule as a flexible 3D search "hit." Such broad hydrophobic features commonly result from binding pockets lined with the long, flexible side chains from methionine, leucine, isoleucine, and valine residues.

Note that there is nothing in the dataset itself to indicate that the ethyleneamine chains need to be fully extended or the direction in which the ammonium hydrogen-bond vector "should" point. The extended chain does in fact allow a good ammonium center overlap from low-energy conformations of the propyleneamine and butyleneamine chains. Since one expects the query to reflect the binding site structure to some degree, it is certainly reasonable to point the hydrogen-bonding vector in the query away from rest of the ligand.

When a flexible 3D search was run in UNITY against the σ receptor antagonist dataset, Query 1 matched ("hit") 51 of the 58 target compounds. Analogs which were missed included **10e, 10f, 10i, 10u,** and **22a.** The hit list obtained was loaded then into a Molecular Spreadsheet and GAST_HUCK charges were applied using the Auto 3D Building option in Selector. The Orientation option was set to NONE and the Basic Modeling option was set to USE_AS_IS so as to retain the conformations and orientations returned by the search engine. CoMFA fields were then calculated using default parameters: a 2 Å grid spacing on a cubic lattice, an sp^3 C^+ probe atom and 30 kcal/mol cutoffs to flatten out potentials within the van der Waals radius.

Running a PLS analysis on these fields[*] gives a moderately complicated (four-component) model with cross-validation statistics of $SE_X = 0.721$ and $q^2 = 0.416$. The latter value is only slightly above the critical value of 0.40 generally used to identify models likely to be reliably predictive.[28,29] As expected for a PLS model, the internal goodness-of-fit statistics are nominally very good—SE 0.194 and r^2 0.958.

Steric factors dominate this model, in that they account for 88% of the explained variance in pIC_{50}. This may be a result, in part, of incorporating the ammonium center into the alignment rule, which leads to the canceling out of the largest electrostatic variations.

9.6. Refining the Query

The tolerances and feature positions in Query 1 could have been modified to pick up the seven "missing" actives, but this would not have improved the model appreciably. One can see why by examining the actual alignment obtained (Plate 9.3, b). Clearly this query is not discriminating enough, so some molecules (e.g., **10d**) hit "backwards"—i.e., the alignment rule is too ambiguous. As a result, the correlation between the molecular fields are disrupted and the predictivity of the model suffers. The real receptor almost certainly differentiates between the highly functionalized central phenyl ring and the distal arylalkoxy rings, but pharmacophoric features are simply too generalized to be specific enough on their own.

This problem comes up quite often when trying to use pharmacophore-based alignments. A good way to deal with it is to mix in some substructural constraints. In this case, the ether oxygens can be used to anchor the central phenyl ring in place, thereby producing a second, more elaborate query which includes three oxygen atoms coupled togeth-

---

[*] Default settings in the SYBYL 6.5 PLS Dialog Box were used: block (CoMFA-Standard) scaling, leave-one-out crossvalidation and no column filtering.

er in a partial match constraint such that one or two of the oxygens must match to qualify as a hit (adding a planar feature and constraints has the same effect). The resulting increase in specificity makes it possible to ease the tolerances on the distal hydrophobic centers from 0.7 Å in Query 1 to 1.5 Å. Plate 9.4, a, shows Query 2 with overlaid exemplars; only the features not present in Query 1 are labeled here. The trio (O-1a, O-1b, and O-1c) of oxygen atoms are tied together via a partial match search constraint (one or two are matched in each hit). Running Query 2 against all 58 analogs again returns 51 hits; **10c**, **10u**, and **22a** were among the seven analogs not picked up in this case. Visual inspection of the conformations returned for Query 2 indicate that a much more satisfying alignment is obtained, at least in qualitative terms. Plate 9.4, b, represents conformations of template molecules identified in the UNITY flexible search based on Query 2.

Moreover, the alignment produced improves the quantitative aspects of the CoMFA substantially. Applying CoMFA to the 47 actives from the hit list for Query 2 (**10ad**, which is one of the inactives, was missed) gave a two-component model with $SE_X = 0.611$ and $q^2 = 0.553$. The improvement in predictivity is particularly significant because it accompanies a decrease in the complexity of the model (from four components to two) vs. the model based on Query 1. The corresponding non-cross-validated goodness-of-fit statistics were $SE = 0.321$ and $r^2 = 0.877$. Somewhat ironically, the drop in r^2 in conjunction with an increase in q^2 is desirable, because it signals a reduction in overfitting by PLS.

As for Query 1, steric factors dominate the model: Their variation accounts for 90% of the variance in pIC_{50} vs. 10% for the electrostatic fields.

9.7. Evaluating the Model

Having obtained a model for which the overall predictivity is satisfactory, a more detailed examination of performance on the individual compounds in the dataset is in order. For those compounds included in the training set, this is best done by examining the relationship between predicted and actual activities and the difference between the two, i.e., the residuals. As shown in Figure 9.2, b, data points are distributed quite evenly along the 1:1 line which defines a perfectly predictive model. Most PLS models consistently underestimate activities of potent compounds to some degree and consistently overestimate the activity of relatively inactive compounds. Inspection of Figure 9.2, b, shows that in this case some such bias is present but its magnitude is small. Moreover, the so-called "qq" plot shown in Figure 9.2, a, indicates that the observed distribution of residuals matches that of a normally distributed error function. In some cases, outliers in the training set can introduce serious distortions in the model obtained; were that the case, the points in Figure 9.2, a, would form a sigmoid curve, rather than lying across the diagonal as they do here.

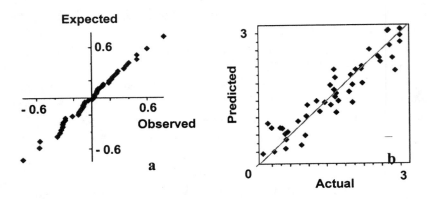

Figure 9.2. Results for the CoMFA model based on the Query 2 alignment. (a) Plot showing the distribution of observed residuals versus the distribution expected, i.e., a normal distribution. (b) Plot showing the predicted pIC_{50} as a function of the actual pIC_{50}. The diagonal represents perfect prediction.

Another important aspect of a CoMFA model is its graphical interpretability. One can obtain well-behaved models with wonderful statistics for which the mapping from fields to structures is difficult or impossible to sort out visually. The best way to visualize CoMFA results is through three-dimensional plots showing the importance of each lattice point to the final model. Plate 9.5 shows molecular fields from the CoMFA model based on the Query 2 alignment rule superimposed on **10g** for reference. Plate 9.5, a, represents contours from steric coefficients at each lattice point multiplied by the standard deviation across the training set at that point (20 and 80% contour levels are shown.)

Yellow sectors denote areas where steric bulk tends to reduce activity; green areas indicate regions where steric bulk contributes favorably and Plate 9.5, b, shows electrostatic STDEV×COEFF contours taken at the 20 and 80% levels. Yellow sectors denote areas where negative charge is desirable, whereas blue areas indicate regions where relatively positive charge is referred. Plates 9.5, c and d, show contours of steric potential around **10g** scaled by the STD×COEFF values for the model at each lattice point (the 18 kcal/mol contour is shown), and contours of electrostatic potential around **10g** scaled by the STD×COEFF values for the model at each lattice point (the +5 kcal/mol contour is indicated in blue and the -0.5 kcal/mol contour is shown in yellow), respectively. Plots to the left (Plate 9.5, a and c) show contributions from steric fields, and the plots to the right (Plate 9.5, b and d) are for the corresponding electrostatic fields. The structure of **10g** is included for reference in all four plots.

The top contour plots (Plate 9.5, a and b) represent the overall model. They are based on the coefficients at each lattice point multiplied by the standard deviation in potential found at that lattice point across the entire training set (the STDEV×COEFF parameter in SYBYL QSAR); this indicates the degree to which variation at each lattice point contributes to the predicted activity. Bulky substituents at the 5 position of the central phenyl ring are disfavored, whereas such substituents contribute positively at the 4 position. Longer alkyl substituents are favored at the ammonium nitrogen, and somewhat longer arylalkoxy groups might be advantageously added at the 3 position.

As noted above, electrostatics contribute relatively little to this model. The major implications are that some electronegative nitrogen substituents such as 3-methoxypropoxy should be considered. Small electropositive substituents at the 2 position might be beneficial, but there is not much available that meets those criteria better than hydrogen itself—methyl or methylthio have some potential, though more radical alternatives such as replacing the central phenyl ring with an N-arylalkylated pyridone are also worth exploring.

The bottom pair of plots in Plate 9.5 (c and d) show field contours for **10g** analogous to those shown in Plate 9.1 except that here the potential at each lattice point is weighted by its contribution to the model using the field focussing option in SYBYL's Advanced CoMFA module. These plots suggest that the symmetry on substitution at the ammonium nitrogen has little net effect (one *N*-propyl group intrudes into a favored region and the other sticks into a disfavored region). Net contributions from the 4-methoxy group and the unsubstituted 3-phenethoxy are good, whereas most of the large region of positive around the ammonium nitrogen center is relatively disadvantageous.

Note that Query 1 and Query 2 perform identically in terms of finding actives—both have hit rates of 88%—yet Query 2 gives a much better CoMFA model. Clearly, a pharmacophore model can actually be quite successful in identifying follow-up candidates without being specific enough to be a useful alignment rule for CoMFA.

9.8. Applicability

A key use for this kind of analysis involves sets of actives such as might be obtained from a high-throughput screening program. Examination will suggest some pharmacophore query which can be used to search virtual libraries for lead follow-up candidates. The corresponding CoMFA model could then be applied as a secondary *in silico* screen to evaluate hits for likely activity. Were this scenario played out for the σ receptor using the antagonists considered here, Query 2 could be made more general by replacing its three explicit oxygens with heavy or hetero atom macros or by imposing a planarity constraint on the central phenyl ring instead. Putting "hits" predicted to be very active into contour plots like those shown in Plate 9.5 can then indicate whether each compound in question really qualifies a lead or falls so far outside the domain of the model as to be irrelevant.

External test sets of compounds not used to generate the final model can give an idea of how common false positives may be in such an application and, as well, indicate the range of structural variation across which the model is likely to be predictive. The four inactive "hits" obtained for Query 2 (**10aa, 10ac, 10w,** and **24**) were predicted to have IC_{50}s of 263, 263, 229, 31 and 3.2 nM, respectively, whereas the observed values were all greater than 1 μM.

The first three predictions reflect the small bias discussed above. They would not qualify for follow-up anyway, though, and so are not false positives. A very high potency is predicted for **24**, which is the *des*-propyl, primary amino analog of the very active **10g**. This is a real but unsurprising discrepancy which reflects the limited range of *N*-substitution patterns included in the training set.

There is no such rationale for the contrast between the observed inactivity of **10w**, and the model's prediction of a moderate potency. On the other hand, given the potency of other very similar compounds in this dataset, the inactivity of **10w** is remarkable by any medicinal chemistry standard.

The combination of a simple three-feature, partial match pharmacophore model with a few constraints based on shared substructural elements produces a flexible search query which can in turn generate a useful and predictive CoMFA model. That model could be of considerable utility when compounds which fit the pharmacophore are being evaluated as lead follow-up candidates.

References

1. Cramer RD III, Patterson DE, Bunce JD: **Comparative Molecular Field Analysis (CoMFA). 1. Effect of shape on Binding of Steroids to Carrier Proteins.** *J Am Chem Soc* 1988, **110**:5959-5967.

2. Martin YC, Kim K-H, Lin CT: **Comparative Molecular Field Analysis: CoMFA.** In: *Advances in Quantitative Structure-Property Relationships,* Vol. 1. Charton M, ed. Greenwich CN: JAI Press, 1996:1-52.

3. Folkers G, Merz A, Rognan D: **CoMFA: Scope and Limitations.** In: *3D QSAR in Drug Design,* Vol. 1. Kubinyi H, ed. Leiden: ESCOM Publishers, 1993:583-618.

4. Livingstone DJ: **Structure Property Correlations in Molecular Design.** In: *Structure-Property Correlations in Drug Research.* Van de Waterbeemd H, ed. Austin: Academic Press, 1996: 81-110.

5. Collantes ER, Tong W, Welsh WJ, Zielinski WL: **Use of Moment of Inertia in Comparative Molecular Field Analysis to Model Chromatographic Retention of Nonpolar Solutes.** *Ana Chem* 1996, **68**:2038-2043.

6. Kellogg GE, Semus SF, Abraham DJ: HINT: **A new method of empirical hydrophobic field calculation for CoMFA.** *J Comp-Aided Mol Des* 1991, **5**:545-552.

7. Klebe G, Abraham U, Mietzner T: **Molecular Similarity Indices in a Comparative Analysis (CoMSIA) of Drug Molecules to Correlate and Predict their Biological Activity.** *J Med Chem* 1994, 37:4130-4146.

8. Klebe G: **Comparative Molecular Similarity Indices Analysis: CoMSIA.** In: *3D QSAR in Drug Design,* Vol. 3. Kubinyi H, Folkers G, Martin YC, eds. Dordrecht: Kluwer/ESCOM, 1998: 87-104.

9. Kroemer RT, Hecht P: **Replacement of steric 6-12 potential-derived interaction energies by atom-based indicator variables in CoMFA leads to models of higher consistency.** *J Comp-Aided Mol Des* 1995, **9**:205-212.

10. Goodford PJ: **A computational procedure for determining energetically favorable binding sites on biologically important macromolecules.** *J Med Chem* 1985, **28**:849-857.

11. *SYBYL* is a registered trademark of Tripos, Inc., St. Louis MO.

12. Wold S: **PLS for Multivariate Linear Modeling.** In: *Chemometric Methods in Molecular Design.* Van de Waterbeemd H, ed. Weinheim: VCH, 1995:195-218.

13. Wold S, Ruhe A, Dunn WJ III: **The collinearity problem in linear regression. The partial least squares approach to generalized inverses.** *SIAM J Sci Stat Comput* 1984, **5**:735-743.

14. Baroni M, Constantino G, Cruciani G, Riganelli D, Valigi R, Clementi S: **Generating Optimal Linear PLS Estimations (GOLPE): An advanced chemometric tool for handling 3D QSAR problems.** *Quant Struct-Activity Relat* 1993, **12**:9-20.

15. Klebe G: **Structural Alignment of Molecules.** In: *3D QSAR in Drug Design*, Vol. 1. Kubinyi H, ed. Leiden: ESCOM, 1993:173-199.

16. Diana GD, Kowalczyk P, Treasurywala AM, Oglesby RC, Pevear DC, Dutko, FJ: **CoMFA analysis of the interactions of antipicornavirus compounds in the binding pocket of human rhinovirus-14.** *J Med Chem* 1992, **35**:1002-1008.

17. Cruciani C, Pastor M, Clementi S: **Region Selection in 3D-QSAR.** In: *Computer-Assisted Lead Finding and Optimization.* Van de Waterbeemd H, Testa B, Folkers G, eds. Weinheim: Wiley-VCH, 1997:379-395.

18. Gamper AM, Winger RH, Liedl KR, Sotriffer CA, Varga JM, Kroemer RT, Rode BM: **Comparative molecular field analysis (CoMFA) of haptens docked to the multispecific antibody IgE(Lb₄).** *J Med Chem* 1996, **39**:3882-3888.

19. Klebe G, Abraham U: **On the prediction of binding properties of drug molecules by comparative molecular field analysis.** *J Med Chem* 1993, **36**:70-80.

20. Cramer RD III, DePriest SA, Patterson DE, Hecht P: **The Developing Practice of Comparative Molecular Field Analysis.** In: *3D QSAR in Drug Design*, Vol. 1. Kubinyi H, ed. Leiden: ESCOM, 1993:443-485.

21. Medvedev AE, Ivanov AS, Veselovsky AV, Skvortsov VS, Archakov AI: **QSAR Analysis of Indole Analogues as Monoamine Oxidase Inhibitors.** *J Chem Inf Comput Sci* 1996, **36**:664-671.

22. Kroemer RT, Koutsilieri E, Hecht P, Liedl KR, Riederer P, Kornhuber J: **Quantitative Analysis of the Structural Requirements for Blockade of the N-Methy-D-aspartate Receptor at the Phencyclidine Binding Site.** *J Med Chem* 1998, **41**:393-400.

23. Wilcox RE, Tseng T, Brusniak M-YK, Ginsburg B, Pearlman RS, Teeter M, DuRand C, Starr S, Neve K: **CoMFA-Based Prediction of Agonist Affinities at Recombinant D1 vs. D2 Dopamine Receptors.** *J Med Chem* 1998, **41**:4385-4399.

24. Nakazato A, Kohmei O, Sekiguchi Y, Okuyama S, Chaki S, Kawashima Y, Hatayama K: **Design, synthesis, structure-activity relationships, and biological characterization of novel arylalkoxyphenylalkylamine ligands as potential antipsychotic drugs.** *J Med Chem* 1999, **42**:1076-1087.

25. *CONCORD* was developed by R. Pearlman at the University of Texas at Austin, and is distributed by Tripos, Inc., St. Louis MO.

26. Gasteiger J, Marsili M: **Iterative partial equalization of orbital electronegativity—A rapid access to atomic charges.** *Tetrahedron* 1980, **36**:3219-3228.

27. *UNITY* is a registered trademark of Tripos, Inc., St. Louis MO.

28. Clark M, Cramer RD III, Jones DM, Patterson DE, Simeroth PE: **Comparative Molecular Field Analysis (CoMFA). 2. Toward its use with 3D-Structural Databases.** *Tetrahedron Comput Method* 1990, **3**:47-59.

29. Clark M, Cramer RD III: **The probability of chance correlation using Partial Least Squares (PLS).** *Quant Struct-Activity Relat* 1993, **12**:137-145.

10

HypoGen: An Automated System for Generating 3D Predictive Pharmacophore Models

Hong Li, Jon Sutter, and Rémy Hoffmann

Abstract

The HypoGen algorithm in Catalyst creates SAR hypothesis models from a set of molecules for which activity values are known. HypoGen selects pharmacophore models that are common among the active compounds but not among the inactive compounds, then optimizes the pharmacophores using simulated annealing. The top pharmacophores can be used to predict the activity of unknown compounds or to search for new possible leads contained in 3D chemical databases. This chapter will illustrate, by showing an example, the general strategy and guidelines of HypoGen.

10

Hypogen: An Automated System for Generating 3D Predictive Pharmacophore Models

Hong Li[†], Jon Sutter[‡], and Rémy Hoffmann[∇]

[†]ChemInnovation Software, Inc.,San Diego, California
[‡]Molecular Simulations Inc., San Diego, California
[∇]Molecular Simulations SARL, Parc Club Orsay Université,
Orsay Cédex, France

10.1. Introduction

One of the most powerful analog-based drug design techniques is the generation of pharmacophore models from a training set. There are a number of programs that generate feature-based pharmacophore models: APEX,[1] HipHop,[2] DISCO,[3] and GASP.[4]

Two algorithms within the Catalyst program suite[5] are used to automatically seek pharmacophore models. HipHop is intended to derive common feature hypothesis models using information from a set of active compounds. HypoGen attempts to derive SAR hypothesis models from a set of molecules for which activity values (IC_{50} or Ki) on a given biological target have been measured. HypoGen generates hypotheses that are a set of features in 3D space, each containing a certain tolerance and weight that fit to the features of the training set, and that correlate to the activity data. These hypotheses can be used to predict the activity of new candidates to synthesize or as search queries in database mining. The purpose of this chapter is to describe the general strategy and the workings of HypoGen and to illustrate it with an example. Some insight into the hypothesis analysis procedure will also be given.

10.2. General Strategy

In Catalyst, pharmacophores are generally referred to as hypotheses. This convention emphasizes the fact that the automatically generated models fit the input data well, but may not necessarily represent the true pharmacophore. Catalyst provides many techniques to analyze (e.g., activity estimation, database mining) and modify hypothesis models (e.g., clustering, merging, addition of excluded volumes, addition of constraints, etc.). Therefore, similar to a scientific hypothesis, a Catalyst hypothesis can be adjusted as new information is obtained. In the remainder of this chapter the terms pharmacophore and hypothesis will be used interchangeably.

The basic idea of the HypoGen algorithm is to optimize hypotheses that are common among the active compounds in the training set but not among the inactive compounds. It constructs the simplest hypotheses that best correlate estimated activities with measured activities. The hypotheses are created in three phases: a constructive, subtractive, and an optimization phase. The constructive phase identifies hypotheses that are common among the active compounds, the subtractive phase removes hypotheses that are common among the inactive compounds, and the optimization phase attempts to improve the initial hypotheses. The resulting hypothesis models contain a set of generalized chemical features in three-dimensional space as well as regression information. Therefore, the hypotheses models can be used as search queries to mine for potential leads from a three-dimensional database or in the form of an equation to predict the activity of a potential lead.

10.3. Methodology

10.3.1. Preparing to Run HypoGen

HypoGen attempts to uncover hypotheses that correlate the data well without overfitting. The user can maximize the odds of finding valid hypotheses by following a few guidelines. This chapter will discuss the user guidelines that should be followed whenever possible.

10.3.1.1. The Training Set

The selection of the training set is obviously very important, since the hypotheses are derived directly from the information in the training set. If the training set contains inadequate or misleading information, the hypotheses generated will likely be invalid. The user should make every attempt to create a training set that is informative and that will not bias the regression. This chapter will discuss some of the areas that should be considered.

The training set should contain clear and concise information. Redundancy in the activity range and structures should be avoided. If a compound has nothing new to teach HypoGen, it probably should not be included. If a compound will likely confuse HypoGen, it should not be used. For example, training set compounds should not contain compounds known to be inactive due to steric interference with the receptor, since HypoGen is not currently equipped to handle such cases.

After inspecting the training set for information problems, it should be checked for factors that may bias the correlation results. Due to the large number of variables being optimized in the process, too few compounds in the training set result in statistically poor fitting. It has been found that the odds of computing a chance correlation increase if the number of compounds in the training set falls below 16. The algorithm also requires a wide range of activity data (4-5 orders of magnitude) to classify compounds as "active" and "inactive." In addition, the activity data should be spread equally through the range.

In this chapter the general guidelines for selecting the ideal dataset were presented. Whenever possible, these guidelines should be followed. Non-ideal training sets can still be used, of course, but the user should be aware that results are suspect.

10.3.1.2. Conformational Coverage

It is known that molecules can adjust their conformations in order to bind to a receptor site; therefore each molecule in the training set is represented by a collection of energetically reasonable conformations. The fit between the potential hypothesis and each compound is evaluated using these pre-calculated conformational models. The conformations (maximum of 256) are created using a poling method to ensure maximum coverage in feature space.[6] It is recommended that the conformational models be generated using the "Best" option in Catalyst for all HypoGen runs.

10.3.1.3. Chemical Features

The hypotheses are constructed using generalized chemical feature definitions. A set of features (maximum 5) can be specified along with their maximum and minimum numbers to construct the hypotheses. The program supports a list of common features (such as H-bond donors, H-bond acceptors, hydrophobic centers, ring aromatic groups, and charged centers) as well as user-defined features.[7] If the hypothesis space is too great, it often can be reduced by using the max/min feature parameters (see Chapter 26 for more detail).

10.3.2. Running HypoGen

HypoGen uses the data selected by the user (i.e., training set, conformational models, chemical features, parameters, etc.) to generate the ten top scoring hypothesis models. As stated previously, this is done in three phases, a constructive, subtractive, and optimization phase. However, before allowing HypoGen to continue, it is a good idea to inspect some initial cost values.

HypoGen calculates the cost of two theoretical hypotheses, one in which the cost is minimal (Fixed cost), and one where the cost is high (Null cost). Each optimized hypothesis cost should have a value between these two values and should be closer to the Fixed cost than the Null cost. The two theoretical cost values, measured in units of bits, are useful guides for estimating the chances for a successful experiment and are available within 15 minutes from the start of the run. The greater the difference between these cost values, the higher the probability for finding useful models. Randomized studies have found that if a returned hypothesis has a cost that differs from the Null hypothesis by 40-60 bits, it has a 75-90% chance of representing a true correlation in the data. As the difference becomes less than 40 bits, the likelihood of the hypothesis representing a true correlation in the data rapidly drops below 50%. Under these conditions, it may be difficult to find a model that can be shown to be predictive. In the extreme situation where the Fixed and Null cost differential is small (<20), there is little chance of succeeding and it is advisable to reconsider the training set before proceeding.

Another useful number is the Entropy of hypothesis space. The number is log to the base 2 of the number of models Catalyst will attempt to optimize during the run. If this number is less than 17, a thorough analysis of all models will be carried out. In general, if the run generates an Entropy greater than 17.0, serious consideration should be given to modifying the training set before proceeding.

10.3.2.1. Constructive Phase

Conceptually speaking, the constructive phase is very similar to the HipHop algorithm.[2] The idea is to generate hypotheses that are common among the active compounds in the training set. This is done in several steps: a) the active compounds are identified, b) all hypotheses (maximum 5 features) among the two most active compounds are identified and stored, and c) those that fit the remaining active compounds are kept.

The algorithm first identifies the lead compounds, which include the most active compound and compounds whose activities satisfy the following condition:

$$MA \times Unc_{MA} - \frac{A}{Unc_A} > 0.0 \qquad (10.1)$$

where MA is the activity of the most active compound, Unc is the uncertainty of the compounds, and A is the activity of the compound in question. If there are more than 8 lead compounds, only the top eight are used.

The program identifies all allowable hypotheses consisting of up to 5 features among the two most active compounds. This is done using a pruned exhaustive search of all the conformations similar to the

HipHop algorithm. Each hypothesis is entered in a high-dimensional data structure.

Finally, HypoGen investigates the remaining active compounds in the list. Only the hypotheses that fit a minimum subset of features of the remaining active compounds are kept. The minimum subset number is controlled by the MinSubsetPoints parameter which has a default of 4.

10.3.2.2. Subtractive Phase

In this phase, the program removes hypotheses from the data structure that are not likely to be useful. The hypotheses that were created in the constructive phase are inspected. If they are common to most of the inactive compounds, they are removed from consideration.

First the inactive compounds are identified. A compound is considered inactive if the activity is 3.5 orders of magnitude greater (adjustable in Catalyst 4.5 release) than the most active compound as shown in Equation 10.2.

$$\log(A) - \log(MA) > 3.5 \qquad (10.2)$$

In Equation 10.2, A is the activity of the compound in question and MA is the activity of the most active compound. Any hypothesis that matches more than half of the compounds identified as inactive is removed.

10.3.2.3. Optimization Phase

The optimization is done using the well-known algorithm simulated annealing. The algorithm applies small perturbations to the hypotheses created in the constructive and subtractive phases in an attempt to improve the score. The steps include selecting a new hypothesis from the data structure, rotating a vectored feature, translating a randomly selected feature in the pharmacophore, adding a new feature, and removing a feature. Acceptance of each step is determined based on a score (see Chapter 26 for more information) that measures the errors in activity estimates from regression and the complexity of the hypothesis. The algorithm will accept all improvements and some detrimental steps based on a probability function. The ten highest scoring, unique pharmacophores (i.e., no duplicates and no direct neighbors in the high-dimensional data structure) are exported.

The activity of each training set compound is estimated using regression parameters. The parameters are computed by regressing a geometric fit value versus -log(activity). The greater the geometric fit, the greater the activity prediction of the compound. The geometric fit is computed using the Fast Fit Compare algorithm of Catalyst. Each hypothesis contains regression parameters which are used to compute part of the hypothesis score and to estimate the activity of future leads.

10.4. Case Study

Many scientific applications have been published that validate the HypoGen[8-16] method. The intent of this chapter is to explain some of the HypoGen output and methods to assess the quality of the hypotheses; therefore a typical study was repeated. Original results were published elsewhere.[15]

The training set consists of 20 di- and tripeptides acting as ACE inhibitors with activity that spanned more than four orders of magnitude (see Table 10.1).

Table 10.1. Members of the training set.

Molecule Name	Activity (nM)	Molecule Name	Activity (nM)
n-Leu-Ala-Pro	700	Glu-Ala-Pro	360000
Val-Trp	1700	Val-Pro	420000
Leu-Ala-Pro	2300	Gly-Phe	450000
Ile-Tyr	3700	Ala-Leu	1.6e+06
Phe-Ala-Pro	4200	Ala-Gly	2.5e+06
Arg-Ala-Pro	16000	Gly-Glu	5.4e+06
Phe-Pro-Pro	78000	Gly-Lys	5.4e+06
Ile-Pro	150000	Pro-Pro	7.5e+06
Ala-Pro	270000	Ala-His	9.0e+06
Ala-Val	300000	Gly-Asp	9.2e+06

One can see from this table that the chemical information contained in this set of peptides is diverse and that each activity class is well balanced. No region of the activity range is under- or overrepresented. This led us to consider this set of molecules to be an appropriate one for HypoGen.

The molecules were sketched in Catalyst. Poled conformations were generated for each molecule using a 10 kcal/mol energy cutoff.[6] Upon inspection of the molecules, it was determined that three generic types of chemical features described most of the functionality. Therefore HypoGen was instructed to select pharmacophore models using hydrophobic centers, H-bond acceptors, and negative ionizable groups.[7] No constraint on the minimum and maximum number of each type of feature in the reported pharmacophores was applied, but only pharmacophores containing five features were considered. All other parameters were left to their default value.

Table 10.2 reports the results for the ten hypotheses generated for the ACE dataset.

Table 10.2. HypoGen results for the ACE dataset.

	Totalcost	Error Cost	RMS	Correl	Feature Definition
Hypo1	85.44	73.60	0.80	0.96	AHHHN
Hypo2	86.11	74.26	0.84	0.95	AHHHN
Hypo3	86.20	74.35	0.84	0.95	AAHHN
Hypo4	86.55	75.04	0.88	0.95	AAHHN
Hypo5	87.23	75.39	0.90	0.95	AAHHH
Hypo6	88.13	76.26	0.95	0.94	AAHHN
Hypo7	89.10	77.16	0.99	0.93	AHHHN
Hypo8	90.05	78.12	1.04	0.93	AHHHN
Hypo9	90.50	78.55	1.06	0.93	AAHHN
Hypo10	92.01	79.27	1.09	0.92	AHHHN

A: HB Acceptor   H: Hydrophobic   N: Negative Ionizable

During a HypoGen run, two output files (<runname>.full and <runname>.log) containing user information are generated. The <runname>.full is a full log file. At the top of this file, interesting information is reported concerning the first two phases of HypoGen (constructive and subtractive phase). Figure 10.1 shows the beginning of the <runname>.full file obtained for this run.

Constructive phase
nleu-ala-pro
NegIonizable avg. hits = 1 HYDROPHOBIC avg. hits = 2.69128 HBA avg. hits = 6.00671
  finished 0 lead
  number of configs = 8383 number of insertions = 8088
val-trp
NegIonizable avg. hits = 1 HYDROPHOBIC avg. hits = 2.82653 HBA avg. hits = 4.71429
  finished 1 lead
  number of configs = 1979 number of insertions = 1939
leu-ala-pro
NegIonizable avg. hits = 1 HYDROPHOBIC avg. hits = 2.52903 HBA avg. hits = 5.84516
  finished 2 lead
  number of configs = 4591 number of insertions = 0
ile-tyr
NegIonizable avg. hits = 1 HYDROPHOBIC avg. hits = 2.9127 HBA avg. hits = 6.69841
  finished 3 lead
  number of configs = 4605 number of insertions = 0
phe-ala-pro
NegIonizable avg. hits = 1 HYDROPHOBIC avg. hits = 2.43617 HBA avg. hits = 5.70745
  finished 4 lead
  number of configs = 4983 number of insertions = 0
(00   NegI HYDR HYDR HYDR) TElems = 0
(00   NegI HYDR HYDR HBA) TElems = 0
(00   HYDR HYDR HYDR HBA) TElems = 0
(NegI HYDR HYDR HYDR HBA) TElems = 292
(00   NegI HYDR HBA HBA) TElems = 0
(00   HYDR HYDR HBA HBA) TElems = 0
(NegI HYDR HYDR HBA HBA) TElems = 540
(HYDR HYDR HYDR HBA HBA) TElems = 823
(00   HYDR HBA HBA HBA) TElems = 0

Figure 10.1. Output of the full file for the ACE dataset (Part 1 of 2)

Results of the constructive phase are shown at the top of the file. HypoGen has identified five compounds as being "active molecules" (see paragraph on the constructive phase). HypoGen starts with the most active molecule, n-leu-ala-pro, and performs a feature mapping using each conformer in the conformational model. An average hit rate

Subtractive phase
gly-asp
NegIonizable avg. hits = 2 HYDROPHOBIC avg. hits = 0 HBA avg. hits = 8.55844
    finished 0 lead
    number of configs = 0 number of insertions = 0
ala-his
NegIonizable avg. hits = 1 HYDROPHOBIC avg. hits = 0 HBA avg. hits = 5.59732
    finished 1 lead
    number of configs = 0 number of insertions = 0
pro-pro
NegIonizable avg. hits = 1 HYDROPHOBIC avg. hits = 1 HBA avg. hits = 4.59184
    finished 2 lead
    number of configs = 0 number of insertions = 0
gly-lys
NegIonizable avg. hits = 1 HYDROPHOBIC avg. hits = 0 HBA avg. hits = 5.46995
    finished 3 lead
    number of configs = 0 number of insertions = 0
gly-glu
NegIonizable avg. hits = 2 HYDROPHOBIC avg. hits = 0 HBA avg. hits = 8.60952
    finished 4 lead
    number of configs = 0 number of insertions = 0
ala-gly
NegIonizable avg. hits = 1 HYDROPHOBIC avg. hits = 0 HBA avg. hits = 5.72222
    finished 5 lead
    number of configs = 0 number of insertions = 0
Total bins containing 0 inactive molecules = 1655
Total bins containing 1 inactive molecules = 0
Total bins containing 2 inactive molecules = 0
Total bins containing 3 inactive molecules = 0
Total bins containing 4 inactive molecules = 0
Total bins containing 5 inactive molecules = 0
Total bins containing 6 inactive molecules = 0
(NegI HYDR HYDR HYDR HBA) TElems = 292
(NegI HYDR HYDR HBA HBA) TElems = 540
(HYDR HYDR HYDR HBA HBA) TElems = 823
Fixed Cost:
    totalcost=79.0896 RMS=0 correl=0
    Cost components: Error=67.2721 Weight=1.12491 Config=10.6926 Mapping=0

Started....

Summary of feature definition hit statistics:
        HBA hits/lead: mean= 5.93 stddev= 1.37
      HYDROPHOBIC hits/lead: mean= 1.47 stddev= 1.13
      NegIonizable hits/lead: mean= 1.15 stddev= 0.37
Entropy of hypothesis space: 10.6926

Figure 10.1. Output of the full file for the ACE dataset (Part 2 of 2)

for each feature is reported (i.e., avg. hits in Figure 10.1), and the sum of the average hits rates is compared to the MinSubsetPoints parameter.* If this value is greater or equal to the MinSubsetPoint parameter, the program will continue, otherwise, it stops. The number of configs (total number of possible hypotheses for this molecule), as well as the number of insertions (total number of possible hypotheses after duplicate removal) are reported. The same procedure is applied to the rest of the active set of molecules, but the number of insertions is only reported for the two most active molecules.

Using all the features (hydrophobic, H-bond acceptor, negative ionizable), the program calculates all the possible feature combinations that contain 7 or less points (the H-bond acceptor feature is characterized by two points) and do not violate the user parameters. In this case, the MinPoints parameter** was set to 4 and the minimum and maximum number of features in the reported pharmacophores was set to 5.

Next, HypoGen moves to the subtractive phase and analyzes the inactive compounds (see paragraph on the subtractive phase). As shown in Figure 10.1, six molecules were identified as being inactive compounds. Similar to the constructive phase, feature mapping is performed on these compounds. HypoGen analyzes all the hypotheses generated from the set of active molecules and will eliminate those who can map more than half of the inactive molecules. In our case, none of the hypotheses generated from the active set of compounds map any of the inactive compounds. The last lines in Figure 10.1 represent the working hypotheses on which the optimization phase will be performed.

An important parameter, the Entropy, or configuration cost, is computed at this stage. This parameter describes the complexity of the hypothesis space HypoGen will have to analyze. Its value in our example (10.6926) means that the number of initial hypothesis choices ($2^{10.69} = 1655$) is reasonable for the optimization. HypoGen works well for training sets with an Entropy up to 17 (which corresponds to 131,072 starting hypotheses). For training sets with an entropy higher

---

* MinSubsetPoints: Controls the minimum number of location constraints (features) required to be found in the next most active molecule(s) during the constructive phase.

** MinPoints: Controls the minimum number of location constraints (features) required for any hypothesis.

than 17, the molecules may be too flexible to allow a correct space coverage during conformational analysis.

As stated previously, important cost parameters that determine the odds of success are printed to the <runname>.full and the <runname>.log files early in the run. Investigation of these parameters, in this study, indicated that the correlations would likely be true and not due to chance. The parameters are the Fixed cost (cost of a perfect hypothesis) and the Null cost (cost of a hypothesis for which we assume there is no structure data and the average of all the activities in the training set is used as the estimate). Refer to Chapter 26 for a more detailed discussion of these cost parameters. In general, the greater the cost range, the higher the statistical significance of the run will be. The difference between the Fixed cost (79.09) and the Null cost (145.69) was 66.6, which is within the appropriate range. Figure 10.2 shows the costs values obtained in our example.

Figure 10.2. Total costs for the ten hypotheses generated with the ACE dataset.

For the ten five-featured hypothesis models, the total costs are close to the fixed cost and range from 85.44 to 92.01.

Among the different cost terms, the Error cost term[*] is the most important one, since one tries to derive SAR hypotheses. An analysis similar to the one represented in Figure 10.2 can be made using only the Error cost component. The Error component has the major effect in establishing the total cost.

Figure 10.3 illustrates this analysis.

---

[*] Error cost: Cost component that increases as the RMS difference between estimated and measured activities for the training set molecules increases. This cost factor is designed to favor models where the correlation between estimated and measured activities is better. The standard deviation of this parameter is given by the Uncertainty parameter.

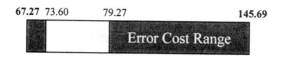

67.27 73.60   79.27   145.69

Error Cost Range

Figure 10.3. Error cost component for the ten hypotheses generated for the ACE dataset.

The output is similar to the one shown in Figure 10.2. However, it gives a better understanding of how well the ten hypotheses predict the activities of the training set molecules.

Other factors besides the cost elements should also be considered when selecting a hypothesis from the top 10. The main assumption made by HypoGen is that an active molecule should map more features than an inactive molecule. In other words, a molecule is inactive because a) it misses an important feature or b) the feature is present but cannot be oriented correctly in space. Based on this assumption, the most active molecule in the dataset should map to all the features of the generated hypotheses. This information is accessible in the <run-name>.log file. The log file is a good source of information to begin checking for problems. This file contains information of each of the top ten hypotheses. The file contains the feature weights, tolerance values, types, and locations. It also lists geometric fit values, mapping information, estimated activities, and errors of estimation for each molecule in the training set. The mapping information can be used to assess the quality of the proposed hypotheses. The mapping column contains a number corresponding to the atom number that mapped to each feature in the hypothesis. An asterisk in this field indicates that the feature did not match. Since the initial hypotheses are derived from the top two active compounds, most hypotheses will match all the features of one of the top two active compounds. Figure 10.4 shows the feature mapping pattern of n-leu-ala-pro on the ten hypotheses.

Note that n-leu-ala-pro misses one feature on the two lowest cost hypotheses, whereas it satisfies this criterion on Hypo3, 4, 5, 6, 8, and 10. As a consequence of the partial mapping of n-leu-ala-pro on the two lowest cost hypotheses, the fit value is smaller and the error between experimental and estimated activities is bigger. In other words, one should focus first on Hypo3, 4, 5, 6, 8, and 10.

	Compound	Fit	Conf		Mappings					Est	Act	Error	Uncert
Hypo1	nleu-ala-pro	7.40	95	+ [21	*	44	26	12]		3900	700	+ 5.6	3
Hypo2	nleu-ala-pro	7.48	134	+ [*	44	26	36	12]		2000	700	+ 2.8	3
Hypo3	**nleu-ala-pro**	**8.05**	**6**	+ [21	1	16	26	12]		**930**	**700**	+ 1.3	3
Hypo4	**nleu-ala-pro**	**8.15**	**6**	+ [1	21	44	26	12]		**440**	**700**	- 1.6	3
Hypo5	**nleu-ala-pro**	**7.87**	**6**	+ [21	1	36	16	26]		**1200**	**700**	+ 1.7	3
Hypo6	**nleu-ala-pro**	**8.58**	**6**	+ [21	1	16	26	12]		**420**	**700**	- 1.7	3
Hypo7	nleu-ala-pro	6.38	105	+ [1	44	36	*	12]		13000	700	+ 18	3
Hypo8	nleu-ala-pro	7.11	134	+ [*	16	26	36	12]		3400	700	+ 4.8	3
Hypo9	**nleu-ala-pro**	**7.75**	**6**	+ [1	21	16	26	12]		**420**	**700**	- 1.7	3
Hypo10	nleu-ala-pro	7.08	68	+ [1	44	26	36	12]		**1000**	**700**	+ 1.4	3

Figure 10.4. Mapping pattern of nleu-ala-pro on the 10 hypotheses generated for the ACE dataset.
Each column between the [ ] refers to one of the five features of the hypothesis.

Before doing more analysis, the hypotheses mentioned above were evaluated against a test set of four molecules (captopril and its enantiomer, enantiocaptopril, enalapril and succinyl proline). This test set is a difficult one since a Zinc-binding interaction is responsible for the binding of Captopril, and this feature is not included in the feature dictionary of Catalyst. Thus, Catalyst does not know how important this interaction is for activity. It is likely that enantiocaptopril must assume a relatively high energy conformation to bind effectively with the ACE receptor. Thus, for the validation, all estimations were calculated using Best fit with an energy limit of 5 kcal/mol. Moreover, we focused on trends rather than on real activities, in order to assess the quality of the hypotheses. Results are shown in Table 10.3.

Table 10.3. Predicted activities for a test set of 4 compounds.

	Act (nM)	Hypo3	ΔE	Hypo4	ΔE	Hypo5	ΔE	Hypo6	ΔE	Hypo8	ΔE	Hypo10	ΔE
SuccPro	484000	1400	1.32	2600	2.22	54000	3.35	2600	1.32	110000	4.91	210000	3.92
Enalapril	4	830	1.13	430	3.18	1900	4.06	520	1.12	2300	0.69	29000	0.69
Captopril	23	11000	2.70	270	2.69	6200	3.98	8200	2.70	16000	2.74	15000	3.98
Enantio-Captopril	nd*	2500	2.87	6700	4.53	1900	0.00	8500	2.87	3500	0.00	6100	0.00

DE: in kcal/mol;   nd: not determined;*
Enantiocaptopril is the inactive isomer of captopril

This table shows that among the ten hypotheses, **Hypo4** performs the best, even though the estimated activities do not map properly to the experimental ones. The hypothesis contains one negative ionizable group, two hydrophobic, and two hydrogen-bond acceptor features. **Hypo4** finds the trend between succinyl-proline and enalapril. Enalapril is predicted to be more active than succinyl proline because of an additional hydrophobic interaction (see Plate 10.1). Moreover, the hypothesis is shown to be stereospecific (see Plate 10.2).

Poor predictivity for both enalapril and captopril are probably the consequence of a) lack of a Zinc-binding function in Catalyst, b) activity of the most active molecule in the dataset (*n*-leu-ala-pro: 700 nM) which makes compounds being much more active (2 orders of magnitude) difficult to predict, and c) all the features in the generated hypotheses are equally weighted and have the same contribution in estimating the activities. Adding more weight on one specific feature may improve the results. Another possibility would have been the creation of a Zn binding function. Such an approach has been shown to be useful.[17]

10.5. Conclusion

In this chapter, we have shown how HypoGen can propose a set of hypotheses from a set of input molecules and activity data. The quality of the results will depend on the structural diversity of the molecules as well as a large spread in the activity data. This procedure returns ten different hypothesis models.

Analysis of the results is performed in different steps. The first step uses cost values that evaluate the simplicity of the models and their statistical significance. Further analyses of the hypotheses focus on the alignment of the molecules on a hypothesis, its ability to discriminate between stereoisomers. Last, evaluation of a series of test molecules will help to further validate the hypothesis model(s). The study case we have shown in this chapter is a difficult one, since a very important function (Zn binding function) is not defined in the Catalyst feature dictionary. This function is replaced by a standard hydrogen-bond acceptor function. However, among the generated hypothesis, one hypothesis identifies correctly the trends observed for the test set of compounds. Different approaches to improve the results on this dataset are suggested.

References

1. Golender V, Vesterman B, Eliyahu O, Kardash A, Kletzin M, Shokhen M, Vorpagel E: **Knowledge-engineering approach to drug design and its implementation in the Apex-3D expert system.** In: *10th European Symposium on Structure-Activity Relationships.* Barcelona: Prous Science, 1994:246-251.

2. Barnum D, Greene J, Smellie A, Sprague P: **Identification of common functional configurations among molecules.** *J Chem Inf Compu Sci* 1996, **36**:563-571.

3. Martin YC, Bures MG, Danaher EA, DeLazzer J, Lico I, Pavlik PA: **A fast new approach to pharmacophore mapping and its application to dopamineric and benzodiazepine agonists.** *J Comput-Aided Mol Des* 1993, **7**:83-102.

4. Beusen D: **Alignment of angiotensin II receptor antagonists using GASP.** Tripos Technical Notes, Nov 1996, **1**(4).

5. *Catalyst v.4.0,* Molecular Simulations Inc., 1998, San Diego, CA, USA.

6. Smellie A, Teig S, Towbin P: Poling: **Promoting conformational variation.** *J Comp Chem* 1995, **16**:171-187.

7. Green J, Kahn S, Savoj H, Sprague P, Teig S: **Chemical function queries for 3D database search.** *J Chem Inf Comput Sci* 1994, **34**:1297-1308.

8. Duffy JC, Dearden JC, Green DSV: **Use of Catalyst in the design of novel non-steroidal anti-inflammatory analgesic drugs.** In: *QSAR and Molecular Modelling: Concepts, Computational Tools and Biological Applications.* Sanz F, Giraldo J, Manaut F, eds. Barcelona: Prous Science Publishers, 1995:289-291.

9. Hoffmann RD, Bourguignon JJ: **Building a hypothesis for CCK-B antagonists using the Catalyst program.** In: *QSAR and Molecular Modelling: Concepts, Computational Tools and Biological Applications.* Sanz F, Giraldo J, Manaut F, eds. Barcelona: Prous Science Publishers, 1995:298-300.

10. Quintana J. Contijoch M, Cuberes R, Frigola J: **Structure-activity relationships and molecular modeling studies of a series of H1 antihistamines.** In: *QSAR and Molecular Modelling: Concepts, Computational Tools and Biological Applications.* Sanz F, Giraldo J, Manaut F, eds. Barcelona: Prous Science Publishers, 1995:282-288.

11. Halova J, Zak P, Strouf O, Uchida N, Yuzuri T, Sakakibara K, Hirota M: **Multicriteria methodology validation using Catalyst™ software system. A case study on SAR of cathecol analogs against malignant melanoma.** *Org React* 1997, **31**(104(1)):31-43.

12. Grigorov J, Weber JMJ, Tronchet CW, Jefford WK, Milhous D, Maric: **A QSAR study of the antimalarial activity of some synthetic 1,2,4-trioxanes.** *J Chem Inf Comput Sci* 1997, **37**:124-130.

13. Kaminski JJ, Rane DF, Snow ME, Weber L, Rothofsky ML, Anderson SD, Lin SL: **Identification of novel farnesyl transferase inhibitors using three-dimensional database searching methods.** *J Med Chem* 1997, **40**(25):4103-4112.

14. Ekins S, Bravi G, Ring BJ, Gillespie TA, Gillespie JS, Vandenbranden M, Wrighton SA, Wikel JH: **Three-dimensional quantitative structure activity relationship analyses of substrates for CYP2B6.** *J Pharmacol Exp Ther* 1999, **288**:21-29.

15. Sprague, PW: **Automated chemical hypothesis generation and database searching with Catalyst.** In: *Perspectives in Drug Discovery and Design,* Vol. 3. Müller K, ed. Leiden: ESCOM Science Publishers B. V., 1995:1-20.

16. Daveu C, Bureau R, Baglin I, Prunier H, lancelot JC, Rault S: **Definition of a pharmacophore for partial agonists of serotonin 5-HT3 receptors.** *J Chem Inf Comput Sci* 1999, **39**:362-369.

17. Scott RS: **Adding extra parameters to the Catalyst force field-an example using ECE inhibitors.** http://www.msi.com/user/groups/catalyst/CatUGM98.html.

Applications in Drug Design

11

Metric for Analyzing Hit Lists and Pharmacophores

Osman F. Güner and Douglas R. Henry

Abstract

In this chapter, a measure of the quality of hit lists obtained from chemical database searching is proposed (the *GH* score—Preliminary work is presented at the 1998 Charleston Conference as a poster. See: http://www.netsci.org/Science/Cheminform/feature09.html). This measure takes into account both the yield (the fraction of active structures hit) and the percentage of actives that are retrieved from the database: the two parameters that need to be maximized to obtain the optimum hit list. By using variable coefficients on these terms and adjusting for the size of the hit list and the database, a flexible but quantitative measure of hit list quality is obtained. We show the application of this measure to several published search results. We also show how the *GH* score can be used to measure the quality of clustering results.

11

Metric for Analyzing Hit Lists and Pharmacophores

Osman F. Güner[†] and Douglas R. Henry[‡]

[†]Molecular Simulations Inc., San Diego, California
[‡]MDL Information Systems, Inc., San Leandro, California

11.1. Introduction

One of the significant steps in the course of pharmacophore model generation is "validation." In the absence of experimental follow-up, the validation of pharmacophore models is typically done by applying the models to databases of compounds with known biological activities. Examples of these types of databases are MDL's Drug Data Report (MDDR) and Comprehensive Medicinal Chemistry (CMC) databases,[1] Chapman & Hall's Dictionary of Drugs,[2] and Derwent's World Drug Index (WDI).[3] Validity of the pharmacophore model is determined by its ability to retrieve known active molecules from these databases. This, of course, only applies to those models that represent known classes of active compounds.

The question of how good a hit list is has been raised for a long time.[4] Many people have considered the yield of the active compounds (i.e., ratio of actives in the hit list to the total number of compounds in the hit list) to decide how successful a query is.[5] This yield, when compared with the ratio of actives in the entire database (i.e., ratio of the active compounds in the database to the total number of compounds in the database) provides a parameter known as "enrichment" or "enhancement".[6] Use of "percent of actives" to evaluate a hit list has been quite rare: To our knowledge, this has been mentioned in only two earlier work.[7,8] One seeks to maximize two parameters, yield and the ratio of actives, to improve the selectivity in a hit list. Maximizing the ratio of actives and yield improves the probability of finding a new potentially active compound (new lead) in the hit list when compared to random selection from the database. However, such an approach does not take into account the size of the hit list and it does not represent well the extreme cases where one retrieves a very large or a very small hit list. For example, if the hit list contains a single compound and that compound is active, then the yield is 100% and the enrichment is a very large number (depending on the size and the number of actives in the database). Such a hit list with a single hit is useless from the perspective of identifying new leads. A relatively small hit list with high selectivity, however, may be quite useful since the false positives in the list can be potentially active and constitute high quality yields. Hence, one should not ignore these extreme cases, but rather deal with them properly.

In this chapter, we propose a simple formula that can be used to score hit lists and provide a quantitative "Goodness of Hit list" (*GH*) score that overcomes the above mentioned limitations.

11.2. Results and Discussion

First let us schematically describe a database and establish the jargon that we use in this chapter. Figure 11.1 represents a hypothetical database that contains a certain number of active compounds. A typical search will then yield a hit list that contains some of the active compounds.

Let us label the number of compounds in the database as D; the number of active compounds in the database as A; and the number of compounds in a search hit list as H_t, where the active compounds in the hit list are represented as H_a. We can now map the database using this terminology (Figure 11.2).

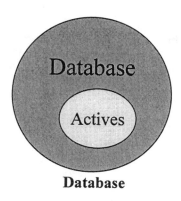 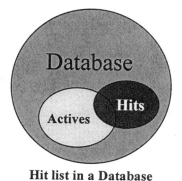

Database	Hit list in a Database

Figure 11.1. Schematic representation of a database and a hit list in a database. Reprinted with permission from reference.[9] © 1999 Wendy Warr & Accociates.

Percent yield of actives:

$$\%Y = \frac{H_a}{H_t} \times 100$$

Percent ratio of the actives in the hit list:

$$\%A = \frac{H_a}{A} \times 100$$

Enrichment (enhancement):

$$E = \frac{H_a / H_t}{A / D} = \frac{H_a \times D}{H_t \times A}$$

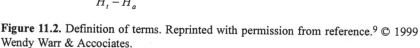

False Negatives:

$$A - H_a$$

False Positives:

$$H_t - H_a$$

Figure 11.2. Definition of terms. Reprinted with permission from reference.[9] © 1999 Wendy Warr & Accociates.

The best hit list is obtained when there is a perfect overlap of the hit list to the known active compounds in the database. This occurs when both conditions $H_a=H_t$ and $H_a=A$, hence $H_a=H_t=A$, are satisfied. This is an ideal case, however, and is nearly impossible to achieve in a real-life situation. In reality, there may be many compounds in the database that may be active but either have not been listed as active, or have not been tested for the specified activity. In either case, these compounds end up in the "false positives" list. Hence, we consider the list of false positives, in this context, as opportunities for potential leads. The objective, then, is to improve the hit list in such a manner that the false positives can contain a large number of potentials of leads. Considering that the ideal hit list is when $H_a=H_t$ (i.e., $\%Y=100$), as well as $H_a=A$ (i.e., $\%A=100$) (see Figure 11.3), a *"good"* hit list, therefore, can be obtained by simultaneously maximizing the percent yield of actives ($\%Y$) as well as the percent of actives in the hit list ($\%A$). Currently, most analyses use either the % yield or the enrichment value to evaluate the search results.[6] For example, in a database of 50,000 compounds with 100 compounds listed as active (for a particular activity), the initial yield in the database (A/D) is $100/50,000 \times 100 = 0.2$. If a search results in a hit list of 500 compounds, 50 of which are active, the search yield ($\%Y$) is 10 (i.e., 10 percent of the compounds are active). This is a significant improvement with an enrichment of 50 (i.e., $10 \div 0.2$). The hit list is 50 times enriched with respect to the random selection from the database. Note that even though enrichment provides an easily comprehensible data, it is directly proportional to, and does not contain any more information, than $\%Y$.

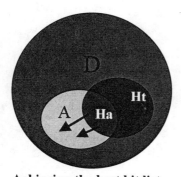   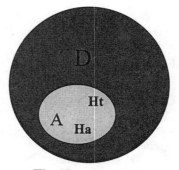

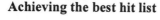   The "best" hit list

Figure 11.3. Hit list definition: the "best."

While this analysis clearly indicates the improvement over random selection, it is incomplete in its identification of how good a hit list is when compared with other hit lists. As we have mentioned earlier, what if the search resulted with a single hit that is active? Then the $\%Y$ is 100 *(very high $\%Y$)* and the enrichment is $100/0.2 = 500$: a very high enrichment value for a useless hit list because it is actually missing 99% of the active compounds in the database *(very low $\%A$)*. More significantly, it does not provide any lead which is the primary objective of 3D searching. The two parameters, $\%Y$ and $\%A$, are not completely independent from each other. In trying to maximize one parameter, one usually compromises the other. It is important to maximize both of the parameters simultaneously. Therefore, we propose that both percent yield *($\%Y$)* as well as percent of the actives in the list *($\%A$)* be considered in the "goodness of hit list" evaluation. If we simply take the linear combination of the $\%Y$ and $\%A$ with weights assigned to each (w_1 and w_2), we obtain:

$$ GH_1 = \frac{w_1\left(\dfrac{H_a}{H_t}\right) + w_2\left(\dfrac{H_a}{A}\right)}{2} $$

or

$$ \boxed{GH_1 = \frac{H_a\left[(w_1 A) + (w_2 H_t)\right]}{2AH_t}} \qquad (11.1) $$

A general case may be considered where the weights are equal to 1: $w_1 = w_2 = 1$ (i.e., maximizing the percent yield is equally important to maximizing the percent of actives retrieved). Then:

$$ GH_1 = \frac{H_a\left(A + H_t\right)}{2H_t A} \qquad (11.2) $$

Equation 11.2 is the very basic GH formula that can be used for some typical cases. Let us now test Equation 11.2 in several hit list scenarios. First, let us define the best and the worst hit list. The best hit list is the one that retrieves all of the actives and nothing else (i.e., $H_t = H_a = A$); whereas the worst hit list is the one that retrieves everything else but the known actives in the database (i.e., $H_a = 0$, $H_t = D - A$).

Note that in true search cases the worst hit list, in this context, is equally valuable as the best one, since in both cases the search was able to differentiate and isolate the known active compounds from the rest. However, since the result was based on a query that was targeting the actives in the database and failed to retrieve any of them, we will use the worst case as described in testing our equation. Also note that in real cases, those compounds that are not listed as active are not necessarily inactive; they may simply be compounds that are not tested for the activity of interest or not listed as such in the database. One of the primary objectives of 3D searching is to identify those compounds that may be good candidates for the proposed activity. Hence the false positives in an optimized hit list will constitute a prioritized list of candidates for a typical pharmaceutical lead identification project. With this caveat in mind, we will now apply six database search scenarios to our equation:

1. The best case: where $H_t = H_a = A$
   Search retrieves all of the actives and nothing else; false negatives = 0, false positives = 0.

2. The worst case: where $H_a = 0$, $H_t = D - A$
   Search retrieves everything in the database except the actives; false negatives = A, false positives = $D - A$

3. Extreme case Y (%Y = 100 with a single hit): where $D = 50,000$, $A = 100$, $H_t = H_a = 1$
   Case where the %Y is 100 (i.e., all the hits in the hit list are active) but retrieves a single hit.

4. Extreme case A (%A = 100 with the entire database in the hit list): where D, $H_t = 50,000$, A, $H_a = 100$
   Case where the %A is 100 (i.e., all of the actives in the database are retrieved together with the rest of the database).

5. Typical good: $D = 50,000$, $A = 100$, $H_t = 200$, $H_a = 80$
   A typical hit list with high %Y and medium %A.

6. Typical bad: $D = 50,000$, $A = 100$, $H_t = 1,000$, $H_a = 50$
   A typical hit list with low %Y and medium %A.

The results of this scenario are represented in Table 11.1.

The *GH score* gives a good indication of how good the hit list is with respect to a compromise between maximum yield and maximum percent of actives retrieved. This table provides an acceptable sorting of the hit lists, from best to worst, via the *GH score*. The two extremes are

Table 11.1. Six database search scenario applied to *GH* (Eqn.11.2).

Case	%Y	%A	Enrichment	false neg.	false pos.	GH$_I$
Best	100	100	500	0	0	1
Typical Good	40	80	200	20	120	0.60
Extreme Y	100	1	500	99	0	0.50
Extreme A	0.2	100	1	0	49,900	0.50
Typical Bad	5	50	25	50	950	0.26
Worst	0	0	0	100	49,900	0

cases where either *%Y* or *%A* is very high while the other component is very low. None of the existing parameters address these extreme cases well. For example, if we ignore the extreme cases, all three parameters, *%Y*, *%A*, and *Enrichment*, sorts the test scenarios correctly: *Best* having the highest score, then *Typical Good*, *Typical Bad*, and the *Worst* cases. Only the *GH* score places the extreme cases in the center. Since the extreme cases maximize one of the parameters only, the *GH* score reaches the limit at 0.5. Note that while *Extreme Y* is very useful, *Extreme A* is not (it does not improve our situation since it retrieves the entire database). Because of the low information content, *Extreme A* should score much lower and the *GH* formula should be modified accordingly. One can argue that extreme cases (both *Y* and *A*) should always be given a low weight. If it so desired, the extreme cases may receive much lower values by using a different formula. In this case, one can take the geometric average of the *%Y* and *%A*, instead of the arithmetic average that we are using. Let's call the geometric average *GH′*. The following formula can be used for this purpose.

$$GH' = \sqrt{\%Y \times \%A}$$

$$GH' = \sqrt{\frac{H_a}{H_t} \times \frac{H_a}{A}}$$

$$GH' = \sqrt{\frac{H_a^2}{H_t \times A}}$$

$$GH' = \frac{H_a}{\sqrt{H_t \times A}} \tag{11.3}$$

We now apply the above formula to our test scenarios to obtain the data listed in Table 11.2.

Table 11.2. Six database search scenario applied to *GH'* (Eqn. 11.3).

Case	%Y	%A	Enrichment	false neg.	false pos.	GH'
Best	100	100	500	0	0	1
Typical Good	40	80	200	20	120	0.57
Typical Bad	5	50	25	50	950	0.16
Extreme Y	100	1	500	99	0	0.10
Extreme A	0.2	100	1	0	49,900	0.04
Worst	0	0	0	100	49,900	0

As discussed above, in this case the *GH'* scores of the two extreme cases are much lower, and they are now placed below the *Typical Bad* hit list. One can use this variation of the *GH* formula if these special cases need to be avoided. However, we believe that one of these special cases (*Extreme Y*) should not be ignored: Small but highly selective hit lists (i.e., high *%Y* but low *%A*: vicinity of *Extreme Y*) are very useful since the fewer false positives in the hit lists can be considered important leads. We define extreme cases as those in which one of the parameters (*%Y* or *%A*) is very high while the other one is very low. Note that when both parameters are high, *GH* score approaches 1.0 (best); or when they are both low, the *GH* score approaches 0.0 (worst). Therefore the extreme cases reaches *GH* score of 0.5 at the limit (i.e., with Equation 11.2). Hence, using the arithmetic mean (*GH$_1$*, Equation 11.2) fits this requirement better than using the geometric mean (*GH'*, Equation 11.3). As mentioned above, we also would like to single out one of the cases, *Extreme Y*, as very useful while hit lists in the vicinity of *Extreme A* are not very useful. In fact, the *Extreme A* represents a case where there is no enrichment in the database at all. Hence, while *Extreme Y* should receive a relatively high *GH* score, *Extreme A* should receive a very low one. One way to increase the distinction of the two extreme cases is by using a heavier weight for the *%Y* parameter in Equation 11.1.

Consideration of weighting the %Y heavier than the %A emphasizes that yield is more important that the ability to retrieve all of the known actives in the database. This is especially the case where multiple binding modes and multiple binding mechanisms may be contributing to the compounds in the database. Since the database search assumes that all of the compounds in the hit list bind to the same active site in the same way, it may not be feasible to retrieve all of listed active compounds with a single pharmacophore model. Therefore, giving the %Y more weight makes more sense. We will therefore modify Equation 11.2 by implementing $w_1 = 1.5$ and $w_2 = 0.5$, keeping the weight total equal to 2 (i.e., $w_1 + w_2 = 2$) as our third test case.

Applying $w_1 = 3/2$, $w_2 = 1/2$ to

$$GH_1 = \frac{H_a[(w_1 A)+(w_2 H_t)]}{2AH_t}$$ (11.1)

we get

$$GH_2 = \frac{H_a\left[\left(\frac{3}{2}A\right)+\left(\frac{1}{2}\right)H_t\right]}{2AH_t}$$

or

$$\boxed{GH_2 = \frac{H_a(3A+H_t)}{4H_t A}}$$ (11.4)

We now apply the same hit list scenarios to the Equation 11.4; results are shown in Table 11.3.

Table 11.3. Six database search scenario applied to GH (Eqn. 11.4).

Case	%Y	%A	Enrichment	false neg.	false pos.	GH_2
Best	100	100	500	0	0	1
Extreme Y	100	1	500	99	0	0.75
Typical Good	40	80	200	20	120	0.5
Typical Bad	5	50	25	50	950	0.33
Extreme A	0.2	100	1	0	49,900	0.25
Worst	0	0	0	100	49,900	0

In this case, *Extreme Y* scored better than *Typical Good,* while *Extreme A* scored lower than *Typical Bad.* We believe that Equation 11.4 gives a better prioritization of hit lists via *GH* score than those with Equations 11.2 and 11.4. However, *Extreme A* still maintains a respectable score with this formula and this forces us to consider a final modification that is more forceful than the weights used. We incorporate a coefficient that is directly proportional to the hit list size when compared with the database size. A simple function like $(1 - H_t/D)$ can work fine. In this case, if one retrieves the entire database, $H_t=D$ and the ratio becomes one and the coefficient becomes zero. Hence, smaller the hit list, larger the coefficient. One last modification is not to penalize the hit list for retrieving the active compounds. Hence using H_t-H_a and $D-A$ instead of H_t and D, respectively, our final *GH* score formula becomes:

$$GH = \left(\frac{H_a(3A + H_t)}{4H_t A} \right) \times \left(1 - \frac{H_t - H_a}{D - A} \right) \qquad (11.5^*)$$

and results are illustrated in Table 11.4.

Table 11.4. Six database search scenario applied to *GH* (Eqn. 11.5).

Case	%Y	%A	Enrichment	false neg.	false pos.	*GH*
Best	100	100	500	0	0	1
Extreme Y	100	1	500	99	0	0.75
Typical Good	40	80	200	20	120	0.5
Typical Bad	5	50	25	50	950	0.16
Extreme A	0.2	100	1	0	49,900	0
Worst	0	0	0	100	49,900	0

The final formula maintained the relative positions of the "good" hit list, where it has lowered the typical bad and zeroed the *Extreme A*. We propose that the above formula (Equation 11.5) gives the best relative positions for the hit list scenarios above. Use of the above *GH* formula will provide the practitioners of 3D searches the ability to evaluate the hit lists when applying different strategies. The *GH* formula can also be used to improve the pharmacophore model during an iterative process of 3D searching. Van Drie[7] explains how one refines the 3D-search query in an iterative fashion until the active compounds but none of the inactive ones are retrieved within a training set of compounds. Clearly *GH* score can also be applied to such an automated query optimization process.

---

* Reprinted with permission from reference.[9] © 1999 Wendy Warr & Accociates.

11.2.1. Application Examples

Let us now test the *GH* formula to some of the earlier published work and compare the results with those provided in the literature. In the Flexible Query paper by Güner, Pearlman, and Henry,[5] Table 11.5 lists the 3D search results in MDDR 3D testing different RMS tolerance, in fixed atomic positions to identify the best tolerance for the follow-up analysis. The query was for ACE inhibitors where 78 compounds were listed as ACE inhibitors (A) in a domain of 977 compounds (D) at MDDR-3D. Equation 11.5 was applied to the hit lists obtained by searching with various tolerance settings. The results are listed in the following table:

Table 11.5. Analysis of fixed positions tolerance in reference.[5]

Tolerance	H_a	H_t	%Y	%A	GH
0.2	60	83	72.3	76.9	**0.716**
0.3	64	91	70.3	82.1	**0.711**
0.5	64	93	68.8	82.1	**0.698**
0.7	64	102	62.7	82.1	**0.647**
1.0	64	114	56.1	82.1	**0.591**
2.0	64	120	53.3	82.1	**0.567**

These results indicate that 0.2 Angstroms was the optimum tolerance for the fixed atoms (albeit only marginally better than 0.3); this is in agreement with the published work.

In the same table in reference[5], the optimized "flexible query" (Q-4) was also compared with pharmacophore models based on literature data (Q-5, Q-6, and Q-7). Again, analysis was carried out with the Equation 11.5 for the results obtained by the queries in Table 11.6:

Table 11.6. Analysis of flexible vs. other queries in reference.[5]

Query	H_a	H_t	%Y	%A	GH
Q-4	64	91	70.3	82.1	**0.711**
Q-5	72	645	11.2	92.3	**0.114**
Q-6	58	560	10.4	74.4	**0.116**
Q-7	24	165	14.5	30.8	**0.157**

The *GH* score for the "flexible query" Q-4 is superior to the other, more traditional, queries. This result is in full agreement with the published analysis. It provides us a quantitative measure to compare the performance of different database search strategies.

We apply the *GH* equation to another earlier work by Henry and Güner, this time, comparing ligand- versus receptor-based queries.[10] MDDR-3D was used in this work that contained 47,926 (D) compounds at which there were 677 and 244 compounds listed as antihypertensives (A1) and angiotensin inhibitors (A2), respectively. We will use both categories in our analysis. The results are listed at Table 11.7.

Table 11.7. Analysis of receptor vs. ligand-based in reference.[11]

Query	H_a	H_t	*%Y*	*%A*	*GH*
Ligand Q-1 (angiotensin inh)	231	4,442	5.20	94.7	**0.251**
Receptor Q-2 (angiotensin inh)	240	5,804	4.14	98.4	**0.245**
Mixed Q-3 (angiotensin inh)	209	4,473	4.67	85.7	**0.227**
Ligand Q-1 (antihypertensive)	506	4,442	11.39	74.7	**0.250**
Receptor Q-2 (antihypertensive)	623	5,804	10.73	92.0	**0.277**
Mixed Q-3 (antihypertensive)	470	4,473	10.51	69.4	**0.231**

In this work, the ligand-based query Q-1 retrieved 4,442 hits at MDDR of which 231 were specifically listed as angiotensinase inhibitors, and 506 as antihypertensives. This results in a *%Y* of 5.20 and *%A* of 94.7. In the case of the receptor-based search, the Q-2 retrieved 5,804 compounds of which 240 were listed as angiotensinase inhibitors. The intuitive analysis presented in the paper[10] indicated that the receptor-based search was more useful since it retrieved 240 of the 244 eligible hits (*%A* = 98.4) with only about a one percent fewer yield than the ligand-based search. Using the data provided in Table I of the paper,[10] we provide the *GH* scores for the three queries listed: Q-1 ligand-based query, Q-2 receptor-based query, and Q-3 a mixed ligand and receptor-based query at Table 11.7.

Evaluating the results for those compounds that are classified as angiotensinase inhibitors, Ligand-based query (Q-1) scored marginally better than the receptor-based query, Q-2. However, when the more general activity class on antihypertensive is considered, the receptor-based query scored considerably better. The mixed query (partly receptor-based, partly ligand-based) performed worse than either receptor- or ligand-based queries did when used alone. This is a case where it is too close to make a call. Receptor-based queries retrieve more active compounds but also more false positives. Since the primary benefit of receptor-based queries is to identify novel classes of compounds that are structurally different than the existing known compounds, the use of a database of known active compounds may not necessarily best way to validate this particular query. Hence, with respect to receptor vs. ligand-based queries, the jury is probably still out. More work needs to be done in this area.

One final example is based on a work published by Sprague and Hoffmann.[8] In this paper, the authors apply two strategies to improve the results of a database search. One strategy involves increasing coverage (%A) by increasing the tolerance for the query; the other strategy involves increasing selectivity (%Y and E) by applying a fit number constraint. This is an ideal case for applying the GH-score evaluation. Let us apply this to their results for the angiotensin II antagonist query (Table 11.8). In Derwent's WDI database of 48,405 compounds that contains 154 angiotensin II blockers, their default query retrieved 1,004 hits of which 135 were listed as active (%Y=85). The first modification involves increasing the tolerance by 20%, and retrieves 97% of the known actives. Alternative modification involves a higher fit requirement, and retrieves a hit list with higher selectivity (%Y=21.6). The combination query seems to be the good compromise and yields the best results according to the authors. Let us see if the GH-score analysis corroborates this observation (see Table 11.8).

Table 11.8. Analysis of angiotensin II blockers results discussed in reference.[8]

Query	H_a	H_t	%Y	%A	GH
Angiotensin II blockers	134	1,004	13.35	87.0	0.312
Angiotensin II blockers (high tolerance)	149	1725	8.64	96.8	0.297
Angiotensin II blockers (fit constraint)	100	462	21.65	64.9	0.322
Angiotensin II blockers (both)	137	997	13.74	89.0	0.320

The GH scores indicate that the constrained search with high fit value is the best strategy, albeit with marginally higher score than the combination query strategy where high fit requirement as well as loose toler-

ances were used. The very close *GH* score for the last two hit lists indicate that both strategies are equally useful. The latter query was proposed as the better case by the authors.

The *GH* formula can also be used to evaluate cluster analysis results.
If, after clustering, we consider each cluster as a hit list, the *GH* formula gives a measure of the homogeneity of the cluster with respect to a
given biological class. This complements the overall cluster criterion of
"percent of actives in active clusters" introduced by Brown and
Martin.[11]

As an example, a total of 1,919 structures that were listed as binding
to a specific receptor active site were selected from the MDDR database. These structures were selected as having activity in eight known
receptors. Table 11.9 lists the Drug Data Report Activity Indexes and
posted activities for the 8 classes of compounds that were included in
this analysis.

Table 11.9. Activity Index values and the patented for the set of compounds
used in cluster analysis.

Activity No.	DDR Activity Index	Patented Activity
1	02454	TNF Inhibitor
2	06245	5HT Uptake Inhibitor
3	09221	Acetylcholine Esterase Inhibitor
4	09248	Prolylendopeptidase Inhibitor
5	12453	Lipid Peroxidation Inhibitor
6	12454	Excitatory Amino Acid Inhibitor
7	52502	Squalene Synthetase Inhibitor
8	54112	H+/K+ATPase Inhibitor

The activity index numbers indicate that the activities are specific, i.e.,
the compounds that are considered are patented due to their ability to
inhibit by binding to a specific active site. This is the closest one can get
to active compounds without doing experimental follow-up.

The structures were characterized by 166 substructure search keys,*
and analyzed by the monothetic cluster analysis method of Kaufman
and Rousseau.[12] Results from the 8-cluster stage are shown in

---

* The MOLSKEYS field in an ISIS® chemical database. These encode simple functional groups and topological features as 166 binary descriptors.

Table 11.10 (where the largest number of active compounds in each cluster is highlighted with bold-italics), along with *GH* (Equation 11.5) calculations in Table 11.11 (where highest *GH* scoring activity group for each cluster is highlighted with bold-italics).

Table 11.10. Cluster analysis result: Hit counts.

Cluster	Act. 1	Act. 2	Act. 3	Act. 4	Act. 5	Act. 6	Act. 7	Act. 8
1	2	*45*	*263*	53	*92*	16	*52*	162
2	1	1	23	0	26	4	10	*201*
3	5	12	91	*202*	48	*27*	16	38
4	0	0	3	3	51	16	0	84
5	17	1	19	1	14	20	7	0
6	17	42	4	7	31	0	17	0
7	0	0	1	0	6	0	40	1
8	*26*	0	0	0	41	0	50	10

Table 11.11. Cluster analysis results: *GH* scores (Eqn. 11.5).

Cluster	Act. 1	Act. 2	Act. 3	Act. 4	Act. 5	Act. 6	Act. 7	Act. 8
1	.006	.104	*.325*	.067	.111	.042	.079	.164
2	.006	.005	.066	.000	.080	.020	.035	*.638*
3	.021	.038	.163	*.458*	.091	.099	.036	.060
4	.000	.000	.015	.016	*.266*	.115	.000	.421
5	.216	.011	.185	.010	.138	*.242*	.072	.000
6	.161	*.355*	.026	.048	.210	.000	.123	.000
7	.000	.000	.016	.000	.096	.000	*.674*	.016
8	*.236*	.000	.000	.000	.261	.000	.344	.059

It is clear that certain clusters tend to contain structures with certain biological activities (cluster 7, for example), while others are more heterogeneous (cluster 1). Examining the raw data does not give as clear a picture of this as examining the *GH* scores, which have a common scale. Highlighting the highest *GH* score for each activity class, one can see that each of the eight classes of compounds is represented as the primary class with each of the eight clusters. Hence, using the *GH* score, we were able to associate ownership for each cluster with a particular activity. Such a distinction is not easy to make at all when reviewing the raw data in Table 11.10. For example, checking the data for Activity 6 in Table 11.10, cluster 3 has more hits (27) than cluster 5 (20); however, the *GH* score for cluster 5 (.242) is higher than that of cluster 3 (.099). This is because cluster 5 contained only 79 hits and 20 out of 79 hits have more significance than 27 out of 439 hits in cluster 3. This behavior observed in Table 11.11 is not random, and compared to the raw data displayed in Table 11.10, it is even less random. Hence, when a maximum-likelihood association analysis is run on autoscaled data from these tables,[13] the resulting Chi-squared statistic is higher for the *GH* measure (1845, P<0.001) versus that for the raw data (1241, P<0.001), implying that the *GH* scores have more power to express the diversity obtained by the cluster analysis. More work is needed and currently planned to verify this conclusion.

11.3. Conclusions

We present the *GH* formula (Equation 11.5) as a convenient way to quantify hit lists obtained from searches with various queries. This can be used not only to quantitatively sort the results with respect to "goodness of hits," but also can be used in automated procedures that will optimize a 3D query (see Miller, Henry, Güner ACS presentation).[14] In addition as exemplified in the paper, the equation can also be used to identify the most appropriate clustering technique for work similar to those published by Brown and Martin.[11] One can also envision use of *GH* scores in the analysis of experimental results obtained from high throughtput screening, or prioritization of combinatorial or virtual libraries.

Acknowledgement

The authors express gratitude to Marvin Waldman for his critical review of this manuscript and for suggesting geometric average as an alterna-

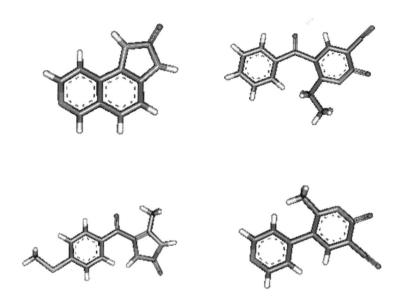

Plate 2.1. Four cardiotonic compounds for which a pharmacophore model will be developed.

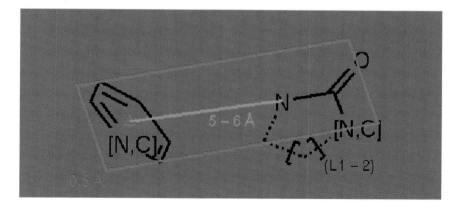

Plate 2.2. The pharmacophore model developed with visual pattern recognition (via ISIS/Draw).

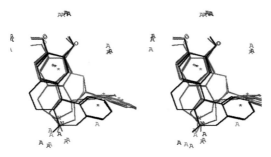

Plate 4.1. Stereopair that shows the superposition of D1 dopaminergic agonists 1, 3-5 according to the pharmacophore identified at 1.0 Å tolerance, but using the conformation selected at 1.8 Å. The points at centers of aromatic rings are marked with an *, site point locations with an A, and atom locations with the atomic symbol.

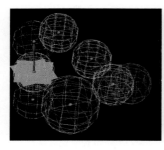

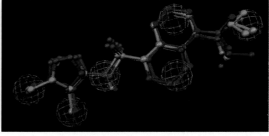

Plate 5.1. Six-feature hypothesis derived for arylpiperazine 5-HT$_3$ antagonists[17] using the Catalyst/HipHop program.[9]

Plate 5.2. The highest ranked (statistically best) six-feature hypothesis for ETA antagonists[16] derived using the Catalyst/HipHop program. Compounds BMS9 (*green*), BMS8 (*blue*) and BMS5 (*red*), are shown aligned onto the hypothesis.

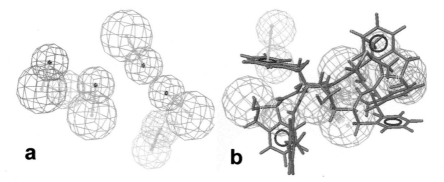

Plate 5.3. (**a**) 6-feature pharmacophore model generated for HIV-1 protease inhibitors using the Catalyst/HipHop program; (**b**) Alignment of the search query (model) onto JE214727 (*blue*) and L-700,41728 (*red*).

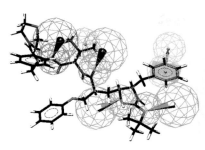

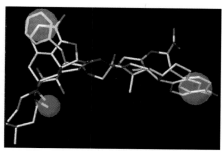

Plate 5.4. Alignment of the search query (model) onto CGP-57813 retrieved from the Derwent Drug Database.

Plate 6.1. Overlay of Leu-enkephalin and hybrid morphine. The transparent globes indicate the elucidated pharmacophore.

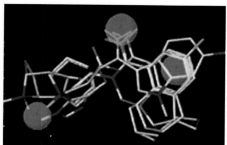

Plate 6.2. Overlay of 5-HT$_3$ antagonists. The elucidated pharmacophore is indicated by the transparent circles.

Plate 6.3. Overlay of six angoitensin II receptor antagonists. The transparent circles indicate the elucidated pharmacophore.

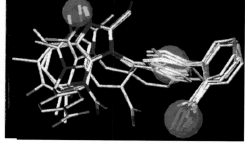

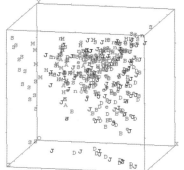

Plate 7.1. A typical pharmacophore key plot.

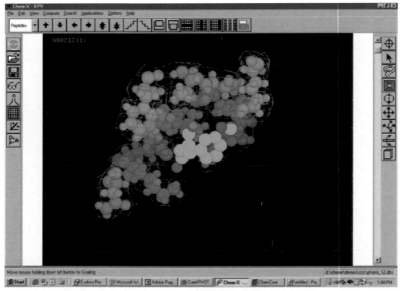

Plate 7.2. A hit molecule bound into the receptor site of Bovine Papilloma Virus using DiR.

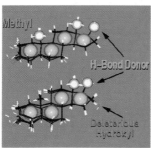

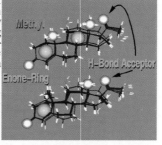

Plate 8.1. Two significant biophores associated with molecules that preferentially bind to testosterone-binding globulin. Presence of a 16-hydroxyl group kills the activity of estriol though it contains the biophore.

Plate 8.2. (right) Two significant biophores associated with molecules that preferentially bind to corticosteroid-binding globulin.

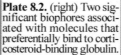

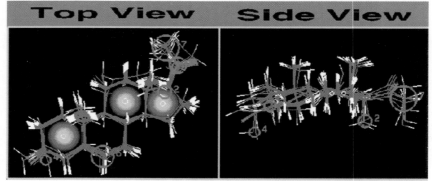

Plate 8.3. Testosterone-binding globulin 3D QSAR model with simple biophore and seven independent variables. Both a top and side view are given to show the secondary sites on the alpha side of the steroids more clearly.

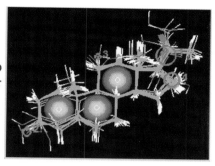

Plate 8.4. Corticosteroid-binding globulin 3D QSAR model with simple biophore and four independent variables.

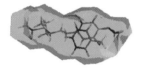

a

b

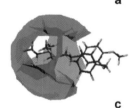

c

d

Plate 9.1. Molecular fields calculated for compound **10g** (see Figure 9.1) plotted as contours (left) and discretely sampled at lattice points (right) for steric (top) and electrostatic (bottom) fields. (See explanation on page 153.)

Plate 9.2. Standardization of conformers by reflection through a common plane. (See explanation on page 160.)

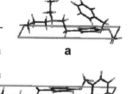

a

b

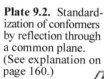

c

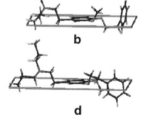

d

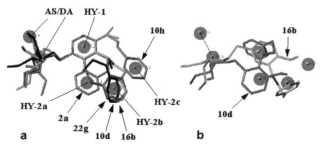

AS/DA HY-1

10h

HY-2a

2a

22g 10d 16b

HY-2b

HY-2c

10d

16b

a

b

Plate 9.3. (**a**) Manual alignment of five structurally diverse active analogs used to generate Query 1. (**b**) Matching conformations found by the UNITY flexible search engine.

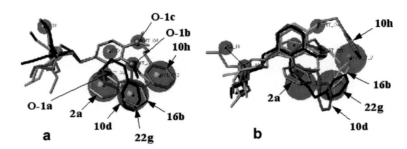

Plate 9.4. (a) Query 2 with overlaid exemplars; only the features not present in Query 1 are labeled here. The trio (**O-1a, O-1b,** and **O-1c**) of oxygen atoms are tied together via a partial match search constraint (one or two are matched in each hit). (b) Conformations of template molecules identified in the UNITY flexible search based on Query 2.

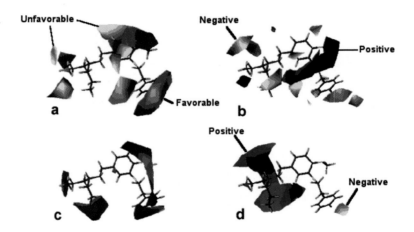

Plate 9.5. Molecular fields from the CoMFA model based on the Query 2 alignment superimposed on **10g** for reference. (See explanation on page 164.)

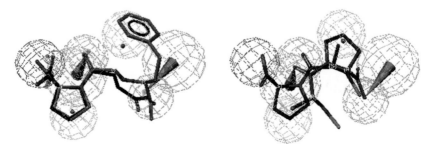

Plate 10.1. Enalapril (*grey*) and Succinyl-proline (*black*) mapped on **Hypo4.**

Plate 10.2. Captopril (*magenta*) and Enantio-captopril (*blue*) mapped on **Hypo4.**

Color code for the spheres:
Cyan: Hydrophobic;   Green: HB Acceptor;   Blue: Negative Ionizable

Plate 12.1. The hypotheses considered for merging: 5HT3.1 on the left and 5HT3.5 on the right.

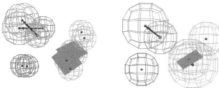

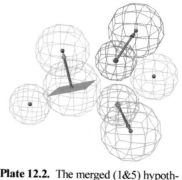

Plate 12.2. The merged (1&5) hypothesis for *selectivity*.

Plate 12.3. The hypotheses HT3.6 and HT3.9 aligned before merger (on the left) and after merger (on the right).

Plate 12.4. Mapping of LY278584 to the merged 6&9 query.

Plate 12.5. The Receptor-ligand hydrogen-bonding positions between methotrexate and DHFR in the X-ray crystal structure of the complex (4dfr).

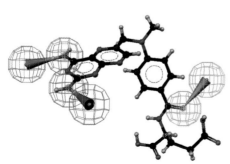

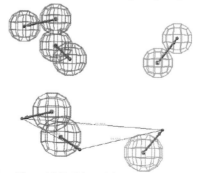

Plate 12.6. Pharmacophore query based on the bound conformation of methotrexate (mapped onto the query).

Plate 12.7. Ligand-based query (top) and receptor-based query (bottom).

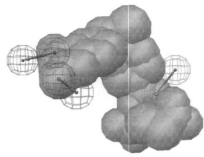

Plate 12.8. Shape query based on methotrexate bound conformation in DHFR.

Plate 12.9. Merged shape and pharmacophore query.

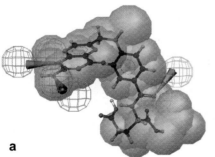

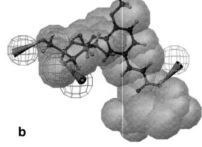

a

b

Plate 12.10. (a) Folate is retrieved with the final merged query. Because folate is listed
as leukocyte and erythrocyte stimulant in the database, it is retrieved as false positive.
However, clearly this can be considered as a correct hit since folate is a substrate for DHFR;
(b) Commercially available chemical from Sigma, a substrate for beta-galactosidase, retrieved from ACD. CAS Registry No: 70622-78-5.

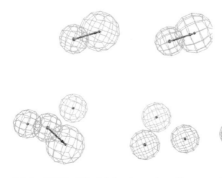

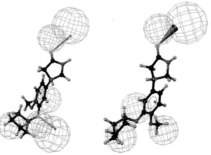

Plate 12.11. The highest scoring diverse
(left) and similar (right) pharmacophore
models obtained from diverse and similar
PDE training sets.

Plate 12.12. Rolipram is mapped onto both
pharmacophore models: Pharmacophore
obtained from the diverse set is on the left,
and similar set is on the right.

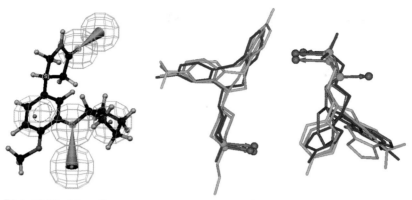

Plate 12.13. Manually generated pharmacophore mapped on to the lowest energy conformation of Rolipram.

Plate 13.1. Flo96 models, D2 (left) and SSRI (right). All conformational energies are within 1 kcal/mol of the global minimum. Note the disagreement in site point direction between sertraline and the other three SSRIs.

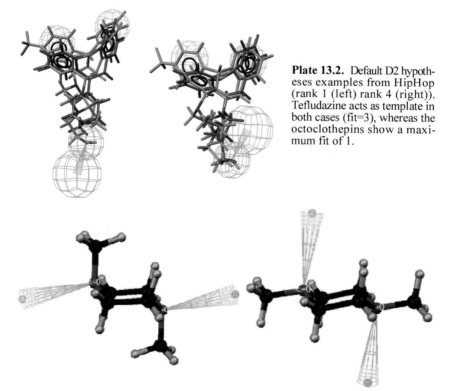

Plate 13.2. Default D2 hypotheses examples from HipHop (rank 1 (left) rank 4 (right)). Tefludazine acts as template in both cases (fit=3), whereas the octoclothepins show a maximum fit of 1.

Plate 13.3. Catalyst conformations and energies for 1,4-dimethylpiperazine (left =3.4 kcal/mol) (right=1.8 kcal/mol). Presumably, the poling forces seek to place features as far from each other as possible. This is not consistent with the most favorable ring conformation of piperazine (right).

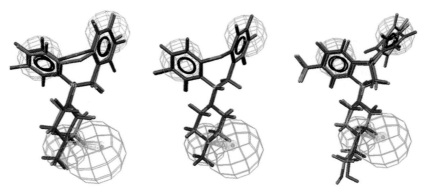

Plate 13.4. MM3* conformations (*red*) fitted to the reference hypothesis and compared to the reference conformations (*green*). From left: (*R*)-octoclothepin (fit=2.5), (*S*)-octoclothepin (fit=2.9) and tefludazine (fit=2.9).

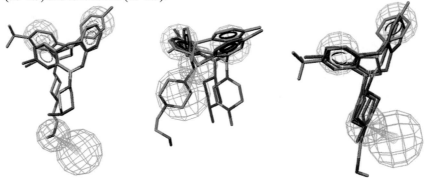

Plate 13.5. Right: Highest ranking HipHop hypothesis based on the MM3* conformational model (octoclothepin barely fit). Middle: Even the uncommon octoclothepin sulfur atom has a higher priority than the common nitrogen, rank 6 (middle). Left: The perfect hypothesis generated by adjustment of the principal and the SuperpositionError parameter (all have fits above 2.6).

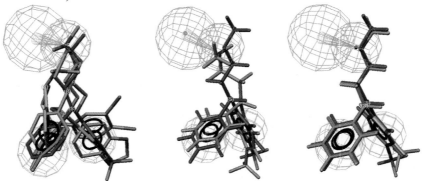

Plate 13.6. The successful SSRI model (right); (fit/energy kcal/mol) Fluoxetine (2.6/0.0), Citalopram (3.0/0.2), Paroxetine (2.5/0.0), and Sertraline (1.3/6.6). The middle picture shows "best fit" of fluoxetine (2.7/9.8) vs. the "correct" one (2.6/0.0) (left).

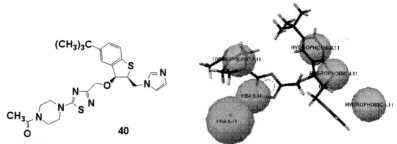

Plate 14.1. Best conformation of **40**, *cis*-isomer, flexibly fit to the lowest-cost Catalyst generated FPT hypothesis. Reprinted with permission from reference[16] in Chapter 14. © 1997 American Chemical Society.

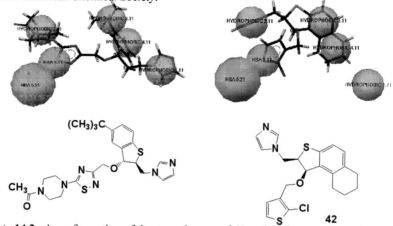

Plate 14.2. A conformation of the *trans*-isomer of **40** and the best conformation of **42** flexibly fit to the lowest-cost Catalyst generated FPT hypothesis. Reprinted with permission from reference[16] in Chapter 14. © 1997 American Chemical Society.

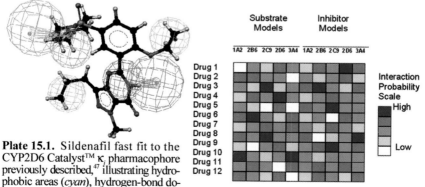

Plate 15.1. Sildenafil fast fit to the CYP2D6 Catalyst™ κ_i pharmacophore previously described,[47] illustrating hydrophobic areas (*cyan*), hydrogen-bond donor (*purple*), and a hydrogen- bond acceptor feature (*green*) with a vector in the direction of the putative hydrogen-bond donor.

Plate 15.2. A theoretical matrix output for interaction probability derived from *in silico* drug metabolizing enzyme 3D QSAR models.

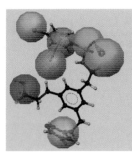

Plate16.1. (left) Compound 16-11 aligned on the lowest cost pharmacophore generated for TXRA antagonist (Tol=1.8 Å). (r =0.89, total cost=114.94, error cost=96.14.)

Plate 16.2. (right) Active Thromboxane Synthase Inhibitors mapped on the highest score common feature pharmacophore.

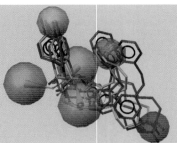

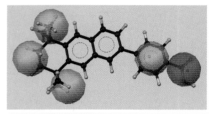

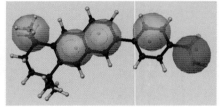

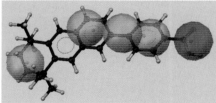

Plate 16.3. Compound 4 mapped on the best hypothesis found for each class of retinoic acid receptor.

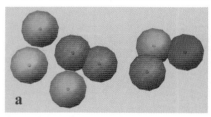

Plate 16.4. Comparing the pharmacophores to analyze the alpha/beta (**a**) and alpha/gamma (**b**) selectivity. (**a**) *orange:* specific to the beta subtype; *green:* specific to the alpha subtype. (**b**) *orange:* specific to the gamma subtype; *green:* specific to the alpha subtype.

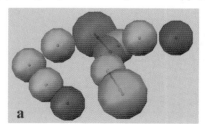

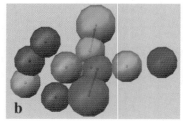

Plate 16.5. Subtype selectivity by comparing the hypotheses. (**a**) alpha/beta selectivity; (**b**) alpha/gamma selectivity.

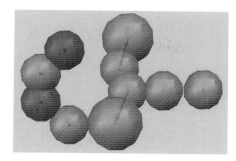

Plate 16.6. Alpha versus Beta/Gamma subtype selectivity.

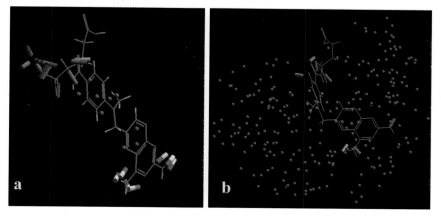

Plate 16.7. Queries generated by the Structure-Based Focusing module in Cerius2. (**a**) mapped on MTX (*blue:* HBD, *Red:* HBA); (**b**) Clusters and Exclusion spheres (*colored by clusters*).

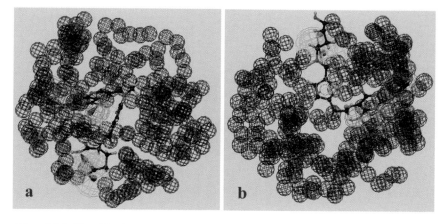

Plate 16.8. Two hits from Derwent WDI: Methotrexate (**a**) and AG-2032 (**b**) mapped on Hypo7.

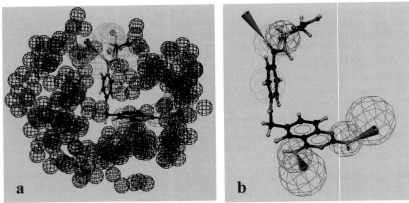

Plate 16.9. Fluorasquin mapped on Hypo3 (**a**) and Hypo10 (**b**).

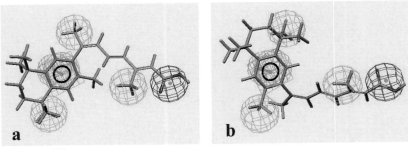

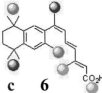

Plate 17.1. (**a**) The first hypothesis gives an estimated RXRα $K_i = 0.88$ for the *blue* mapping. (**b**) The first hypothesis gives an estimated $K_i = 3.2$ nM for the *red* mapping. (**c**) The *green* features are mapped in both orientations.

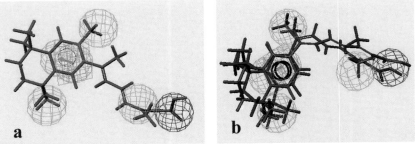

Plate 17.2. (**a**) RXRa3.1 maps best to the C-3' methyl group on the naphthyl ring for an all-*trans* olefin compound. (**b**) RXRa3.1 maps the all-*trans* olefin compound (*red*), without a C-3' methyl group, missing the C-3 olefin methyl contact, while compound **3** (*blue*) maps to all features.

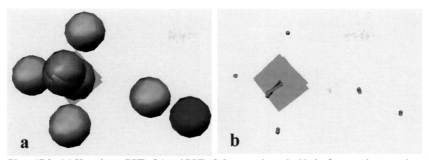

Plate 17.3. (**a**) Hypotheses RXRα3.1 and RXRα3.6 are overlapped with the feature tolerances shown (**b**) The first (*blue*) and sixth (*red*) hypotheses feature centroids overlap four common features.

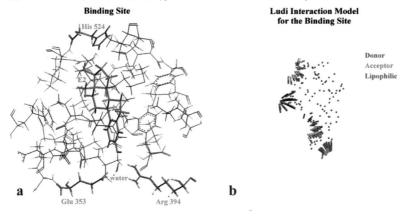

Plate 18.1. (**a**) Binding site of ERα. Residues within 9.0 Å of the bound E2 ligand's geometric center are shown. Three residues and a crystallographic water molecule thought to be important for hydrogen-bonding are labeled and displayed with heavier lines. The bound E2 ligand colored red and drawn with heavier lines is also displayed. (**b**) Ludi interaction model for the ERα binding site. Donor features are displayed as *blue* and *white* rays, acceptors as *gray* and *red* rays, and lipophilic features as *gray* spheres.

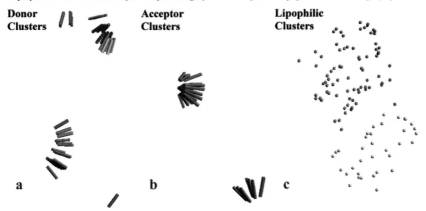

Plate 18.2. Clustering of the interaction model features by type. For clarity in distinguishing between the clusters, plates have been magnified and slightly rotated from the other plates. (**a**) Four donor clusters. (**b**) Two acceptor clusters. (**c**) Four lipophilic clusters.

Cluster Centers of Interaction Model
(Overlaid on the E2 Ligand)

His 524

Gly 521

Thr 347

Leu 346

Glu 353

Arg 394

H₂O

4 Donor
2 Acceptor
4 Lipophilic

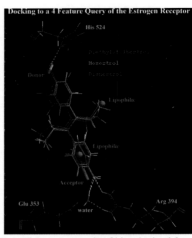

Docking to a 4 Feature Query of the Estrogen Receptor

Plate 18.3. Cluster centers of the interaction model overlayed on the bound E2 ligand. The features have been labeled with their assigned numbers to allow for comparison with Table 18.1. The numbers are colored by feature type and each hydrogen bond donor and acceptor is labeled with the receptor residue number which produced that feature.

Plate 18.5. An example of hits obtained for a 4-feature query. Docked conformations of the three most active ligands examined in this study are shown with the features of the query which retrieved them. Also shown with yellow dashed lines are the hydrogen bonds formed between the docked conformations and several receptor residues.

Hits File MDL SD Format	Donor	Acceptor	Comprising the Query Lipophilic	Diethylstilbestrol	Hexestrol	Dienestrol	E2	Coumestrol	Estrone	17α-estradiol	Moxestrol	β-zearalanol	Estriol	4-hydroxy-E2	2-hydroxy-E2	5-androstenediol	Genistein	3β-androstanediol	Norethynodrel	4-androstenedione	3α-androstanediol	Norethindrone	BisphenolA	5α-dihydrotestosterone	Dehydroepiandosterone	Nandrolone	Methoxychlor	Testosterone	Progesterone	Represented
feat4_112.sd	2		2,3,4	1	1	1	0	0	0	0	0	0	0	0	0	0	0	0	0	0	0	0	0	0	0	0	0	0	3
feat4_159.sd	4	2	1,3	1	1	1	1	0	0	1	0	0	0	0	0	0	0	0	0	0	0	0	0	0	0	0	0	0	5
feat4_166.sd	4		1,3,4	1	1	0	1	0	0	1	0	0	1	0	1	0	0	0	0	0	0	0	0	0	0	0	0	0	6
feat4_181.sd		2	2,3,4	1	1	0	0	0	0	0	0	0	0	0	0	0	0	0	0	0	0	0	0	0	0	0	0	0	2
4 Feature Totals				5	21	4	15	1	2	7	0	0	11	11	7	6	3	8	1	7	6	0	18	0	2	0	0	0	0
feat5_100.sd	1	1	2,3,4	0	1	0	0	0	0	0	0	0	0	0	0	0	0	0	0	0	0	0	0	0	0	0	0	0	1
feat5_134.sd	2,4		1,3,4	1	1	0	1	0	0	1	0	0	1	0	0	0	0	0	0	0	1	1	0	0	0	0	0	0	7
feat5_188.sd	4	2	1,3,4	0	0	0	1	0	0	1	0	0	0	0	0	0	0	0	0	0	0	0	0	0	0	0	0	0	2
feat5_195.sd	1		1,2,3,4	0	1	1	0	0	0	0	0	0	0	0	0	0	0	0	0	0	0	0	0	0	0	0	0	0	2
5 Feature Totals				1	1	1	3	6	0	1	2	0	0	3	3	0	1	0	2	0	2	2	0	5	0	0	0	0	0
feat6_90.sd	1	1	1,2,3,4	0	1	0	0	0	0	0	0	0	0	0	0	0	0	0	0	0	0	0	0	0	0	0	0	0	1
feat6_106.sd	2,3		1,2,3,4	0	0	1	0	0	0	0	0	0	0	0	0	0	0	0	0	0	0	0	0	0	0	0	0	0	1
feat6_132.sd	3	1	1,2,3,4	0	1	0	0	0	0	0	0	0	0	0	0	0	0	0	0	0	0	0	0	0	0	0	0	0	1
feat6_138.sd	4	1	1,2,3,4	0	1	0	0	0	0	0	0	0	0	0	0	0	0	0	0	0	0	0	0	0	0	0	0	0	1
6 Feature Totals				0	3	1	0	0	0	0	0	0	0	0	0	0	0	0	0	0	0	0	0	0	0	0	0	0	0

Ligands with Decreasing RBA →

COLORS: steroids, synthetic estrogens, phytoestrogens, industrial chemicals

Plate 18.4. Examples of hits obtained for individual queries. A value of "0" indicates that no hits were obtained for the particular ligand with that particular query. A value of "1" indicates that there were hits for 1 or more conformations of the particular ligand with that particular query. The "Represented" column indicates the number of ligands which had hits for a particular query. The "Totals" rows indicate the number of queries which produced hits for a particular ligand.

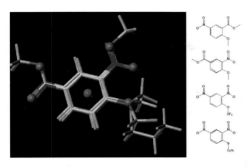

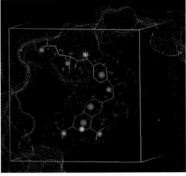

Plate 19.1. Example of database conformers with a common three-dimensional pharmacophore fingerprint overlayed for pharmacophore based docking. Acceptor points are colored *red* and ring centroids *purple*. The two-dimensional structures of the overlayed conformers are depicted on the right.

Plate 19.2. A set of approximately 100 site points generated with MCSS2SPTS for the DHFR structure. Acceptor sites are colored *red*, donor sites *blue*, dual sites which can match both acceptors and donors *yellow*, and ring centroids *purple*. Spheres indicate site points which overlay with similar features in MTX bound to DHFR. MTX is shown colored by element, a molecular surface for DHFR is in *white*, and the box used for the MCSS and subsequent DOCK calculations is in *orange*.

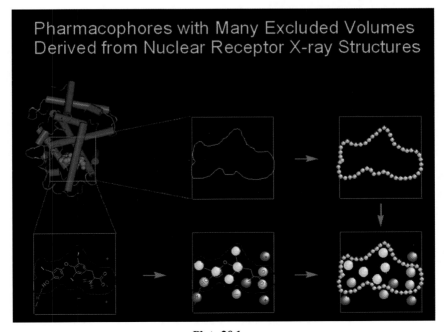

Pharmacophores with Many Excluded Volumes
Derived from Nuclear Receptor X-ray Structures

Plate 20.1.

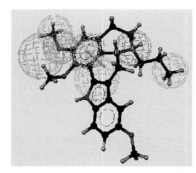

Plate 21.1. The docking-derived α_{1A} pharmacophore with IQC mapped (without excluded volumes). The mesh spheres are location constraints and are color-coded according to the feature (*blue*: hydrophobic group; *red*: positive ion; *brown*: aromatic ring [larger sphere depicts the interacting aromatic system on the protein, blue grid the plane of the aromatic system on the ligand]; *green*: H-bond acceptor [the larger sphere again depicts the location of the interacting group on the protein]). The atoms of IQC are color-coded according to element type (*black*: carbon; *white*: hydrogen; *red*: oxygen; *blue*: nitrogen). Reprinted with permission from reference[33] in Chapter 21. © 1999 Molecular Simulations Inc.

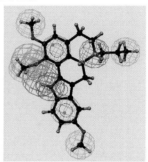

Plate 21.2. The docking-derived α_{1A} pharmacophore with excluded volumes. The features are shown as solid spheres. *Black* spheres: excluded volumes. (Other colors: see Plate 21.1.)

Plate 21.3. The docking-derived α_{1B} pharmacophore with IQC mapped (without excluded volumes). For colors see Plate 21.1 with the following addition: The *light blue* spheres define aromatic hydrophobic groups, and the *purple* spheres are location constraints for an H-bond donor (smaller sphere on the ligand, larger sphere on the protein.)

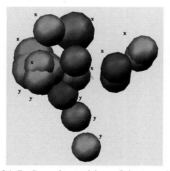

Plate 21.4. The docking-derived α_{1B} pharmacophore with excluded volumes. (See Plates 21.1, 21.2, and 21.3 for colors and symbols.)

Plate 21.5. Superimposition of the two docking-derived pharmacophores. (See Plates 21.1 and 21.3 for explanation of the symbols.)
x: Common features for both pharmacophores,
y: Features unique to the α_{1B} pharmacophore,
z: Features unique to the α_{1A} pharmacophore.

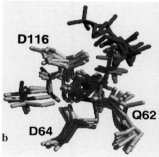

a

b

D116

Q62

D64

Plate 22.1. (a) The process for overlaying the binding sites from the MUSIC studies using methanol molecules to determine the binding sites for hydroxyl groups within the active site of HIV-1 integrase. Each cluster from the MUSIC simulation is represented by its probe with the most favorable interaction energy. D64, D116, Q62, and the magnesium ion from the MD structures are shown in *gray* (the magnesium ion was not present during the MUSIC calculations but was used to overlay the active sites of the 11 snapshots from the MD simulations). The methanol are colored from *dark blue* to *yellow* to *bright red* in order of the time reference from the MD simulations (0-500 ps at 50 ps intervals). (b) The final overlay, seen at the far right in a, is shown with all six positions for hydrogen-bond donors highlighted in different colors. The color-coding in b does not correspond to the color-coding in a except that D64, D116, Q62, and the magnesium ion are still shown in *gray*.

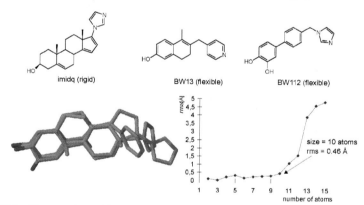

imidq (rigid)

BW13 (flexible)

BW112 (flexible)

HO

HO

HO

OH

size = 10 atoms
rms = 0.46 Å

Plate 23.1. The superimposition of three P450c17 (human) inhibitors and the corresponding Pareto diagram of the best GA run out of 40 runs.

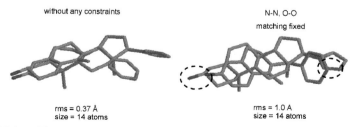

without any constraints

N-N, O-O

matching fixed

rms = 0.37 Å
size = 14 atoms

rms = 1.0 A
size = 14 atoms

Plate 23.2. Different superimpositions of two cytochrome P450c17 (human) inhibitors. The left one (imidq, flexible) has been performed without any restrictions; in the right one (BW13, flexible) the nitrogens and hydroxyl groups are required to appear in every match list.

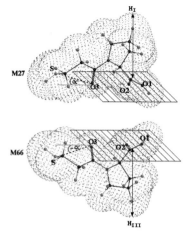

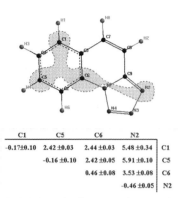

C1	C5	C6	N2	
-0.17±0.10	2.42 ±0.03	2.44 ±0.03	5.48 ±0.34	C1
	-0.16 ±0.10	2.42 ±0.05	5.91 ±0.10	C5
		0.46 ±0.08	3.53 ±0.08	C6
			-0.46 ±0.05	N2

Plate 24.2. The active fragment (pharmacophore) responsible for rice blast activity contains four directly nonbonded atoms, more precisely, four charges situated at distances shown in the submatrix of activity (ECSA). Reprinted with permission from reference[12] in Chapter 24. © 1999 Kluwer Academic Publishers.

Plate 24.1. Illustration to chirality influence on the activity: Compound M27[14] has the groups H_I and a positive angle α, while for its enantiomer (M66) α is negative and it has the H_{III} group but not H_I. Reprinted with permission from reference[14] in Chapter 24. © 1999 American Chemical Society.

Plate 25.1. Example overlap of several ACE inhibitors using Sculpt Paste Overlap with additional manual tethers.

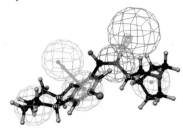

Plate 26.1. The top scoring HypoGen pharmacophore aligned to the most active compound in the training set. The purple feature with two blobs corresponds to the hydrogen-bond donor. The other feature with two blobs corresponds to the ring aromatic group and the remaining features are hydrophobic groups.

Plate 26.2. The top scoring variable tolerance pharmacophore aligned to the most active compound in the training set. The red, single blob feature on the right corresponds to the positive ionizable group. The other single blob features correspond to the hyprophobic groups and the feature with two blobs corresponds to the hydrogen-bond acceptor.

Plate 26.3. The top scoring variable weight pharmacophore aligned to the most active compound in the training set. The feature types are identical to the variable tolerance pharmacophore model. The weights are 2.6, 2.0, 2.0, and 2.6, respectively, beginning with the hydrogen-bond acceptor group, moving clockwise to the positive ionizable group and continuing clockwise to the remaining hydrophobic groups.

tive approach to the arithmetic average method that is applied to *GH* calculations. The authors also recognize one of the referees' comments that have helped improve the analysis presented in this chapter.

References

1. *MACCS-Drug Data Report (MDDR)* and *Comprehensive Medicinal Chemistry (CMC)* are drug databases available from MDL Information Systems, Inc. San Leandro, CA, USA.

2. *Dictionary of Drugs*, formerly available from Chapman & Hall; now from Healthworks Ltd., Leeds, UK.

3. *World Drug Index (WDI)*, available from Derwent Information Ltd. London, UK.

4. Martin YC, Bures MG, Willett P: **Searching databases of three-dimensional structures.** In: *Reviews in Computational Chemistry,* Vol. 1, Lipkowitz KB, Boyd DB, eds. New York: VCH Publishers, 1990:213-263.

5. Güner OF, Henry DR, Pearlman RS: **Use of flexible queries for searching conformationally flexible molecules in databases of three-dimensional structures.** *J Chem Inf Comput Sci* 1992, **32**:101-109.

6. Haraki KS, Sheridan RS, Venkataraghavan R, Dunn DA, McCulloch R: **Looking for pharmacophores in 3-D databases: does conformational searching improve the yield of actives?** *Tetrahedron Comp Meth* 1990, **3**(6C):565-573.

7. Van Drie JH: **3D database searching in drug discovery.** In: *Network Science,* Vol. 1, Issue 3, 1995; http://www.netsci.org/Science/Cheminform/feature06.html

8. Sprague PW, Hoffmann R: **CATALYST pharmacophore models and their utility as queries for searching 3D databases.** In: *Computer Assisted Lead Finding and Optimization—Current Tools for Medicinal Chemistry.* Van de Waterbeemd H, Testa B, Folkers G, eds. Basel: VHCA, 1997:230-240.

9. Güner OF, Hoffmann R, Li H: **Techniques and strategies in 3D data mining.** In: *Report by Wendy A. Warr on 217th ASC National Meeting and Exposition, Anaheim, California, March 12-25, 1999.* London: Wendy Warr & Associates:1999:50-53.

10. Henry DR, Güner OF: **Techniques for searching databases of three-dimensional (3D) structures with receptor-based queries.** In: *Electronic Conference on Trends in Organic Chemistry (ECTOC-1).* Rzepa HS, Goodman JM, eds. Royal Society of Chemistry publications (1995). http://www.ch.ic.ac.uk/ectoc/papers/guner/

11. Brown RD, Martin YC: **Use of structure-activity data to compare structure-based clustering methods and descriptors for use in compound selection.** *J Chem Inf Comput Sci* 1996, **36**:572-584.

12. Kaufman L. and Rousseeu P. J: *Finding Groups in Data—An Introduction to Cluster Analysis.* New York: Wiley, 1990:280-311.

13. Haberman SJ, Gulila Z: **The analysis of multivariate contingency tables by restricted canonical and restricter association models.** *J Amer Stat Assoc* 1988, **83**:760-771.

14. Henry DR, Miller MA, and Güner OF: **Optimization of pharmacophore search queries for structure-based drug design.** *ACS, 213th National Meeting,* April 13-17, 1997, paper COMP-39.

12

Strategies for Database Mining and Pharmacophore Development

Osman F. Güner, Marvin Waldman,
Rémy Hoffmann, and Jong-Hoon Kim

Abstract

Three-dimensional (3D) database searching is an essential part of a computational chemistry operation in the pharmaceutical and agrochemical industry. While the primary objective of 3D searching is to identify new leads and new classes of compounds that possess desired biological activities, the technique is also used in focusing combinatorial libraries. The ability to ask "good" questions in a 3D searching experiment is very important as the quality of the results depend heavily on the quality of the search query. We are proposing a way to determine if the query (question) is good or not based on evaluation of search results that are performed in a drug database with known biological activities. In this paper, we present several database search scenarios where each scenario is complemented with several alternative queries or search strategies. The performance of each query is analyzed using various metrics, including percent yield ($\%Y$), percent ratio of actives ($\%A$), Enrichment (E), and Goodness of Hit list (GH). A rich set of strategies for developing pharmacophore models and database search techniques are proposed. The strengths and weaknesses of each database searching technique are discussed.

12

Strategies for Database Mining and Pharmacophore Development

Osman F. Güner,[†] Marvin Waldman,[†]
Rémy Hoffmann,[‡] and Jong-Hoon Kim[∇]

[†]*Molecular Simulations Inc., San Diego, California*
[‡]*Molecular Simulations SARL, Parc Club Orsay Université,
Orsay Cédex, France*

[∇]*Cheil Jedang Inc., Ichon-si, Kyonggi-do, South Korea*

12.1. Introduction

The following metrics are used to analyze the hit lists, where D is the database domain (number of compounds in the database), A is the number of active compounds in the database, H_t is the number of compounds in a hit list, and H_a is the number of active compounds in a hit list.

Percent yield of actives (%Y):

$$\%Y = \frac{H_a}{H_t} \times 100$$

The percentage of the known actives in the hit list. The higher the value, the more selective the query. The false positives ($H_t - H_a$) in the hit list may include compounds that are potentially active; hence, higher yields provide fewer but of higher quality potential leads.

Percent ratio of the actives in the hit list (%A):

$$\%A = \frac{H_a}{A} \times 100$$

The percentage of the known active compounds retrieved. The higher the value, the more coverage. The list of actives may include compounds from different classes or compounds that may bind in a different mode. Hence, it is usually not possible to retrieve all of the compounds, and higher coverage may be obtained only by compromising the selectivity.

Enrichment or Enhancement (E):

$$E = \left(\frac{H_a/H_t}{A/D} \right) = \frac{H_a \times D}{H_t \times A}$$

Indicates how many times more enriched the hit list is, with respect to the database domain. For example, an enrichment value of 2 indicates that it is two times more probable that one can randomly pick an active compound from the hit list then that from the database.

Goodness of Hit list (GH):

$$GH = \left(\frac{H_a(3A + H_t)}{4H_t A} \right) \times \left(1 - \frac{H_t - H_a}{D - A} \right)$$

Weighted linear combination of %Y and %A. Usually these two parameters compete with each other (i.e., an increase in one of the parameters results in the decrease of the other). This weighted formula provides us with the ability to compare hit lists obtained from alternative methods. The formula works best if the comparison is made within the same domain, i.e., the same database (see Chapter 11).

12.2. Methods

All of the 3D searches presented in this paper are performed with the Catalyst software[1] and using the BEST flexible searching technique unless otherwise noted. Searches are performed at Derwent's World Drug Index (WDI)[2] to obtain a hit list (H_t) and the number of active percent yield of actives (%Y), percent ratio of the actives in the hit list (%A), the enrichment (E), and the Goodness of Hit list (GH) are calculated and the results are analyzed based on these parameters.

We used 96-4 version of Derwent's WDI in this project. The database contains 48,405 compounds (D=48,405). The number of active compounds in the database is determined either by a keyword search at the Activity Keyword (PT) field, or the Mechanism of Action (MA) field. Since 9,776 compounds in the database have empty PT field and of the 38,629 remaining compounds, 3,393 are listed as TRIAL-PREP with no other activity information, we decided to set our domain to those compounds that have non-empty MA field (D=10,318) instead. Hence, all of the searches presented in this paper use a 10,318 subset of WDI, and the active compounds are identified with a keyword search on the Mechanism of Action (MA) field. Note that a "false positive" in a hit list does not necessarily means that the compound is inactive: It means that the compound is not listed for the specific activity that we are interested in. In fact, those false positives may contain our potential new leads.

12.3. Results and Discussion

12.3.1. Use of Query Clustering and Merging

In a typical project, one can manually develop several pharmacophore models (or hypotheses). With the more automated pharmacophore development tools, such as HipHop,[3-4] one can easily get dozens of different pharmacophore models. It is possible to post-process these models and merge them to have a better representation of the ligand-receptor interaction. Query clustering tools can be used to analyze the variation in the models to help decide which ones to merge. Two different strategies can be applied for pharmacophore merging:

1. Improve the ratio of known actives in a hit list. With a higher yield of actives, one can have more confidence in a query that it will retrieve potential leads from a database of compounds with unknown activities. For this objective, you should try to merge two queries that have some common features but are reasonably different (i.e., select queries from different clusters).

2. Maximize the number of actives in a hit list. With a higher number of active compounds in your hit list, you are generalizing your query to allow compounds that may be in different classes. For this objective, you should try to merge two queries that are reasonably similar (i.e., from the same cluster).

We applied these techniques to the hypotheses obtained for 5-HT3 antagonists based on a training set of 23 antagonists with an activity range between 0.2 to 1400 nM. Using the top hypothesis, one gets a correlation of 0.8275 with respect to predicted vs. actual activities.

Hypotheses were obtained using the default HypoGen settings in the Catalyst program. Table 12.1 is the result of "average linkage" clustering of these 10 hypotheses.

Table 12.1. Cluster Analysis results for the top ten 5HT3 hypotheses.

Number of Clusters	2	3	4	5	6	7	8	9
5HT3.1	1	1	1	1	1	1	1	1
5HT3.2	2	2	2	2	2	2	2	2
5HT3.6	2	2	2	2	2	2	2	3
5HT3.9	2	2	2	2	2	2	2	3
5HT3.5	2	2	3	3	3	3	3	4
5HT3.3	2	3	4	4	4	4	4	5
5HT3.7	2	3	4	4	4	5	5	6
5HT3.10	2	3	4	4	4	5	6	7
5HT3.4	2	3	4	5	5	6	7	8
5HT3.8	2	3	4	5	6	7	8	9

If we are seeking higher selectivity (objective 1), then we should consider merging 5HT3.1 with any one of the other nine hypotheses (see column 2 that places 5HT3.1 into one cluster and the rest into another). If we are seeking higher coverage (objective 2), then we should consider merging, for example, 5HT3.6 and 5HT3.9 (see the last column at Table 12.1 where the two hypotheses are still in the same cluster).

We pursued both objectives. Upon comparison of 5HT3.1 with the other nine hypotheses, we identified 5HT3.5 as a good compliment. The merging of these two hypotheses results in a 5-feature query. Plate 12.1 displays 5HT3.1 and 5HT3.5.

The hypotheses contain color-coded chemical features. The diameters of the location constraints (spheres) indicate the tolerance: A compound is a hit when it simultaneously satisfies all constraints. The cyan-colored spheres indicate hydrophobic groups, the green-colored feature indicates a surface accessible hydrogen bond acceptor group and the direction of the hydrogen bond, the purple-colored object indicates a hydrogen-bond donor group and the direction of the bond, and the orange-colored object indicates an aromatic ring and the ring plane. The detailed chemical definition of these features has been published.[5]

Plate 12.2 displays the merged hypothesis (obtained by merging the two hypotheses with 1.2 Angstroms tolerance).

Following the second objective (i.e., merging similar queries to increase coverage), we merged the hypotheses HT3.6 and HT3.9. These are the two most similar hypotheses per cluster analysis. In this case, we keep the number of features the same and merge all 4 features of one hypothesis with the corresponding ones of the other. Plate 12.3 displays the two hypotheses HT3.6 and HT3.9 before and after merger. On the left, the two hypotheses are overlaid onto each other to show the relative similarity in the models; on the right is a single hypothesis as the result of merger. The merged hypothesis has larger tolerance values for all features (to accommodate both hypotheses), and hence it is expected retrieve a larger hit list. The feature with red color in the merged hypothesis represents a positive ionizable group (i.e., a basic center).

Database searches are performed on the 10,318 (D) compound subset of the 96-4 version of Derwent's WDI. Searching the MA field for the keyword "antiserotonins" we identified that there are 255 active compounds (A) in our database. The results are displayed in Table 12.2.

The merged (1&5) hypothesis retrieved 11 fewer active compounds than the original query (53 instead of 64), while the hit list was 222 compounds fewer. Hence, it performed slightly worse with respect to the original 5HT3.1 query. While the %Y decreased slightly from 3.39%

to 3.18%, the *%A* also decreased slightly from 28.4% to 23.6%. Hence, the results obtained from the merged(1&5) query resulted with a lower *GH* score. In short, the merger of hypotheses 1 & 5 has not improved the quality of the hit list.

Table 12.2. Comparison of results with HT3.1 and the merged queries. Reprinted with permission from reference.[6] © 1999 Wendy Warr & Accociates.

Query	# Actives (Ha)	# Hits (Ht)	%Y	%A	Enrichment (E)	GH score
Database	225	10,318	2.18	100.0	1.0	0
HT3.1	64	1,889	3.39	28.4	1.6	0.079
Mrgd(1&5)	53	1,667	3.18	23.6	1.5	0.070
Mrgd(6&9)	174	3,772	4.61	77.3	2.1	0.147

On the other hand, the impact of merged (6&9) hypothesis is simply astounding. The query retrieved about 1/3 of the database, but more importantly, it retrieved over 3/4 of all the active compounds in the database. The significant increase in the *%A*, with this strategy, was as expected; however, unexpectedly, this increase is accompanied also by an increase in *%Y*. Usually, an increase in *%A* is accompanied by a decrease in *%Y*. In this case, the yield has improved from 3.39 to 4.61, while the percent of actives retrieved increased from 28.4 to a remarkable 77.3. The enrichment (which is directly proportional to the changes in *%Y*) has increased from 1.6-fold to 2.1-fold. Consequently, the *GH* score has increased, fairly dramatically, from 0.079 to 0.147. Clearly, the strategy of merging similar hypotheses, in this particular case, has improved the results considerably. Plate 12.4 displays one of the highly active compounds from the training set, LY278584, a 5HT3 antagonist patented by Eli Lilly. Note the excellent fit of the features of the drug to the constraints in the query.

Why it was possible to manually improve upon a hypothesis that is generated with a fully automated method that takes into consideration the biological activities and uses sophisticated statistical tools to develop a predictive model? The Hypothesis 5HT3.1 correlates reasonably well (r=0.828) with the activities of 23 5HT3 antagonists in the training set. However, we are testing the performance of the hypothesis at a 10,318 compound database that contains a diverse set of compounds. Furthermore, most of the 23 compounds in the training set are not in the database. The 6&9 merged query, for example, correlate the activities of the 23 compounds in the training set rather poorly (r=0.609), however, it performs much better in the full database. One reason for this variance may be that hypotheses 6 and 9 separately represent groups of compounds that are slightly different, whereas the merged query may include a superset, and better represent active compounds that are structurally more diverse. Another reason may be that the training set may be too restrictive in representing the active compounds in the database. The fact that we were able to improve 5HT3.1 is an excellent demonstration that one should consider the machine-generated hypotheses not as the final model, but as a working model that can be improved upon as more information about the problem becomes available.

Based on this single experiment, we have seen that the merging of selected pharmacophore models can improve the quality of the search results, and tools such as pharmacophore clustering and merging can be useful alternative techniques to be added to the repertoire of researchers who are using 3D database searching techniques in drug design.

12.3.2. Receptor-Based versus Ligand-Based Pharmacophore Models

The traditional pharmacophore model development techniques based on a series of known active molecules has been the primary thrust in 3D searching for a long time. Lacking any receptor information, these so-called *analog-based design* methods has been a considerably successful aspect of 3D searching technology. However, with the increasing availability crystal structures of protein-ligand complexes, *structure-based design* is now also possible for the pharmacophore development tasks. We expect that the enhanced pharmacophore models that maintain a precise geometric relationship existing in the receptor site will increase the "novelty" in the hit list, since we are less dependent on the already known series of active compounds.

Drugs that bind to a common receptor do not necessarily have similar functional groups precisely overlapped.[7-8] In such cases, it makes good sense to apply a receptor-based approach to pharmacophore models. The details of this approach have already been published[9] and can be summarized simply as incorporating the geometric relationships of the hydrogen-bonding sites at the receptor active site into the queries' projected points. The primary benefit of this approach is that it opens up the possibility to retrieve compounds that are geometrically novel, i.e., compounds that are not necessarily geometrically similar to the set of known active compounds that the query is originally is based on. This approach is a modification of an otherwise ligand-based query, where the projected points that map onto the receptor active site for hydrogen-bonding interactions are constrained precisely based on receptor geometry.

Consider the complex between methotrexate and dihydrofolate reductase. The active site of DHFR together with methotrexate (in orange color) of the X-ray crystal structure (Brookhaven Protein Databank: 4dfr) is displayed in Plate 12.5. The three hydrogen-bonding interactions between the ligand and the receptor are identified. The distances between the receptor binding sites are displayed. Based on this information, we can manually develop a pharmacophore model by mapping the three hydrogen-bonding features onto the bound conformation of methotrexate. The ligand-based query is displayed in Plate 12.6. The figure displays how the bound conformation of methotrexate fits the query.

This query can be converted into a receptor-based query in two ways: First, the location constraints that represent the site point in the query (i.e., the complementary hydrogen bonding site at receptor) can be removed and replaced by distance constraints centering around the actual distances that we measure in the crystal structure (see Plate 12.5). The second modification involves increase in the size of the location constraint from the default value of 1.5 Å to 2.0 Å for the ligand hydrogen-bonding centers. This change provides the molecules more flexibility with respect to the location of their hydrogen-bonding sites, as long as they can still bind to a fixed location at the receptor site. The two queries are displayed in Plate 12.7, and results are represented in Table 12.3.

We used two slight variations for the receptor-based queries. In Receptor-1, we used distance constraints based on the distances measured from the bound conformation of methotrexate; in Receptor-2, we used distance constraints based on the distances measured at the receptor site. All three queries yield very similar results. A larger number of hits were retrieved with the receptor-based queries, as well as a larger number of active compounds compared to the ligand-based search results. However, the increase in %A and decrease in %Y for receptor-based hit lists cancel each other's effect, and the result is very similar

GH scores. As far as the expected improvement in results with receptor-based queries, the jury is still out. One can argue that since one of the assumed benefits of the receptor-based query is to identify compounds that are geometrically different than the known existing active compounds, testing the quality of the hit list with a database of compounds with known activities is not a good approach. The ultimate success of the quality of the hit list can be measured with the observed experimental results. Fortunately, today it is possibly to apply the *GH* formula to the results of a high throughput screening (HTS) experiment. Hence, most pharmaceutical research groups can quickly validate their proposed hit lists with a follow-up HTS experiment.

Table 12.3. Comparison of results with ligand-based query vs. the receptor-based queries.

Query	# Actives (Ha)	# Hits (Ht)	%Y	%A	Enrichment (E)	GH score
Database	80	10,318	0.78	100.0	1.0	0
Ligand-based	25	1,437	1.74	31.3	2.2	0.079
Receptor-1	28	1,954	1.43	35.0	1.8	0.080
Receptor-2	26	1,816	1.43	32.5	1.8	0.076

12.3.3. Use of Shape versus Pharmacophore versus Merged Pharmacophore/Shape Queries

We use the same bound conformation of methotrexate (from Brookhaven Protein Databank: 4dfr) to construct a shape, pharmacophore, and merged shape/pharmacophore queries to compare and contrast the results. Methotrexate is listed in WDI as a folate-antagonist (Mechanism of Action field), of which there are 80 in WDI.

First we convert the bound conformation of methotrexate into a shape query as shown in Plate 12.8 (methotrexate itself has been mapped onto the query to demonstrate the match) using the default set for the constraints. A search with this query at the 10,318 compound subset of WDI retrieved 2,244 hits, of which 13 are listed as folate-antagonists (%Y= 0.58). Considering that there are 80 compounds in the database also listed as folate antagonists, the percent of actives that are retrieved is 16.25 (%A=16.25); the overall enrichment that the hit list presents $13/2{,}244 \div 80/10{,}318 = 0.8$. The fact that the enrichment value is below 1 indicates that the hit list is poorer (in this case 20% poorer) than the original database with respect to the ratio of active compounds. Clearly, shape search alone is not selective for compounds of specific activity. Therefore, it should either be used as post- or pre-processing of other more chemically relevant searches like pharmacophore searches, or it should be used within a merged pharmacophore/shape query.

Why does the search retrieve a hit list that is poorer than the original database itself with respect to the ratio of actives? Of the 2,244 hits there were only 13 actives. One way of looking at the shape search results is to sort the hits with respect to their similarity values. Hence, compounds that satisfy the shape constraint best will be at the top of the list, and the worst will be at the bottom. We then look at the top 1,000, 500, and 100 compounds in this hit list to see how many of the active compounds are in these groups. Shape similarity is calculated by comparing the volume descriptors of the query and the hits with a Tanimoto-based calculation.[10] Hence one can tighten the hit list is by using a higher similarity cutoff. The default shape similarity value is set to 0.5. Higher similarity cutoff values retrieves a smaller list, but they tend to fit the shape better. The database search results are displayed in the Table 12.4.

Table 12.4. Comparison of results with shape search based on methotrexate bound conformation: top 1000, 500, and 100 compounds.

Query	# Actives (Ha)	# Hits (Ht)	%Y	%A	Enrichment (E)	Similarity Cut-off	GH score
Database	80	10,318	0.78	100.0	1.0	0.0	0
Shape	13	2,244	0.58	16.25	0.8	0.50 (default)	0.035
Top 1,000	10	1,000	1.00	12.50	1.3	0.57	0.035
Top 500	8	500	1.60	10.00	2.1	0.59	0.035
Top 100	5	100	5.00	6.25	6.5	0.62	0.053

The selectivity and enrichment increases gradually as we increase the cutoff value for the Tanimoto similarity. The improvement is not spectacular, but it is consistent. However, because the percent of actives also reduce with the increasing similarity cutoff, the variation in the *GH* score is not much. Only when we look at the top 100 or further does the increase in *%Y* overtake the decrease in *%A* and produce higher *GH* scores. In conclusion, if one must use shape query alone, we recommend higher similarity cutoff values, or evaluation of a smaller part of the hit list that is in the top tier with respect to similarity value. However, a better approach would be to incorporate some chemistry onto the shape that one can obtain by merging a shape query with a pharmacophore query.

How do the shape search results compare with the results obtained from pharmacophore, or merged queries? When developing a pharmacophore-based query, the scientist must make a decision regarding which parts of the molecule are involved in hydrogen bonding or lipophilic interactions. Even with the availability of the bound ligand-receptor complexes, this is a non-trivial decision and there may be several alternative pharmacophore models that could be considered. In this case, we checked close contacts between methotrexate and DHFR as displayed in Plate 12.5 and identified two Hbond-donor points and one acceptor position. Plate 12.6 displays the final pharmacophore-based query overlaid on methotrexate. The search retrieved 1,114 hits, of which 23 are listed as folate-antagonists. The pharmacophore query retrieved a hit list that is about half the size of the one from the shape search, and with about twice the number of actives. Clearly, the pharmacophore search returns superior results (with respect to all four analysis metrics) computed to the shape query alone.

The final search involves the merged query displayed in Plate 12.9. This query not only constrains the shape of the compounds, but also incorporates chemical properties onto the shape. The combination is a very powerful query that focuses our attention to a handful of high quality hits. Search with this query retrieved only 20 hits of which 4 are listed as folate-antagonists.

Let us evaluate the results from these three searches together as listed in Table 12.5.

We see a very dramatic change in the hit list size and profile with these three approaches. The hit list size changes dramatically from 2,244 to 1,144 to 20 with shape, pharmacophore, and merged queries, respectively, while the number of active compounds in these lists change slightly from 13 to 23 to 4. This profile results in a major change in the %Y, as well as the Enrichment. In short, shape search alone has very poor selectivity, unless the top tier is selected based on similarity value. Pharmacophore-based (traditional) searches are much more selective and the hit lists obtained are enriched with respect to the original database configuration. However, the merged shape/pharma-cophore searches are extremely tight and very highly selective. These searches can be very useful when one needs a fast way of retrieving a handful of compounds from a library of thousands. The small hit list in this case of 20 compounds is heavily enriched with respect to folate antagonism. Four active compounds in a list of twenty compounds provide a yield of 20% and 25.8-fold enrichment of the database. This is a very selective hit list. The objective of merged query is to rapidly focus on a few high quality leads. Hence, the 16 compounds that are not listed as folate-antagonist are considered potentially very good leads. Upon investigation of the false positives of the last search, we have identified hits that include compounds like folic acid itself (see Plate 12.10, a). The reason it is considered a false positive is because it is listed as erythrocyte stimulant. In fact, folic acid is the natural substrate of DHFR and the pharmacophore model was correctly able to identify it as a compound that can bind to the DHFR active site. Once one develops such a highly selective query, it is best to try the query out on a database of commercially chemicals or the corporate database, to identify potential leads. Plate 12.10, b, displays a commercially available chemical retrieved with the merged query.

Table 12.5. Comparison of results with shape, pharmacophore, and merged queries with the receptor-based pharmacophore query. Reprinted with permission from reference.[6] © 1999 Wendy Warr & Accociates.

Query	# Actives (Ha)	# Hits (Ht)	%Y	%A	Enrichment (E)	GH score
Database	80	10,318	0.78	100.0	1.0	0
Shape (FAST)	13	2,244	0.58	16.3	0.8	0.035
Pharm. (FAST)	23	1,144	2.01	28.8	2.6	0.077
Merged (FAST)	4	20	20.00	5.0	25.8	0.163

In short, merged pharmacophore/shape queries provide a very powerful means to quickly focus a library of thousands of compounds into a handful of high quality leads.

The objective of optimizing a database search query by improving its performance using a database of compounds with known activities is to use it to retrieve high quality leads from other databases. Once an optimum query is obtained, it can be used to search databases with unknown activities, corporate libraries, or databases of commercially available chemicals to retrieve hit lists that may contain potential leads. The hit lists obtained from searching these corporate or commercial databases are expected to yield a high ratio of potentially active compounds. The better the query (i.e., those with higher *GH* scores), the more likely it is that good leads will be identified from the hit lists obtained from at query. For example, when we take this query and search MDL's Available Chemicals Directory[11] (ACD) with it, we retrieve 27 hits, most of which are either folic acid, methotrexate, aminopterin, or amethopterin derivatives that structurally are very close to methotrexate itself. However, there are also several hits that are structurally very diverse and these hits may constitute different classes of potential leads. Plate 12.10, b displays a hit from ACD, 2-methoxy-4(2-nitrovinyl)-phenyl beta-D-galactopyranoside, which is a chromgenic substrate for beta-galactosidase. It is a commercially available chemical and may be considered a potential lead or a synthetic precursor for a lead.

12.3.4. The Significance of Training Set Selection: Using Similar versus Diverse Compounds

One important aspect of automated pharmacophore model generation is selection of the "training set." To develop a more selective and useful 3D search queries, should we provide the program a series of similar compounds or diverse ones? This is the question that we would like to address in this chapter. We will use rolipram (Figure 12.1), a phosphodiesterase IV inhibitor, as our reference molecule to which similarity and diversity will be based on.

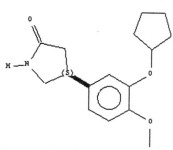

Figure 12.1. Rolipram, a phosphodiesterase IV inhibitor used as a reference molecule for our similarity and diverse selections.

Our test case is phosphodiesterase IV inhibition. We select all the priority patented compounds that specifically cover PDE IV inhibition from the 96-2 version of MDDR.[12] There are 82 compounds in this list. We move these 82 compounds into Cerius[2],[13] where topological descriptors for each of them are computed. The list of compounds is grouped into nine clusters via Ward's hierarchical clustering method; finally the centroid of the nine clusters are isolated to constitute the diverse set of PDE IV inhibitors (Figure 12.2).

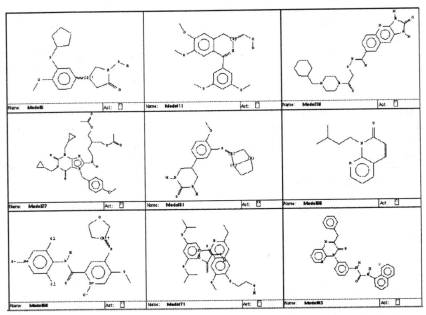

Figure 12.2. The nine most diverse PDE IV inhibitors among the 82 patented compounds.

The similar set is identified based on 2D similarity search using ISIS/Host via Cerius[2].DBAccess.[13] The top eight compounds that are most similar to rolipram are extracted and together with Rolipram constitute the 9 similar compounds (Figure 12.3).

The feature-based alignment of the compounds in each training set is performed by HipHop.[3-4] The top hypotheses obtained from the similar and diverse sets are displayed in Plate 12.11. The one on the left is obtained from the diverse set; one on the right is from the similar set.

Both hypotheses have a somewhat similar set of features. The top hypothesis obtained from the diverse training set has two hydrogen-bond acceptors and two lipophilic groups. However, the third-highest scoring hypothesis has one hydrogen-bond acceptor and three lipophilic groups, much like the top hypothesis obtained from the similar training set.

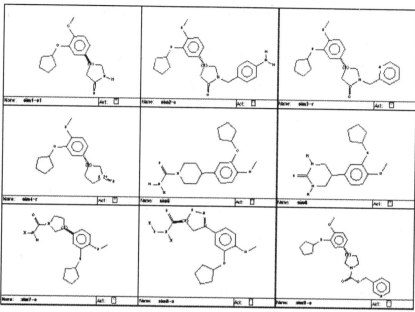

Figure 12.3. The nine most similar PDE IV inhibitors to rolipram.

In the 10,318 compound subset of WDI for which the MA field is filled, there are 207 compounds listed as phosphodiesterase inhibitors. Search with the diverse query retrieved 1,158 hits, of which 62 are known active compounds. Conversely, search with the similar query retrieved 841 hits, of which 48 are listed as phosphodiesterase inhibitors; 35 of these PDE inhibitors are common to both searches. Plate 12.12 displays how rolipram maps to both of these hypotheses. The hit list analysis is provided in Table 12.6.

These results are interesting. First of all, it is clearly expected that the diverse query will retrieve more active compounds than the similar one since the more generic query is based on a set of diverse compounds. The similar query is based on compounds that have identical frames where the primary differentiation is made by substituting different groups to the amide nitrogen in rolipram. Just by eyeballing the compounds in the similar training set, one can visually recognize the pattern and identify the pharmacophoric features. On the other hand, the diverse training set contains compounds with significant topological differences to the extend that it is not possible to identify any pattern visually. Yet HipHop was able come up with a hypothesis that performs very similar to the one obtained from the similar set. It demonstrates one of the benefits of computer-aided design: In those cases where the pharmacophoric pattern is not visually apparent, fully automated computational methods (like HipHop) are very useful.

Table 12.6. Comparison of results with queries obtained from diverse and similar compounds.

Query	*# Actives (Ha)*	*# Hits (Ht)*	*%Y*	*%A*	*Enrichment (E)*	*GH score*
Database	207	10,318	2.01	100.0	1.0	0
Diverse	73	1,589	4.59	35.3	2.3	0.105
Similar	51	986	5.17	24.6	2.6	0.091

Percent yield in the hit lists from diverse search is 4.59%, slightly less than the 5.17% of the similar set. However, the percent of the actives retrieved by the diverse search is 35.3%, about 10% higher than the one obtained from similar set. Because of this, the GH score for the diverse query is higher. This result indicates that when we are faced with selecting candidate compounds for a training set for pharmacophore model building, we should opt for information-rich, structurally diverse compounds as long as they are all binding to the same receptor site.

12.3.5. Manual versus Automated Pharmacophore Model Generation

How do manually generated pharmacophore models compare with the ones obtained from automated tools? Using rolipram (see Figure 12.1), we manually developed a pharmacophore model and compare the search results with the models obtained from the HipHop runs (see previous chapter). The procedure for manual query development involves visual analysis of the compound; identification of pharmacophoric sites; and mapping of chemical features to the pharmacophoric sites. One aspect of this approach is the selection of the conformation of the reference molecule. In the absence of bound conformation, we typically use the lowest energy conformation.

Another aspect is the selection of the pharmacophoric centers. In this case, we used what we have learned from the previous experiment. Therefore, the pharmacophore model that we have manually developed based on the lowest energy conformation of rolipram is similar to the one that came out of HipHop analysis on the diverse training set (see Plate 12.13). Performing searches at WDI resulted with the hits listed in Table 12.7.

Table 12.7. Comparison of results from searches with manual query with queries obtained from diverse and similar compounds.

Query	# Actives (Ha)	# Hits (Ht)	%Y	%A	Enrichment (E)	GH score
Database	207	10,318	2.01	100.0	1.0	0
Diverse BEST	73	1,589	4.59	35.3	2.3	0.105
Similar BEST	51	986	5.17	24.6	2.6	0.091
Manual BEST	66	1,595	4.14	31.9	2.1	0.094

The manual query generated a hit list that is larger than both HipHop queries, with a respect-able yield ($\%Y = 5.06\%$). Its performance is very similar to the performance of the diverse query. Because of fact that rolipram is a semi-rigid small compound, it was possible to manually build pharmacophore models that perform quite well by simply using the global minimum energy conformation of the compound. This approach is especially valid if a bound conformation of the ligand is available. For larger and more flexible compounds, automated systems will probably still be the better choice.

12.3.6. Rigid versus Flexible Searching

The rigid versus flexible searching has been a major issue during the earlier developments of the 3D searching technology. One can deal with the flexibility issue in three areas:

1. Flexibility in the database: storing multiple conformations in the database.[14]

2. Flexibility in the query: use of flexible queries in single conformation databases.[15-16]
3. Flexibility during searching: on-the-fly generation of conformations during search time.[17-18]

Earlier days of the evolving 3D searching technology, the first approach
was abandoned due to combinatorial issue of conformation generation
for flexible molecules and due to difficulties in assuring the bound conformation is stored in the database. The second approach is a viable one,
but has been considered as an interim approach to the conformational
flexibility problem. Hence, once the technology for on-the-fly conformational driving was developed, the third approach was considered the
best approach: storing single conformation in a database and manipulating the conformations during the search.[17-18] At least this was the
case until it was possible to have an adequate representation of the conformational space in databases with multiple conformations.[19-21] This
new capability intrigued us to revisit the first approach and re-evaluate
the relative performances of these methods.

   In this chapter, we compare the results obtained from rigid searches
in multi-conformation database (WDI) to flexible searching in the same
database. The flexible searching method in Catalyst (BEST) involves a
full optimization of compounds on-the-fly, and does not limit the flexibility to torsion space as in the case with other approaches.[13] We use the
same queries that have been developed in the previous four chapters and
conduct flexible searches on the same database. The advantage of the
BEST search is that it will always retrieve more hits than the FAST
search. This is because regardless of how well the conformational space
is represented in the database, there may be some valid hits that will be
missed with the FAST approach, simply because none of the conformations in the database could map to the query. The disadvantage of the
BEST search is that it requires 5-10 times longer CPU time to complete
a search, compared to the FAST approach. The question is how well the
flexible BEST searches compare with the rigid FAST searches with
respect to the metrics that we have used to analyze hit lists throughout
this project. The results are presented in Table 12.8

   In all cases, the BEST search retrieved more hits and more active
compounds. However, when evaluating the performance from the perspective of yields, percent of actives, enrichment and *GH* score, we see
that the FAST search performance is practically equal to the BEST one.

In three out of four cases, the *GH* score difference was in the one-in-one-thousandth range. For all practical purposes, rigid and flexible search produced results of equal quality. Only in one case, the methotrexate-based pharmacophore search, did the flexible searching produced slightly better results (*GH*=0.081 vs. 0.080). In all other cases, the results were either same or slightly in favor of FAST search.

Table 12.8. Fast (rigid) Vs Best (flexible) search results [D=10,318, A=225 for ht3, A=80 for mtx, and A=207 for pde].

Query	# Actives (Ha)	# Hits (Ht)	%Y	%A	Enrichment (E)	GH score
Merged (6&9)-[ht3] FAST	173	3,724	4.65	76.9	2.13	0.147
Merged (6&9) [ht3] BEST	174	3,772	4.61	77.3	2.12	0.147
Pharm [mtx]- FAST	21	476	4.11	26.25	5.69	0.094
Pharm [mtx]- BEST	24	870	2.76	30.00	3.56	0.088
Receptor-1 [mtx] FAST	25	1,335	1.87	31.3	2.42	0.080
Receptor-1 [mtx] BEST	26	1,454	1.79	32.5	2.31	0.081
Similar [pde] FAST	48	841	5.71	23.2	2.84	0.093
Similar [pde] BEST	51	986	5.17	24.6	2.58	0.091
Manual [pde] FAST	61	1,205	5.06	29.5	2.52	0.099
Manual [pde] BEST	66	1,595	4.14	31.9	2.06	0.094

In conclusion, these results indicate that conducting rigid searches in a multi-conformation database produces hit lists that have very similar quality to those produced with flexible searching. Whereas flexible search produces hit lists that are indisputably more complete, it typically requires up to a magnitude of order more CPU resources compared to rigid searching. This study demonstrates that with regards to the ability to fully represent the conformational flexibility in a database via reg-

istering diverse set of conformation, rigid searching provides a performance that is very close to that obtained from a fully flexible searching.

12.4. Conclusions

One of the most important aspects of performing a successful 3D search
is the search query itself. Given a query, 3D search will always retrieve
hits; however, quality of the hit list is depends on how "good" the query
is. In this work we present various strategies to define the query.
Sometimes this query is a hypothesis (i.e., a predictive model), other
times it is a pharmacophore model (i.e., containing the essential elements, of compounds, that are responsible for the biological activity).
Queries can be obtained via fully automated methods, or can be constructed manually, or designed with receptor geometry considerations.
Regardless of the source of the query, one needs to assess the quality of
the query by analyzing the hit lists, and then use the information to
improve the query.

We test the queries by searching a drug database with known biological activities and expect to retrieve the known active compounds from
the database. If we fail to retrieve any of the known active compounds
then, perhaps, our model is not adequately representing the pharmacophore for that therapeutic category (unless we are identifying a
"novel" class of compounds; and this can become apparent once the
experimental screening is done). If we do retrieve some but not all of
the active compounds (which is the most common case), then we use
the *GH* score to compare and improve the queries. We also take advantage of the "imperfect" databases by having a careful look at the "false
positives," because the most likely place to find new leads are within
these false positives. What we mean by the "imperfect" database is the
fact that all of the compounds in the database are not necessarily tested
for all activities, and that the false positives may prove to be active in
one particular category should they be tested for that activity. With the
advent of high throughput screening, it is now possible to send the
entire contents of a hit list and obtain activity data quickly. Therefore,
we recommend that once a query is optimized, it should be used to

search "corporate databases" or databases of available chemicals to retrieve candidates for testing.

While we propose that the strategies described in this paper and the *GH* score assessment of hit lists should be used to optimize the working pharmacophore model at databases with known biological activities, note that the technique can also be used to focus a list of active compounds as a post-HTS processing, or to prioritize a virtual library as a pre-HTS processing.

References

1. *Catalyst v.4.0,* available from Molecular Simulations Inc. San Diego, CA, USA.

2. *World Drug Index v.96.02,* available from Derwent Information Ltd. London, UK

3. Sprague PW: **Automated chemical hypothesis generation and database searching with Catalyst.** In: *Perspectives in Drug Discovery and Design.* Vol. 3. Müller K, ed. Leiden: ESCOM Science Publishers B. V., 1995:1-20.

4. Barnum D, Greene J, Smellie A, Sprague P: **Identification of common functional configurations among molecules.** *J Chem Inf Comput Sci* 1996, **36**:563-571.

5. Greene J, Kahn S, Savoj H, Sprague P, Teig S: **Chemical function queries for 3D database search.** *J Chem Inf Comput Sci* 1994, **34**:1297-1308.

6. Güner OF, Hoffmann R, Li H: **Techniques and strategies in 3D data mining.** In: *Report by Wendy A. Warr on 217th ASC National Meeting and Exposition, Anaheim, California, March 12-25, 1999.* London: Wendy Warr & Associates:1999:50-53.

7. Tintelnot M, Andrews P: **Geometries of functional group interactions in enzyme-ligand complexes Gauges for receptor modeling.** *J Comput-Aid Mol Des* 1989, **3**:67-84.

8. Taylor R, Kennard O, Verschiel, W: **Geometry of the N-H...O=C hydrogen bond. 1. Lone-pair directionality.** *J Am Chem Soc* 1983, **105**:5761-5766.

9. Henry DR, Güner OF: **Techniques for searching databases of three-dimensional (3D) structures with receptor-based queries.** In: *Electronic*

Conference in Trends in Organic Chemistry (ECTOC-1). Rzepa HS, Goodman JM, eds. Royal Society of Chemistry Publications (1995). http://www.ch.ic.ac.uk/ectoc/papers/guner/.

10. Hahn M: **Three-dimensional shape-based searching of conformationally flexible compounds.** *J Chem Inf Comput Sci* 1997, **37**:80-86.

11. MDL Information Systems, Inc. San Leandro, CA, USA.

12. *MACCS Drug Data Report v. 96-2,* available from MDL Information Systems, Inc. San Leandro, CA, USA.

13. *Cerius² version 3.6,* available from Molecular Simulations Inc. San Diego, CA, USA.

14. Murrall NW, Davies EK: **Conformational freedom in 3-D databases.** *J Chem Inf Comput Sci* 1990, **30**:312-316.

15. Güner OF, Henry DR, Pearlman RS: **Use of flexible queries for searching conformationally flexible molecules in databases of three-dimensional structures.** *J Chem Inf Comput Sci* 1992, **32**:101-109.

16. Güner, OF, Henry DR, Moock TE, Pearlman RS: **Flexible queries in 3D searching. 2. Techniques in 3D query formulation.** *Tetrahedron Comput Method* 1990, **3**(6C):557-563.

17. Moock TE, Henry DR, Ozkabak AG, Alamgir M: **Conformational searching in ISIS/3D databases.** *J Chem Inf Comput Sci* 1994, **34**:184-189.

18. Hurst T: Flexible 3D searching: **The directed tweak technique.** *J Chem Inf Comput Sci* 1994, **34**:190-196.

19. Smellie A, Teig,SL, Towbin P: Poling: **Promoting conformational coverage.** *J Comp Chem* 1995, **16**:171-187.

20. Smellie A, Kahn SD, Teig, S: **An analysis of conformational coverage. 1. Validation and estimation of coverage.** *J Chem Inf Comput Sci* 1995, **35**:285-294.

21. Smellie A, Kahn SD, Teig S: **An analysis of conformational coverage. 2. Applications of conformational models.** *J Chem Inf Comput Sci* 1995, **35**:295-304.

13

Pharmacophore Modeling by Automated Methods: Possibilities and Limitations

Morten Langgård, Berith Bjørnholm, and Klaus Gundertofte

Abstract

The core problem in the art of pharmacophore development is the complex task of locating the common spatial pharmacophoric elements among active ligands.

In this study, we have investigated the possibilities and limitations for automated or semi-automated computational methods for pharmacophore development exemplified by the programs Catalyst and Flo96. The discussion is focused on how well the methods can reproduce two well-known pharmacophore models. The philosophy behind the programs as well as the influence of user-controlled options is likewise discussed. The evaluation reveals several possible pitfalls but does also demonstrates the potential of the methods if used correctly.

13

Pharmacophore Modeling by Automated Methods: Possibilities and Limitations

Morten Langgård, Berith Bjørnholm, and Klaus Gundertofte

H. Lundbeck A/S, Copenhagen-Valby, Denmark

13.1. Introduction

Traditionally it has been a tedious and time-consuming job to develop valid pharmacophore models by use of conventional methods. By conventional methods, we mean combined conformational analysis and manual alignment of identified pharmacophores according to the active analogue approach.[1]

In order to deal with the huge amount of data coming from HTS and combinatorial chemistry, some kind of automation of this process is required. This situation has been realized and new concepts for addressing the problem have been developed; some also have been made commercially available.[2,3]

In this study we will evaluate the scope and limitations of a few of these methods. In order to do so, we have chosen the simple path of asking the question: How well can these automated methods reproduce already known "conventional" pharmacophore models?

13.1.1. The Pharmacophore Models

The "conventional" pharmacophore models applied as references are the dopamine (D2) model[4] and the serotonin re-uptake[5] (SSRI) (see Figures 13.1 and 13.2). The D2 model in this study is a core model represented by three key pharmacophore elements derived from a series of papers covering various selectivity aspects of the model in comparison with other monoamine receptor modulators.[6,7] An essential characteristic of the model is that only one set of low-energy conformations for the underlying enantiomers of octoclothepine (Figure 13.1, a) can accommodate a common pharmacophore.

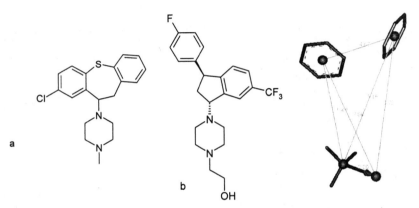

Figure 13.1. (*R*)- and (*S*)-Octoclothepin (**a**), (1*R*,3*S*)-Tefludazine (**b**), and the D2 pharmacophore represented by two aromatic centroids and a basic nitrogen with its putative receptor interaction site point.

The SSRI model is based on several potent and selective serotonin re-uptake inhibitors including the four marketed products considered in this study: citalopram, fluoxetine, sertraline and paroxetine (Figure 13.2). The full model explains stereoselectivity of the individual compounds as well as their selectivity towards the norepinephrine re-uptake site.

It is interesting to note that the two models, which are independently built from different sets of molecules, end up representing a virtually identical core pharmacophore model. This implies that the models used here are oversimplified representations of the original models. The models are not considered true key answers but serve as references for discussing the result.

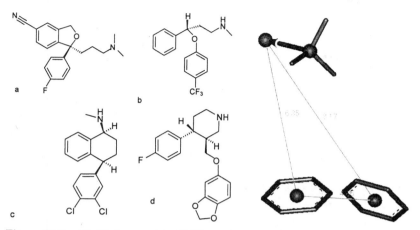

Figure 13.2. (*S*)-Citalopram (**a**), (*S*)-Fluoxetine (**b**), (1*S*,4*S*)-Sertraline (**c**), (3*S*,4*R*)-Paroxetine (**d**), and the SSRI pharmacophore. In this pharmacophore there is no common overlap of the basic nitrogen atoms but only the putative site points associated with these.

13.2. The Methods

There are several commercially available software packages on the market aimed for assisting a drug discovery program.[8] Some of these include methods for automatic search and alignment of common structural features. A few of these packages have combined algorithms for conformational search and alignment, which again can be coupled with a regression analysis routine based on given activities.

In this study, the two programs Catalyst[9] and Flo96[10] are considered. In order to evaluate the programs, it is necessary to emphasize the underlying philosophy and the special features of the two as done below. However, the reader is referred to the original papers for a detailed description.[11-14]

13.2.1. Flo96

Flo96 is a package of modules for structure-based drug design including fast, flexible docking of ligands in a binding site and template fit-

ting routines for more direct pharmacophore modeling.[13,14] In this
study, we will only use the template fitting part.

For template fitting, Flo96 uses the module QXP (quick explore) with
its TFIT (template fit) procedure. The philosophy behind the TFIT procedure is to carry out a full conformational search and similarity (template) match of two or more molecules simultaneously. The TFIT procedure involves a modified AMBER force field, a superposition force
field, and various Monte Carlo conformational search and rigid body
alignment algorithms.

The superposition force field is unique and central to Flo96. It therefore needs special attention though the concept is very simple. QXP
automatically assigns short-range attractive forces between similar
atoms in different molecules. The assignment of "similar atom types" is
based on the chemical properties: Polarity, charge, and hydrogen bonding (an atom typing like c1, c2, and c3 for atoms having negative, neutral, and positive formal charges, respectively, can illustrate the concept
of charge property assignment).

The superposition force field that acts between molecules consists of
a distance dependent potential function as shown in Figure 13.3. The
energy-scaling coefficient (K_{sup}), the inter-atomic distance (dist), and
the cutoff distance (d_{cut}) determine the attractive energy (E_{sup}) between
a pair of similar atoms. The maximum possible reward for perfect
superposition is three times K_{sup} for the case where two atoms have all
three similarity types in common (−9 kJ for the default settings of −3 kJ
for K_{sup} and 3 Å for d_{cut}).

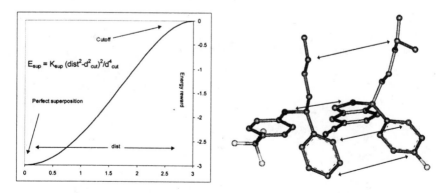

Figure 13.3. The superposition potential (left) and examples of similar atoms (right).

In the template fitting procedure, the normal intramolecular non-bonded energies are replaced by the superposition energies. The internal energies are calculated by the normal force field (E_{int}) ignoring non-bonded energies. The two force fields are working together, and the co-minimization of the energy will ideally result in structures with optimal superimposition and maintained low conformational energy.

The combined QXP module can be described as a repeating sequence of search, alignment, and energy minimization steps. Solutions that pass a predefined energy window and a similarity check are kept as the result and ranked by total energy ($E_{tot}=E_{sup}+E_{int}$) in the output.

Flo96 can handle molecules both as templates (fixed) or freely moving (perturbed) models. In practical terms, the program will efficiently handle up to about five individual molecules at a time. The mode of action is easily controlled by a color-coding scheme: Fixed models are yellow, moving models are green, and orange means that the model can move but will not be perturbed in the search algorithm. Fixed template molecules do not need to be in a continuous model but can be any part or fragment of a molecule. This allows known pharmacophore models to be constructed and used as fixed templates. The concept may also be applied for building pseudo-receptors, but this is beyond the scope of this study.

13.2.2. Catalyst

Catalyst[9] is a package that can be used for multiple purposes in the drug discovery program as demonstrated in many chapters of this book. In the present study, we have only been looking at Catalyst for the purpose of generating pharmacophore models.

It must be realized that the minimal "training sets" and the redundant information used in this study may be considered a violation of the recommended rules for using Catalyst.[15] However, the purpose of the study is not to derive a predictive hypothesis using the module HypoGen, but only to reproduce the known pharmacophore pattern. The descriptions of the program will therefore be restricted to the details important for understanding the behavior in this context.

Central to Catalyst is the generation of conformational models for the molecules in question. A conformational model is a pool of low-energy conformations generated by the module "Confirm." "Confirm" is a quasi-exhaustive search module based on a modified CHARMM force field with a poling algorithm designed for creating coverage of the conformational space.[11] The role of the poling algorithm is to add penalty functions to the force field based on chemical features (poles) that will tend to push chemically identical features apart. It is important to note that these conformational models do not necessarily hold the local energy minimum structures since the poling algorithm directly modifies the energy surface of the force field. The conformational energies are only used to keep the energy below a given threshold and for sorting the conformations.

Pharmacophore models are called hypotheses in Catalyst and are created by the module HipHop. A hypothesis is a three-dimensional configuration of pre-defined chemical features that can be mapped on a molecule. The algorithms inside HipHop are designed for identifying the best configurations for the mapped features common to the selected set of molecules.[12] Hypotheses generated by HipHop are ranked in the output according to a maximum likelihood algorithm that also considers the rarity of the configurations. HipHop has a compare/fit algorithm for finding the best match between the conformations and the hypothesis, but this information it not used for the ranking of hypotheses.

13.3. Results and Discussion

13.3.1. Flo96

With the exception of sertraline in the SSRI model, Flo96 manages to produce common superimposed low-energy conformations of the compounds in both the D2 and the SSRI model in close agreement with the conformations in the published pharmacophores models (Plate 13.1).

The case of sertraline is special in the sense that the fit of sertraline in the reference model is focusing on site points rather than optimal molecular overlap. When the TFIT procedure seeks to find the best overall combination of low internal energy and high superposition reward, it will discard the reference conformation due to low superposition energy. The optimal conformation of sertraline found by Flo96 superimpose well with the other molecules in the model but the nitrogen lone pair is pointing in the wrong direction (Plate 13.1 (right)). This behavior is a clear consequence of the concept and demonstrates that Flo96 should be used with caution for cases where site points are more important than molecular overlap.

In order to explore the efficiency and robustness of the method, several different approaches have been tried. The careless "default" method of simply assigning all involved molecules as moving models at the same time has demonstrated a remarkable robustness. This method is also the best choice if the user wants all the models to "learn" equally from each other. However, it is not beneficial in terms of computational time since it scales exponentially with the number of molecules. Use of more than five molecules at a time cannot be recommended and may also occasionally result in non-exhaustively searched results. Several approaches of having a different number of molecules in play at the same time have been tested for the SSRI and the D2 models but without any notable differences in the result. This shows that the TFIT method is effective for problems concerning relatively small sets of medium-sized, sufficiently diverse molecules as those considered here. It should be noted that it was necessary to increase the number of steps in TFIT from 100 (default) to 300 in order to find the exact same solution for every trial. This again increases the computational time required but no tests exceeded one hour CPU time (195MHz R10k).

A slight tendency for TFIT to get trapped in a single solution pocket has been noted in other studies performed with Flo96 (data not shown). Occasionally it happens that a TFIT run results in a set of very similar solutions. This does not necessarily imply that the "solution" is wrong but care should be taken before accepting the result. The reason for this behavior is a natural consequence of the way the superposition force field works—the more structural similarity, the more they glue together. For instance, a good overlap of a common indole ring can gain up to 60 kJ in superposition reward per molecule for the total energy (default settings). Such large rewards can dominate the conformational energy contribution and thereby strongly bias the outcome of a TFIT run. A key issue in this discussion is the balance between the internal force field and the superposition force field. The default value for the superposition force field seems to work well in most cases, like in this study. However, the user may want to decrease the weight if very large superposition rewards are encountered. In the current version of Flo96, it is not possible to "switch off" individual atoms from the superposition forces field, which would be a functional option for more advanced use.

In Flo96 it is possible to guide superposition between molecules by the use of zero order bonds. These bonds will add a harmonic distance dependent constrain (5 kJ/(Å^2 mol)) between atoms during energy minimization. Another possibility in Flo96 is to use fixed templates, either as a whole molecule or just the pharmacophoric elements. This is particularly useful if a pharmacophore is already known, and the user wants to search for low-energy conformations of other ligands to fit the same pharmacophore.

13.3.2. Catalyst

The Catalyst case is far more ambiguous than the Flo96 story. In short, Catalyst excels in reproducing the published SSRI pharmacophore model, whereas it is dubious if a plausible D2 model can be generated at all with Catalyst.

For the generation of hypotheses, HipHop was conducted to search only for the same composition of standard features, in both cases, namely the two aromatic hydrophobes and a single hydrogen-bond acceptor (HBA), which will map the basic nitrogen. All other settings were default values. Prior to the HipHop run, conformational models for the molecules were generated by Confirm using the "best" algorithm and energy threshold at 10 kcal/mol.

It is convenient to use the problematic D2 pharmacophore as a base for the discussion of the work done by Catalyst. Examples of the result from the first "default" trail with HipHop are shown in Plate 13.2. All three features can be mapped onto the conformations of tefludazine and the two enantiomers of octoclothepin. However, it is also evident that none of the proposed hypotheses are in agreement with the reference model.

The first thing to note is that none of the underlying conformations of the hypotheses seem to be low-energy conformations. In fact, a careful examination of the conformational models generated by Confirm revealed that there were hardly any conformations present with the expected low-energy di-equatorial arrangement of the 1,4-disubstituted piperazine ring (Plate 13.3 (right)). This finding is somewhat surprising since the equatorial/chair conformation is correctly predicted as the global energy minimum by the Catalyst force field (Plate 13.3). The explanation for this strange behavior must be related to the poling algorithm. In other words, it seems like the diversity-promoting forces (poles) are overruling the bare force field to such an extent that the most favorable conformations of the piperazine moiety are discarded.

The second thing to note is that the mapping of the HBA is located on the oxygen of tefludazine rather than the common basic nitrogen, resulting in a very poor fit for the octoclothepins (Plate 13.2). This peculiar course of action can be ascribed to HipHop's regression model in which the rarity of a configuration is estimated. One parameter in this model is a measure of the dispersion of the feature location in the configuration. For the D2 case, it means that the scoring function will prefer the HBA to be on the ether oxygen rather than on the common nitrogen since the dispersion will be greater. This may result in high-ranking hypotheses in which some of the model structures barely fit, as in this case (see Plate 13.2). If such an unwanted situation is recognized before a HipHop run, it is possible for the user to change the priority order for the molecules by assigning different principal values. However, this kind of immediate knowledge is normally not obvious in the initial phase of a pharmacophore development.

Another possible way of increasing the fit score between structures and hypotheses is by reducing the SuperpositionError parameter. The usage of both the principal and the SuperpositionError value will be illustrated in the following.

A feasible workaround for the fact that no conformation in the Confirm models would match the reference pharmacophore was to import a conformational model generated by another method. In this case, a set of conformations from a MacroModel[16] conformational search, using the MM3* force field, was imported to Catalyst and used as a new conformational model.

Each of the models for the three compounds had several conformations closely related to those present in the reference model. These conformations could easily be located by Catalyst if a hypothesis based on the reference structures alone was provided to the program (Plate 13.4).

Based on these observations, it was surprising that HipHop, granted the MacroModel conformations, still failed in generating any hypothesis close to the reference model (Plate 13.5). However, by adjusting the SuperpositionError (from 1 to 0.5) and setting the principal value for the two octoclothepins (=2) and tefludazine (=1), almost perfect models were generated (Plate 13.5 (right)). This illustrates how important the settings of these parameters can be.

The chemical relevance between the hypotheses and the individual compounds can only be established by use of the compare/fit module. In this module, the fit of a molecule to the hypothesis is measured and the quality of the mapping is indicated by a fit value. The maximum fit value will be three in the case of the D2 model since there are three possible features to fit (fit values are given on the individual figures). The conformational energies for the individual conformers are not considered in the fit process, which means that the user has to locate these manually by browsing the model. In other words, Catalyst is considering all conformations within a model to be equally valid.

To summarize, there are two major reasons for the poor performance of Catalyst in the D2 case. One is the incorrect treatment of piperazine ring structures in the conformational models by Confirm. The other is the complete lack of connection between the HipHop regression model and the underlying structures in terms of best overlap of common feature. In addition, it does not make much sense that a dispersion factor in a rarity algorithm can overrule the otherwise perfect fit of a common feature.

Bearing this in mind, it is interesting to note how remarkably well HipHop reproduces the SSRI model (Plate 13.6). Both the pharmacophore and the underlying structures, including sertraline, presented by Catalyst are almost indistinguishable from the published model. The only minor discrepancy is that the suggested highest fit conformation of fluoxetine is one with a high conformational energy (Plate 13.6 (middle and left)). However, the "correct" conformation was present in the conformational model and could easily be replaced without compromising the quality of the fit. In general, there were no problems encountered for the Confirm conformational models in the SSRI case. The SSRI study clearly demonstrates that the concept of Catalyst will succeed in many situations.

12.4. Conclusion

Returning to the original question: Is automated pharmacophore modeling possible? To judge from this story, the short answer must be—not completely.

This does not imply that the evaluated programs are unsuccessful. To be fair, the vendors have never said that this should actually be possible. Hopefully, this evaluation has demonstrated that many of the usual tedious tasks in the pharmacophore development can be automated by these methods. However, it should also be clear that a "blind" trust in these algorithms might result in more confusion than real information. The user has to have sufficient expert knowledge of the methods and a good amount of chemical common sense in order to control and evaluate the models generated by these methods.

Having sounded all these alarms, it is appealing to see how fast, efficient, and helpful these methods can be.

References

1. Marshall GR, Barry CD, Bosshard HE, Dammkoehler RA, Dunn DA: **The conformational parameter in drug design: The active analog approach.** In: *Computer-Assisted Drug Design.* Olson EC, Christoffersen RE, eds. American Chemical Society Symposium, Vol. 112, Washington DC: American Chemical Society, 1979:205-226.

2. (a) Murcko MA: **Recent advances in ligand design methods.** In: *Reviews in Computational Chemistry*, Vol. 11. Lipkowitz KB, Boyd DB, eds. New York: VCH Publisher, 1997:1-66; (b) Clark DE et. al.: **Current issues in de novo molecular design.** In: *Reviews in Computational Chemistry*, Vol. 11. Lipkowitz KB, Boyd DB, eds. New York: VCH Publisher, 1997:66-126.

3. Loew GH, Villar HO, Alkorta I: **Strategies for indirect computer-aided drug design.** *Pharmaceutical Research* 1993, **10**(4):475-486.

4. Liljefors T, Bøgesø KP: **Conformational analysis and structural comparisons of (1R,3S)-(+)- and (1S,3R)-(-)-tefludazine, (S)-(+)- and (R)-(-)-octoclothepin, and (+)-dexclamol in relation to dopamine antagonism and amine-uptake inhibition.** *J Med Chem* 1988, **31**:306-312.

5. Gundertofte K, Bøgesø KP, Liljefors T: **A stereoselective pharmacophoric model of the serotonin re-uptake site.** In: *Computer-Assisted Lead Finding and Optimization. Current Tools for Medicinal Chemistry.* Weinheim: Wiley-VCH, 1997:443-459.

6. Andersen K, Liljefors T, Gundertofte K, Perregaard J, Bøgesø KP: **Development of a receptor-interaction model for serotonin 5-HT2 receptor antagonists. Predicting selectivity with respect to dopamine D2 receptors.** *J Med Chem* 1994, 37:950-962.

7. Bøgesø KP, Liljefors T, Arnt J, Hyttel J, Pedersen H: **Octoclothepin enantiomers. A reinvestigation of their biochemical and pharmacological activity in relation to a new receptor-interaction model for dopamine D-2 receptor antagonists.** *J Med Chem* 1991, 34:2023-2030.

8. Examples other than Catalyst and Flo96:
   (a) DISCO and GASP by Tripos, http://www.tripos.com.
   (b) FlexS by GMD, http://cartan.gmd.de/flex-bin/FlexS.
   (c) Chem-X by Oxford Molecular, http://www.oxmol.co.uk/prods/chem-x/phtech.html

9. Molecular Simulations Inc, 9685, Scranton Road, San Diego, CA 92121, USA

10. Thistlesoft, 603 Colebrook Road, Colebrook, Connecticut 06021, USA.

11. Smellie A, Teig S, Towbin P: **Poling: Promoting conformational variation.** *J Comp Chem* 1995, 16:171-187.

12. Barnum D, Green J, Smellie A, Sprague P: **Identification of common functional configurations among molecules.** *J Chem Inf Comput Sci* 1996, 36(3):563-571.

13. McMartin C, and Bohacek RS: **Flexible matching of test ligands to a 3D pharmacophore using a molecular superposition force field: Comparison of predicted and experimental conformation of inhibitors of three enzymes.** *J Comput-Aided Mol Des* 1995, 9:237-250.

14. McMartin C, and Bohacek RS: **QXP: Powerful, rapid computer algorithms for structure-based drug design.** *J Comput-Aided Mol Des* 1997, 11:333-344.

15. Document by Peter Sprague, http://www.msi.com/support/catalyst/hypogen.html

16. *MacroModel v.6.5,* http://www.schrodinger.com.

14

Database Mining Using Pharmacophore Models to Discover Novel Structural Prototypes

James J. Kaminski, Dinanath F. Rane, and Marnie L. Rothofsky

Abstract

Generation of a three-dimensional pharmacophore model (hypothesis) that correlates the biological activity of a series of farnesyl protein transferase (FPT) inhibitors, exemplified by the prototype 1-(4-pyridylacetyl)-4-(8-chloro-5,6-dihydro-11H-benzo[5,6]cyclohepta[1,2-b]pyridin-11-ylidene)piperidine, Sch 44342, **1**, with their chemical structure was accomplished using the three-dimensional quantitative structure-activity relationship (3D-QSAR) software program, *Catalyst*. Based on the in vitro FPT inhibitory activity of a training set of compounds, a five-feature hypothesis containing four hydrophobic and one hydrogen bond acceptor region was generated. Using this hypothesis as a three-dimensional query to search our corporate database identified 718 compounds (hits). Determination of the in vitro FPT inhibitory activity using available compounds from this hit list identified five compounds. These compounds represent three structurally novel classes that exhibited *in vitro* FPT inhibitory activity, $IC_{50} \leq 5$ μM. From these three classes, a series of substituted dihydrobenzothiophenes was selected for further structure-FPT inhibitory activity relationship studies. The results from these studies are discussed in this chapter.

14

Database Mining Using Pharmacophore Models to Discover Novel Structural Prototypes

James J. Kaminski, Dinanath F. Rane, and Marnie L. Rothofsky

Schering-Plough Research Institute, Kenilworth, New Jersey

Identifying the optimal drug candidate during the discovery process is difficult given the often conflicting desires and needs of such diverse groups as chemists, pharmacologists, toxicologists, product development, and clinical professionals involved in the drug development process. While the intrinsic therapeutic potency of the selected compound is of prime importance, there is no doubt that the overall progress of drug development can be enhanced if the drug candidate chosen also possesses physicochemical and metabolic properties that positively influence its chemical synthesis, metabolism, pharmaceutical formulation, and pharmacodynamic profile (bioavailability).

Once the lead structure in any therapeutic area of interest has been identified, optimization of its activity profile using a specific armamentarium of selected *in vitro* and *in vivo* pharmacological assays is customarily accomplished by conducting a systematic structure-activity relationship (SAR) study directed by chemical synthesis. Although the primary goal of the SAR study is to maximize the potency of the potential drug candidate in the various biological models examined, modification of the physical/chemical properties of the drug candidate is considered more often by the medicinal chemist in the discovery phase, rather than in the development phase with the design of the dosage form. In most instances, the physical/chemical properties of the drug candidate are modified in an attempt to maximize its efficacy, to maximize its delivery (transport) to the site of action, and to minimize any potential drug safety issues while still satisfying preclinical development criteria. The nature of the modified physical/chemical properties of the drug candidate are determined solely by virtue of the chemical structure of the target compound proposed for synthesis. The process as described above is largely empirical in nature, and the results of such SAR studies, in many cases, are qualitative at best.

In an attempt to more accurately identify promising drug candidates from a series of compounds of interest, approaches to improve the direction provided by empirical SAR studies have been attempted over the last thirty years by investigators who have incorporated and extended the principles of thermodynamics[1] and physical organic chemistry[2] to biological systems. The results from these initial studies made it possible for Hansch and his coworkers in the early 1960s to develop the most widely used and well-known method of quantitative structure-activity relationships: QSAR.[3-6] Since the derived Hansch equations attempted to correlate thermodynamic and other related parameters to biological activity without using the formal structure of thermodynamics, this approach to drug design became known as the extrathermodynamic approach. The multiparameter equations that relate the biological activity of an analogue to the electronic, steric, and hydrophobic effect of its substituents have been termed extrathermodynamic relationships. *In toto*, the overall objective of any QSAR study is to identify parameters that will give a statistically significant correlation with the observed biological activity of a series of molecules. Once these parameters have been identified, the resulting equation can be used to predict (calculate) the biological activity of unknown analogues. While this quantitative statistical approach appears to be less empirical, the successful prediction (calculation) of biological activity is more complex, and the translation of this information to guide further structural modifications of the lead compound is not readily apparent.

During the last sixty years, it has become more recognized and accepted that the three-dimensional (3D) conformation, or shape of a (bio)molecule is uniquely interrelated with expression of the biological activity and function of the (bio)molecular entity. The interrelationship between the 3D structure of the (bio)molecule and expression of its biological activity and function is so tightly coupled that a better understanding of the molecular conformation and the nature of the intermolecular interactions occurring with a bound substrate might provide the basis for the "rational design" of novel target molecules that could interact with greater precision, affinity, and effect than naturally occurring ligands.

The only known method for precisely determining the 3D structure of any (bio)molecule is by single crystal X-ray analysis. However, relatively few biomolecules that are therapeutic targets have had their solid-state structure successfully determined by X-ray crystallography, and even fewer crystallographic structures exist for biomolecules that also contain their substrate, or ligand, bound. Thus, in the absence of detailed structural information, alternative approaches have evolved which might mimic investigation of the interactions occurring between biomolecules and substrate molecules. One such approach has its genesis in the generation and utilization of pharmacophore models in the emerging field of three-dimensional quantitative structure-activity relationships (3D QSAR).

Recently, the discovery of the tricyclic farnesyl protein transferase (FPT) inhibitor 1-(4-pyridylacetyl)-4-(8-chloro-5,6-dihydro-11H-benzo[5,6]cyclohepta-[1,2-b]pyridin-11-ylidene) piperidine, Sch 44342, 1, was reported.[7] Sch 44342, 1, is a unique example of a novel nonpeptide, nonsulfhydryl-containing FPT inhibitor that exhibits substantial selectivity against geranyl geranyltransferase-1 (GGPT-1) and kinetically competes with the RAS protein, but not with farnesyl pyrophosphate (FPP), in binding to FPT. Significant effort has been expended to optimize the *in vitro* FPT inhibitory potency and the in vivo pharmacological profile of this series of FPT inhibitors by conducting a systematic structure-FPT inhibitory activity relationship (SAR) study directed by chemical synthesis.[8-12] This effort culminated with the selection for clinical evaluation of R-(+)-4-[2-[4-(3,10-dibromo-8-chloro-6,11-dihydro-5H-benzo[5,6]-cyclohepta[1,2-b]pyridinyl)-2-oxoethyl]-1-piperidinecarboxamide, Sch 66336, 36, as a potential anti-cancer agent.[13]

Sch 44342 , 1   Sch 66336 , 36

Concomitant with this effort has been an analysis of the FPT inhibitory activity data determined *in vitro* for these compounds using Catalyst, a 3D QSAR software program.[8,14] One application of this program is the generation of hypotheses that attempt to correlate the biological activity observed for a series of compounds to their chemical structure.[15] The hypotheses generated are three-dimensional descriptions of a pharmacophore model proposed for the series of compounds examined. The hypotheses are represented by the chemical features that describe the series of compounds, for example, hydrophobic groups, hydrogen-bond donors, hydrogen-bond acceptors, positive and negative ionizable groups, etc. The hypotheses generated may be used to estimate the biological activity of proposed targets allowing a rank ordering of synthetic priorities. In addition, the hypotheses generated may also be used as three-dimensional queries to search databases of proprietary and/or commercially available compounds. These three-dimensional searches could identify structurally novel analogues that might exhibit the biological activity of the prototype. The results obtained from searching our corporate database using a Catalyst generated FPT hypothesis as a three-dimensional query have been reported recently[16] and are discussed further here.

From the analogues prepared to investigate the structure-FPT inhibitory activity relationship of the series exemplified by the prototype 1-(4-pyridylacetyl)-4-(8-chloro-5,6-dihydro-11H-benzo[5,6]cyclohepta[1,2-b]pyridin-11-ylidene)piperidine, Sch 44342, **1**, a training set of compounds was selected for Catalyst analysis, Figure 14.1. The compounds in the training set included the most active FPT inhibitors in the series, and each compound possessed something new to teach Catalyst during hypothesis generation. In addition, the compounds in the training set were structurally distinct from a chemical feature point of view, and represented the diversity of the series. Each compound in the training set was considered as a collection of energetically reasonable conformations, and in cases where the chirality of an asymmetric center was not specified, Catalyst generated and considered alternative stereoisomers.

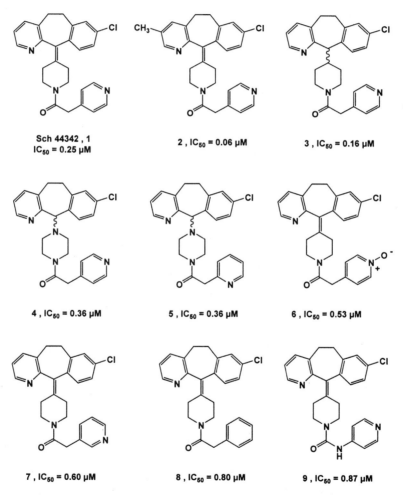

Sch 44342 , 1
IC_{50} = 0.25 µM

2 , IC_{50} = 0.06 µM

3 , IC_{50} = 0.16 µM

4 , IC_{50} = 0.36 µM

5 , IC_{50} = 0.36 µM

6 , IC_{50} = 0.53 µM

7 , IC_{50} = 0.60 µM

8 , IC_{50} = 0.80 µM

9 , IC_{50} = 0.87 µM

Figure 14.1. (Part 1) Training set of selected farnesyl protein transferase (FPT) inhibitors and their determined *in vitro* FPT inhibitory activity. The figure is reprinted with permission from reference.[16] © 1997 American Chemical Society.

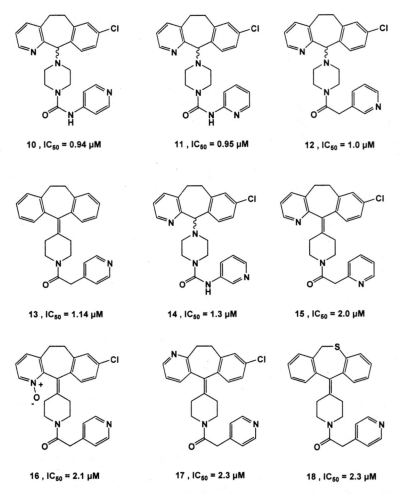

10 , IC$_{50}$ = 0.94 µM   11 , IC$_{50}$ = 0.95 µM   12 , IC$_{50}$ = 1.0 µM

13 , IC$_{50}$ = 1.14 µM   14 , IC$_{50}$ = 1.3 µM   15 , IC$_{50}$ = 2.0 µM

16 , IC$_{50}$ = 2.1 µM   17 , IC$_{50}$ = 2.3 µM   18 , IC$_{50}$ = 2.3 µM

Figure 14.1. (Part 2)   Training set of selected farnesyl protein transferase (FPT) inhibitors and their determined *in vitro* FPT inhibitory activity.

The range of *in vitro* FPT inhibitory activity exhibited by these select-ed compounds spanned four orders of magnitude (10^{-1}-10^{3} µM), and the compound distribution was evenly populated over the activity range. Using this training set, FPT hypotheses (pharmacophore models) were generated. When generating hypotheses, Catalyst tries to minimize a cost function consisting of three terms. One term-the weight cost-that increases in a Gaussian form as the feature weight in a model deviates from an idealized value of two. The second term-the error cost-penal-

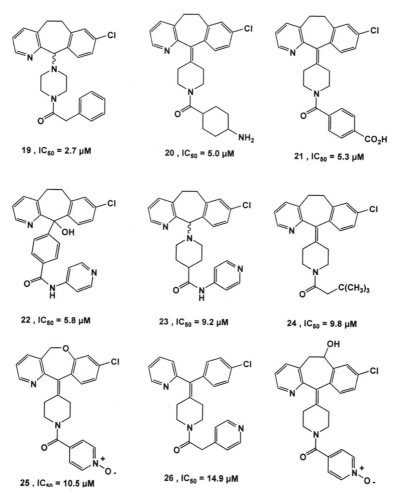

19 , IC$_{50}$ = 2.7 μM

20 , IC$_{50}$ = 5.0 μM

21 , IC$_{50}$ = 5.3 μM

22 , IC$_{50}$ = 5.8 μM

23 , IC$_{50}$ = 9.2 μM

24 , IC$_{50}$ = 9.8 μM

25 , IC$_{50}$ = 10.5 μM

26 , IC$_{50}$ = 14.9 μM

Figure 14.1. (Part 3) Training set of selected farnesyl protein transferase (FPT) inhibitors and their determined *in vitro* FPT inhibitory activity.

izes the deviation between the estimated activities of the training set and their experimentally determined values. The third term-the configuration cost-penalizes the complexity of the hypothesis. This is a fixed cost which is equal to the entropy of the hypothesis space. The overall cost of a hypothesis is calculated by summing over the three cost factors. Of these three, the error cost contributes the most in determining the cost of a hypothesis. During hypothesis generation, Catalyst calculates the cost of two theoretical hypotheses: the ideal hypothesis, in which the

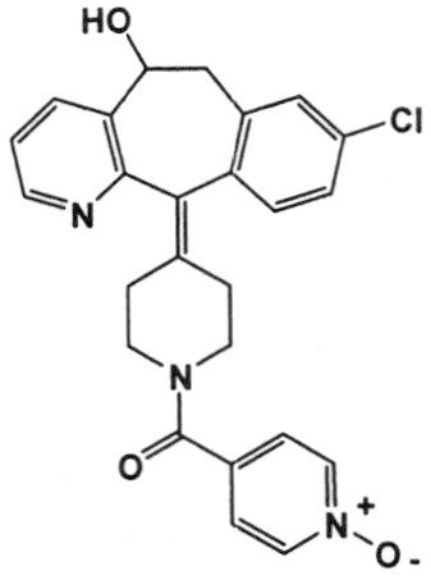

28 , IC_{50} = 34.0 μM

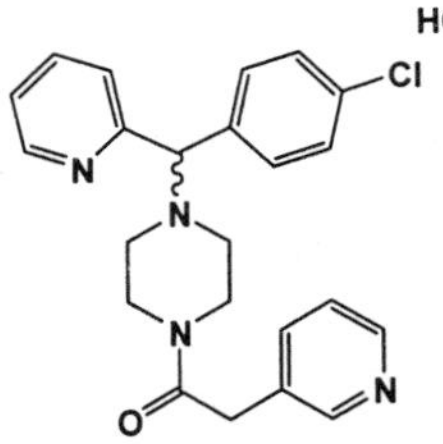

29 , IC_{50} = 38.3 μM

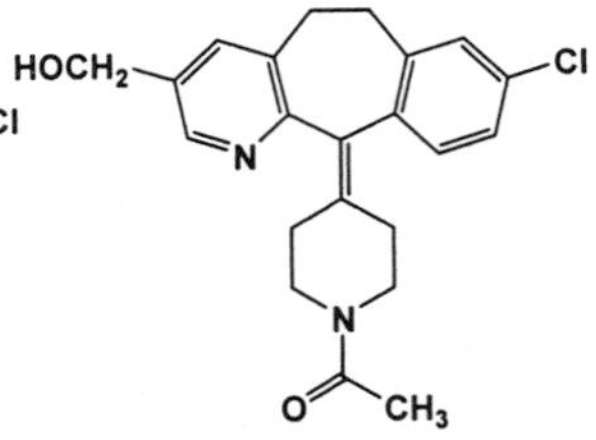

30 , IC_{50} = 41.0 μM

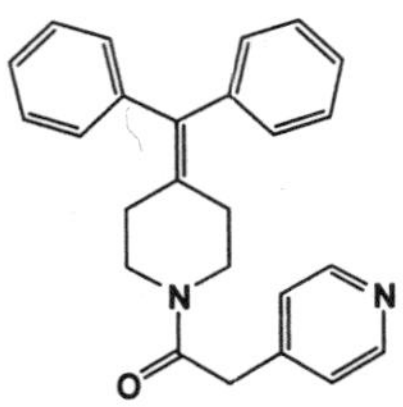

31 , IC_{50} = 48.4 μM

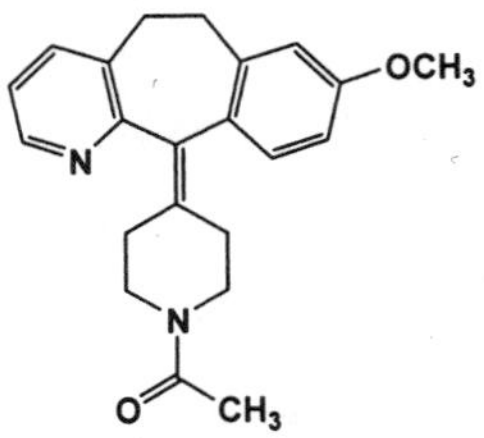

32 , IC_{50} = 56 μM

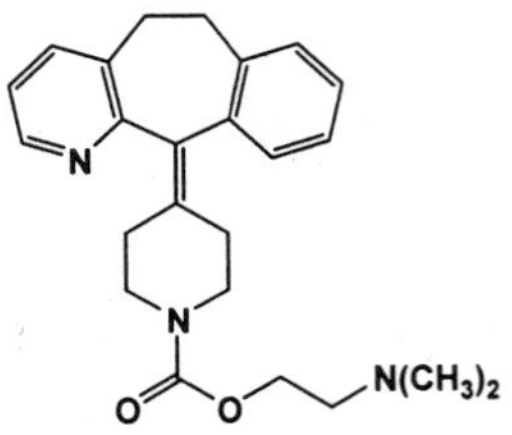

33 , IC_{50} = 79 μM

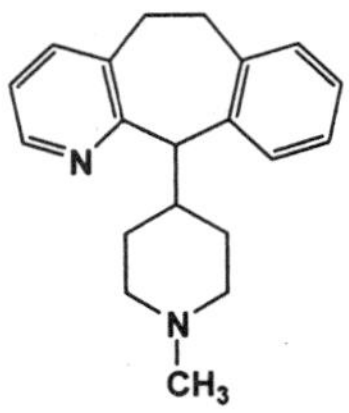

34 , IC_{50} = 724 μM

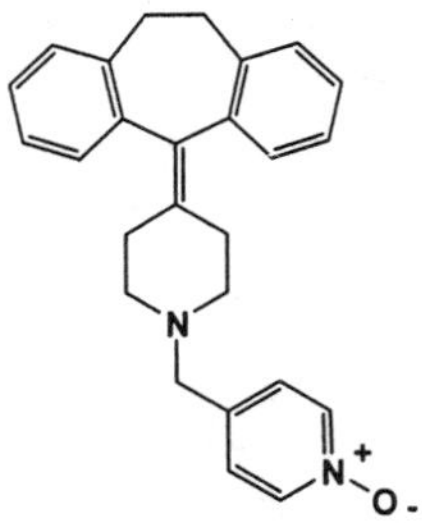

35 , IC_{50} = 1832 μM

Figure 14.1. (Part 4) Training set of selected farnesyl protein transferase (FPT) inhibitors and their determined *in vitro* FPT inhibitory activity.

error cost is minimal and the slope of the activity correlation line is one; and the null hypothesis, where the error cost is high and the slope of the activity correlation line is zero. The greater the difference between these two costs, the higher the probability of generating a useful model.

The FPT hypothesis chosen from the alternatives generated was that which exhibited the lowest cost value and resided closest to the ideal hypothesis (see Figure 14.2).[15] The FPT hypothesis is a collection of chemical features distributed in three-dimensional space that is intended to represent groups in the molecule that participate in important binding interactions between drugs and their receptors. The pharmacophore model produced consisted of four hydrophobic regions and one hydrogen-bond acceptor site in a specific three-dimensional orientation. Each of the five features in this model were equally weighted.

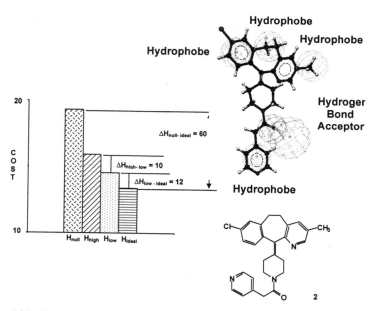

Figure 14.2. Best conformation of **2** flexibly fit to the lowest-cost Catalyst generated FPT hypothesis (Pharmacophore model). Reprinted with permission from reference.[16] © 1997 American Chemical Society.

Using **2**, IC_{50} = 0.06 μM, as an example, a flexible fit of the best conformer of this molecule maps to the lowest-cost Catalyst-generated FPT hypothesis as described in Figure 14.2. The four hydrophobic regions of the hypothesis are the 3-methyl group on the pyridyl portion of the tricyclic system, the 5,6-ethano bridge of the tricyclic system, the aromatic ring of the 8-chlorophenyl portion of the tricyclic system, and the 4-pyridyl ring of the picolinamide attached to the pendant piperylidenyl ring. The hydrogen bond acceptor identified in the FPT hypothesis generated is the carbonyl group of the γ-picolinamide attached to the pendant piperylidenyl ring.

A regression line of "measured" versus "estimated" FPT inhibitory activity for the training set, expressed as -log [IC_{50}], based on the lowest-cost Catalyst-generated FPT hypothesis, exhibited a correlation coefficient (r^2) = 0.91 and a root mean square deviation RMS = 0.84. Using these criteria, comparison between the "estimated" activity of the compounds in the training set relative to their experimentally observed activity is in the worst case, within one order of magnitude, and in most cases, is within a five-fold difference.[16]

In cases where one chiral center is present in the molecule, the generated FPT hypothesis exhibits a preference for the S-stereoisomer relative to the R-stereoisomer. For example, the "estimated" FPT inhibitory potency of the S - (-) stereoisomer of **4**, IC_{50} = 0.014 µM, is greater than the "estimated" FPT inhibitory potency of the R - (+) stereoisomer of **4**, IC_{50} = 0.65 µM. This observation is consistent with the "measured" FPT inhibitory potency determined for the enantiomers of **4**, the S - (-) stereoisomer, IC_{50} = 0.14 µM relative to the R - (+) stereoisomer, IC_{50} = 0.49 µM.[8] In general, this observation is consistent with the FPT inhibitory potency determined for enantiomers of several other analogues in the series (the S-stereoisomer exhibits a greater FPT inhibitory potency relative to the R-stereoisomer.)

The FPT inhibitory activity predicted for compounds which were not part of the training set, but contain chemical features on which the FPT hypothesis was based, is usually within a four- to five-fold difference. However, consistent with other QSAR methods, activity predictions for compounds outside the training set are inaccurate and can be misleading. For example, the "estimated" FPT inhibitory activity of the peptide CVWM, IC_{50} = 0.007 µM, is approximately two orders of magnitude different from its experimentally "measured" FPT inhibitory activity, IC_{50} = 0.525 µM.

The lowest-cost Catalyst-generated FPT hypothesis was also used as a three-dimensional query to search the Schering-Plough Research Institute's corporate database and resulted in the identification of 718 compounds. Examination of these compounds revealed that 626 structures were unique, only 330 were available, and determination of their *in vitro* FPT inhibitory activity was initiated.

From the structures examined, only five compounds (5/330 = 1.5%), exhibited an *in vitro* FPT inhibitory potency of $IC_{50} \leq 5$ µM (see Figure 14.3). The 1.5-% value obtained from this focused assessment of the corporate database is approximately a two-fold improvement compared to determining the FPT inhibitory activity of a larger subset of the corporate database. High-throughput screening (HTS) of approximately 84,000 structures identified 2468 compounds which exhibited FPT inhibition = 50% at 20 μg/ml. From these compounds, only twenty-two (22/2468 = 0.9%) exhibited an in vitro FPT inhibitory potency of $IC_{50} \leq 5$ μM.

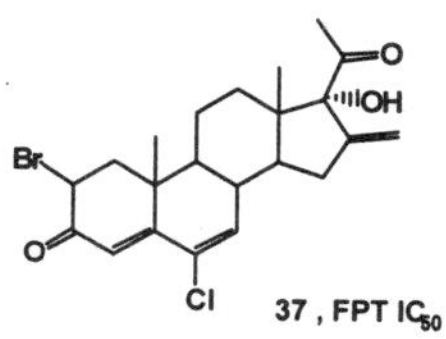

37 , FPT IC_{50} = 1.8 μM

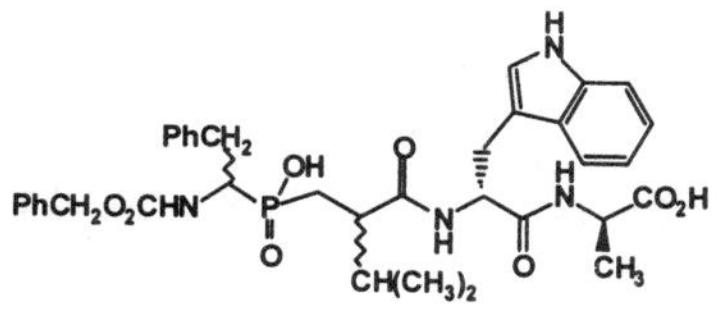

38 , FPT IC_{50} = 1.0 μM

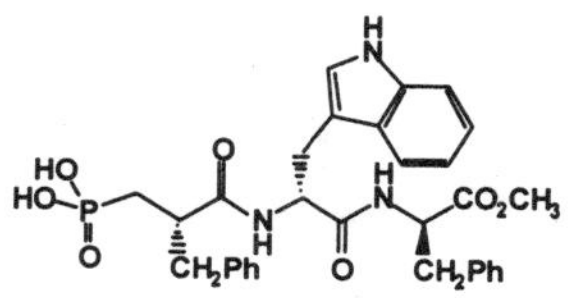

39 , FPT IC_{50} = 0.7 μM

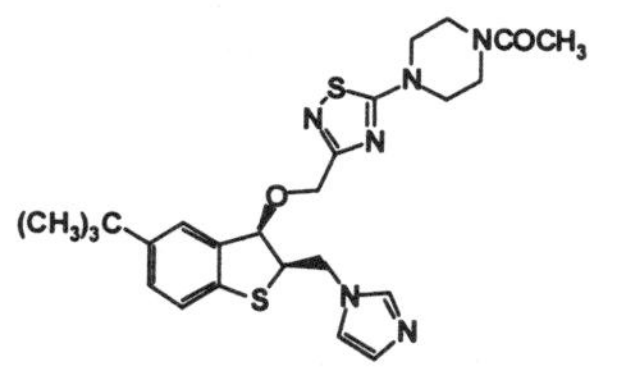

40 , FPT IC_{50} = 4.8 μM

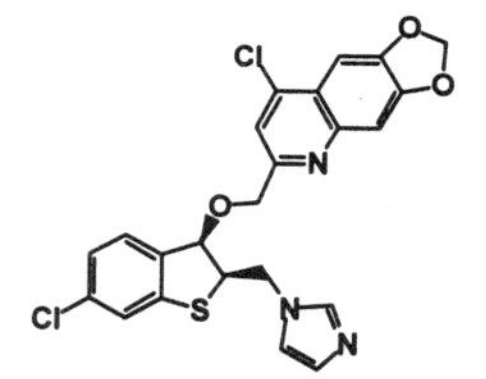

41 , FPT IC_{50} = 2.5 μM

Figure 14.3. Novel compounds exhibiting *in vitro* FPT inhibitory activity $IC_{50} \leq 5$ μM identified by searching the Schering—Plough Research Institute Corporate database using the lowest-cost Catalyst generated FPT hypothesis.

Of the five compounds identified, one is steroid-based, **37**, two are peptide-based, **38** and **39**, and two, **40** and **41**, are derived from a series of "azole" antifungals which were clinically investigated as topical agents.[17] From a chemical point of view, the "azole" antifungals represent a novel class of FPT inhibitors that are structurally distinct from the "tricyclic" series of compounds, as well as other known FPT inhibitors. On that basis, the FPT and GGPT-1 inhibitory activities of these initial leads were profiled further.[16]

The FPT inhibitory potency of **40** and **41** was independently confirmed using a secondary assay (the FPT inhibitory potencies of **40** and **41** determined using the FPT Ras/TCA assay were $IC_{50} = 5.3$ µM and $IC_{50} = 3.1$ µM, respectively). Selectivity between FPT and GGPT-1 inhibitory activity for **40** and **41** was also demonstrated (the GGPT-1 inhibitory potencies of **40** and **41** were $IC_{50} > 39$ µM and $IC_{50} = 1.4$ µM, respectively). In addition, the lack of significant FPT inhibitory activity exhibited by other "azole" antifungal agents. Ketoconazole ($IC_{50} > 46$ µM) and fluconazole (% Inhibition = 3 at 20 µg/ml) suggested that the FPT inhibitory activity of these compounds may not be coupled to their antifungal activity. These observations encouraged us to determine the *in vitro* FPT inhibitory potency of other available analogs from this series.[16]

The structure-FPT inhibitory activity relationships determined from the preliminary study are summarized in Figure 14.4, and the most active FPT inhibitors identified from the initial leads were **42** and **43**.

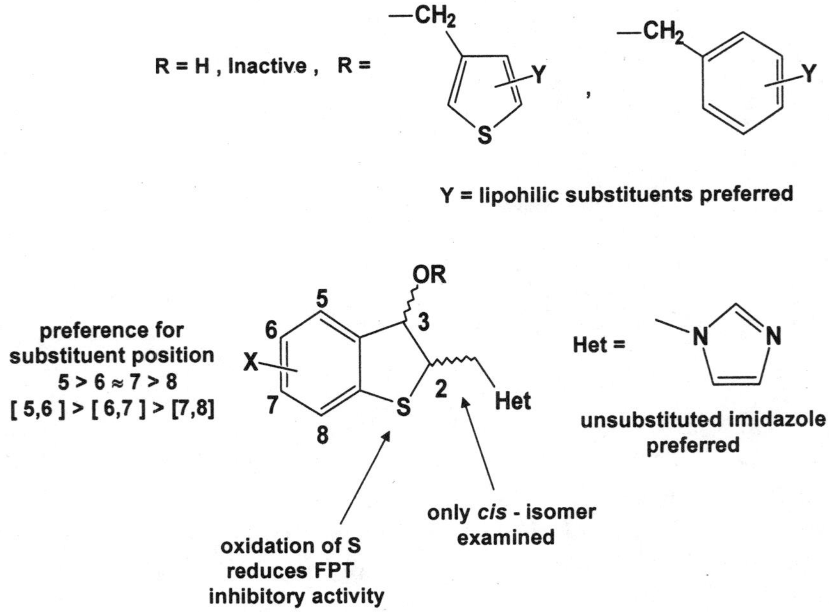

Figure 14.4. Preliminary structure—FPT inhibitory activity relationships of the substituted dihydrobenzothiophenes.

While the FPT inhibitory potency of **42** (FPT IC_{50} = 0.2 μM and GGPT-1 IC_{50} = 16.8 μM) and **43** (FPT IC_{50} = 0.3 μM and GGPT-1 IC_{50} = 0.7 μM) are comparable to each other, the FPT to GGPT-1 selectivity of **42** (84) is greater than the FPT to GGPT-1 selectivity of **43** (2).

Using one of the initial lead compounds, **40**, as an example, a flexible fit of the cis-isomer of this molecule maps to the lowest-cost Catalyst-generated FPT hypothesis as described in Plate 14.1. Only three of the four possible hydrophobic regions of the FPT hypothesis map to the molecule: the piperazine ring of the side chain and the aromatic ring and sulfur atom of the dihydrobenzothiophene ring system. The hydrogen-bond acceptor in the generated FPT hypothesis is identified as the sulfur atom in the thiadiazine ring system.[18] The estimated FPT inhibitory activity for the cis-isomer of **40**, IC_{50} = 3.8 μM, based on the generated FPT hypothesis, is in excellent agreement with its experimentally measured FPT inhibitory activity, IC_{50} = 4.8 μM. This observation is particularly surprising since only four of the five features of the FPT hypothesis map to the molecule.

Interestingly, the trans-isomer of **40**, flexibly fit to the lowest-cost Catalyst-generated FPT hypothesis, maps to all five features of the hypothesis (see Plate 14.2). More importantly, an estimate of the FPT inhibitory activity of this isomer based on the model, IC_{50} = 0.18 μM, suggests that the *trans*-isomer could be as potent as **42**, the best compound identified from the structure-FPT inhibitory relationship study, IC_{50} = 0.2 μM. In addition, the FPT inhibitory potency of **42** might also be improved by further analogue synthesis. Since **42** maps to only four of the five features of the lowest-cost Catalyst-generated FPT hypothesis (see Plate 14.2), introduction of functionality in **42** which might interact with the fifth feature of the hypothesis could impart enhanced FPT inhibitory activity to the compound.

In summary, using a training set of novel farnesyl protein transferase (FPT) inhibitors, exemplified by the prototype 1-(4-pyridylacetyl)-4-(8-chloro-4-(8-chloro-5,6-dihydro-11H-benzo[5,6]cyclohepta[1,2-b]pyridin-11-ylidene) piperidine, Sch 44342, **1**, a three-dimensional pharmacophore model (hypothesis) was generated which successfully correlated the FPT inhibitory activity observed for this series of these compounds to their chemical structure. Using the lowest-cost Catalyst-generated FPT hypothesis as a three-dimensional query to search a database of compounds identified several other structurally novel analogues that exhibited the biological activity of the prototype. Investigating the structure-FPT inhibitory activity relationships of one of the identified series using the lowest-cost Catalyst-generated FPT hypothesis demonstrated that it was useful for assessing the relative merits of proposed synthetic targets prior to their synthesis. In addition, the lowest-cost Catalyst-generated FPT hypothesis was useful in the conceptual design of other novel FPT inhibitor targets in the series.

References

1. Ferguson J: **The use of chemical potentials as indices of toxicity.** *Proc R Soc London*, 1939, Ser. B, **127**:387-403.

2. Hammett LP: *Physical Organic Chemistry.* New York: McGraw-Hill, 1940.

3. Hansch C, Muir RM, Fujita T, Maloney PP, Geiger F, Streich M: **The correlation of biological activity of plant growth regulators and chloromycetin derivatives with Hammett constants and partition coefficients.** *J Am Chem Soc* 1963, **85**:2817-2824.

4. Fujita T, Iwasa J, Hansch C: **A new substituent constant, p, derived from partition coefficients.** *J Am Chem Soc* 1964, **86**:5175-5180.

5. Martin YC: Quantitative *Drug Design.* New York: Marcel Dekker, 1978.

6. Ramsden CA: Quantitative drug design. In: *Comprehensive Medicinal Chemistry*, Vol. 4. Hansch C, ed. New York: Pergamon Press, 1990.

7. Bishop WR, Bond, R, Petrin J, Wang L, Patton R, Doll R, Njoroge G, Catino J, Schwartz J, Windsor W, Sayto R, Schwartz J, Carr D, James L, Kirschmeier P: **Novel tricyclic inhibitors of farnesyl protein transferase.** *J Biol Chem* 1995, **270**:30611-30618.

8. Mallams AK, Njoroge FG, Doll RJ, Snow ME, Kaminski JJ, Rossman R, Vibulbhan B, Bishop WR, Kirschmeier P, Liu M, Bryant MS, Alvarez C, Carr D, James L, King I, Li Z, Lin C-C, Nardo J, Petrin J, Remiszewski S, Taveras A, Wang S, Wong J, Catino J, Girijavallabhan V, Ganguly AK: **Antitumor 8-chlorobenzocycloheptapyridines: A new class of selective, nonpeptidic, nonsulfhydryl inhibitors of Ras farnesylation.** *Bioorg Med Chem* 1997, **5**:93-99.

9. Njoroge FG, Doll RJ, Vibulbhan B, Alvarez C, Bishop WR, Petrin J, Kirschmeier P, Carruthers NI, Wong JK, Albanese MM, Piwinski JJ, Catino J, Girijavallabhan V, Ganguly AK: **Discovery of novel nonpeptide tricyclic inhibitors of Ras farnesylation.** *Bioorg Med Chem* 1997, **5**:101-114.

10. Njoroge FG, Vibulbhan B, Rane DF, Bishop WR, Petrin J, Patton R, Bryant MS, Chen KJ, Nomeir AA, Lin C, Liu M, King I, Chen J, Lee S, Yaremko B, Dell J, Lipari P, Malkowski M, Catino J, Doll RJ, Girijavallabhan V, Ganguly AK: **Structure-activity relationship of 3-substituted N-(pyridinylacetyl)-4-(8-chloro-5,6-dihydro-11H-benzo[5,6]cyclohepta[1,2-b]pyridin-11-ylidene)piperidine inhibitors of farensyl protein transferase: Design and synthesis of in vivo active antitumor compounds.** *J Med Chem* 1997, **40**:4290-4301.

11. Mallams AK, Rossman RR, Doll RJ, Girijavallabhan V, Ganguly AK, Petrin J, Wang L, Patton R, Bishop WR, Carr DM, Kirschmeier P, Catino J, Bryant MS, Chen KJ, Korfmacher WA, Nardo C, Wang S, Nomeir AA, Lin CC, Li Z, Chen J, Lee S, Lipari P, Liu M: **Inhibitors of farnesyl protein transferase. 4-amido, 4-carbamoyl and 4-carboxamido derivatives of 1-(8-chloro-6,11-dihydro-5H-benzo[5,6]-cyclohepta[1,2-b]pyridin-11-yl)piperazine and 1-(3-bromo-8-chloro-6,11-dinyhdro-5H-benzo[5,6]-cyclohepta[1,2-b]-pyridin-11-yl)piperazine.** *J Med Chem* 1998, **41**:877-893.

12. Njoroge FG, Vibulbhan B, Pinto P, Bishop WR, Bryant MS, Nomeir AA, Lin C, Liu M, Doll RJ, Girijavallabhan V, Ganguly AK: **Potent, selective and orally bioavailable tricyclic pyridylacetamide n-oxide inhibitors of farnesyl protein transferase with enhanced in vivo antitumor activity.** *J Med Chem* 1998, **41**:1561-1567.

13. Njoroge G, Taveras A, Kelly J, Remiszewski S, Mallams AK, Woli R, Afonso A, Cooper A, Rane D, Liu Y, Wong J, Vibulbhan B, Pinto P, Deskus J, Alvarez C, Rosario J, Connoly M, Wang J, Desai J, Rossman R, Bishop WR,

Patton R, Wang L, Kirschmeier P, Bryant M, Nomeir A, Lin C, Liu M, McPhail A, Doll RJ, Girijavallabhan V, Ganguly AK: (+)-4-[2-[4-(3,10-dibromo-8-chloro-6,11-dihydro-5H-benzo[5,6]-cyclohepta[1,2-b]pyridinyl)-2-oxoethyl]-1-piperidinecarboxamide (Sch 66336): A very potent farnesyl protein transferase inhibitor as a novel antitumor agent. *J Med Chem* 1998, **41**:4890-4902.

14. *Catalyst, v2.1.* Molecular Simulations, Inc., Burlington, MA.

15. Sprague PW: **Automated chemical hypothesis generation and database searching with Catalyst.** In: *Perspectives in Drug Discovery and Design*, 1995, **3**:1-20.

16. Kaminski JJ, Rane DF, Snow ME, Weber L, Rothofsky ML, Anderson S, Lin SL: **Identification of novel farnesyl protein transferase inhibitors using three-dimensional database searching methods.** *J Med Chem* 1997, **40**:4103-4112.

17. Rane DF, Pike RE, Puar MS, Wright JJ, McPhail AT: **A novel synthesis of cis-1-[[6-chloro-3-[(2-chloro-3-thienyl)methoxy]-2,3-dihydrobenzo[b]thien-2-yl]methyl]-1H-imidazole. A new class of azole antifungal agents.** *Tetrahedron* 1988, **44**:2397-2402.

18. Allen FH, Bird CM, Rowland RS, Raithby PR: **Hydrogen-bond acceptor and donor properties of divalent sulfur.** *Acta Cryst* 1997, Sect. B: Struct Sci **B53**(4):696-701.

15

Predicting Drug-Drug Interactions in Silico Using Pharmacophores: A Paradigm for the Next Millennium

Sean Ekins, Barbara J. Ring, Gianpaolo Bravi, James H. Wikel, and Steven A. Wrighton

Abstract

Improving the success of drug development is increasingly being recognized as dependent upon absorption, distribution, metabolism, and excretion (ADME) properties. The ability to predict such characteristics before a molecule reaches *in vitro* testing would be a valuable asset to any pharmaceutical company. This chapter describes preliminary computational pharmacophore models that have been used to successfully predict cytochrome P450-mediated drug-drug interactions. We suggest that these pharmacophores represent an initial shift in the drug metabolism paradigm and that the technique is equally applicable for other enzymes and transporters in drug metabolism as well as pharmacokinetic parameters. Ultimately, pharmacophore approaches represent a faster screen than *in vitro*, with the additional advantage of utility for virtual design of molecules with more favorable ADME.

15

Predicting Drug-Drug Interactions in Silico Using Pharmacophores: A Paradigm for the Next Millennium

Sean Ekins, Barbara J. Ring, Gianpaolo Bravi, James H. Wikel, and Steven A. Wrighton

Lilly Research Laboratories, Eli Lilly and Co., Indianapolis, Indiana

15.1. Introduction

In an attempt to contain spiraling costs, the pharmaceutical industry is striving to enhance the likelihood of success for molecules in drug development. One way to improve this process is to identify why failure occurs and then monitor subsequent drug candidates for this behavior. All major pharmaceutical companies have now recognized the importance of drug metabolism, polymorphic cytochrome P450s (CYPs), and the need to decrease attrition caused by a candidate compound having undesirable drug-drug interactions. The route taken to arrive at the present state of the art in drug metabolism has been well reviewed along with some discussion of potential future research directions.[1] The most recent trend is towards the use of high-throughput screening for metabolism and drug interactions.[2] However, we would like to take a different approach and outline how predictions have played an important role in drug metabolism and will continue to do so through the next millennium. Looking back twenty years, 1979 was a simpler time for drug metabolism departments in the pharmaceutical industry. This was prior to the days of combinatorial synthesis and high-throughput screening when the time and costs of drug development along with the number of developed drugs were significantly different to those today. Twenty years ago there were only a few CYPs identified and they were predominantly located in the liver. In addition, in drug development *in vitro* studies of metabolism were infrequent as this technology was poorly understood and the emphasis was on *in vivo* studies. Up until the late 1980s, there was even little apparent concern as to identifying which CYP was involved in metabolism of a molecule or whether a candidate was likely to cause drug-drug interactions *in vitro*. However, some surprisingly prescient predictions for the future of drug metabolism were made in 1979. First, it was recognized that the intestine had tremendous metabolic capabilities, including the microflora, that were poorly understood.[3] Second, it was suggested that drug metabolism scientists and medicinal chemists should work more closely on structure activity relationships.[4] Finally it was suggested that drug metabolism scientists should begin to understand how substrates bind to different CYPs and what determines their specificity.[5]

Fast forward 20 years to the present, in which many hundreds of CYPs have now been identified across phyla.[6] A typical drug metabolism group in industry today produces an incredible amount of information using *in vitro* studies with expressed drug metabolizing enzymes, hepatocytes, liver slices, and subcellular fractions.[7] Further these studies utilize models of not only the various experimental animals but also human. But perhaps the most important difference between the pharmaceutical industry today and 20 years ago is the reliance of both discovery and development scientists on the prediction of potential drug-drug interactions and pharmacokinetic variability as early as possible,[8] with the associated implications for drug metabolism and toxicology.[9] Theoretically, these techniques are used to limit predictable failures in the more costly later stages of development.[10] In reality, the situation is often more complex, with many other factors, such as toxicity, contributing to the termination of a candidate in development. The FDA has recognized the importance of drug-drug interaction studies and has issued guidelines for *in vitro* studies, suggesting how to perform and interpret them to their satisfaction.[11] In addition, the FDA is currently circulating a draft guidance on *in vivo* drug interactions in which the predictions by *in vitro* studies are put into perspective.

So what does the next millennium hold for predictions in drug metabolism, drug interactions and pharmacokinetic variability? Recently published pharmacophores for CYPs suggests that a battery of computational approaches may eventually be implemented to winnow down the number of molecules requiring the labor-intensive *in vitro* techniques that are presently used to assess drug-drug interactions and metabolism. Clearly this is an area that needs to be investigated as it also represents a mechanism for minimizing utilization of animal and human tissues *in vitro*. This would ultimately result in faster screens for drug interaction probability and undesirable metabolism at the very earliest stages of drug discovery. An approach such as this may even be useful prior to molecule synthesis. Computational models would also be tools for the medicinal chemist to test (virtually) molecules and efficiently synthesize bioactive molecules with favorable CYP inhibition and metabolism profiles. The potential challenges required for implementation of computational technology need to be seriously considered. Using the predictions and developments in drug metabolism over the past 20 years to guide us, we intend to highlight where prediction by computational models of drug-drug interactions and metabolism is now, where we think it should be, and how we can ultimately get there.

15.2. Shifting the Drug Metabolism Paradigm

The guiding principle of drug discovery in the coming decades may not necessarily be the "more and faster" paradigm of combinatorial chemistry and high-throughput screening when it comes to finding the next blockbuster drug.[12,13] What continues to be a priority in the pharmaceutical industry is failure limitation in the latter stages of development, particularly as the costs accrued at these stages are great and increasing.[14] Since drug-drug interactions and high pharmacokinetic variability may cause rejection of a molecule as a useful therapeutic entity, an evaluation of these characteristics as early and reliably as possible would be incredibly valuable. If such information was available in the discovery phase it could direct chemical syntheses away from structures with a high likelihood of drug-CYP interaction. For example, studies indicate that clinically relevant and undesirable drug-drug interactions occur widely in oncology.[19] In many other therapeutic areas drug-drug interactions represent 1-2% of clinically relevant adverse drug reactions (ADRs).[20-22] At present, CYP2D6 appears to cause the most concern with respect to pharmacokinetic variability due to its polymorphic expression, ability to metabolize a large proportion of therapeutic drugs, and the potential for different responses within varying populations.[23] However, it must be noted that there are many drugs that are commercially successful in spite of their being potent CYP2D6 inhibitors.

With the recent measurement of high levels of CYP3A in the gastrointestinal tract,[24] drug interactions and metabolism in organs other than the liver are now also being actively pursued.[25] Further, it has become apparent that there are relationships between drug transport, metabolism, and metabolite transport. The most well characterized is the interrelationship between CYP3A4 and P-glycoprotein (Pgp), both from the point of overlapping substrate specificities[26] and co-regulation of expression.[27] The consequences of this may be of importance for new investigational drugs if they are found to interact with either the drug metabolizing enzyme or transporter.[28] It may also be worth considering that the binding sites for CYPs may be similar to target receptors, enzymes, and transporters, which extends the importance of understanding drug-CYP interactions on much a broader scale.[29] Clearly, the scope of understanding drug-CYP interactions now goes well beyond the liver and these enzymes alone.

Lin and Lu have suggested that the processes for determining the consequences of clinically relevant drug interactions *in vitro* are complicated.[15] Good predictions are dependent upon the concentrations of both substrate and inhibitor used in the *in vitro* studies and their relationship to the *in vivo* situation.[15] Obviously it is desirable to pick a therapeutic agent which is not a potent CYP or non-target enzyme inhibitor. Hence knowledge of the likelihood of concurrent use and therapeutic index of potentially interacting drugs are major criteria in facilitating extrapolation of *in vitro* results to *in vivo* predictions.[15] In order to predict drug-drug interactions, we must be able to clearly define and understand the mechanisms of inhibition of the drug-metabolizing enzymes. In addition, the metabolic fate of the drug (and potentially active metabolites), the enzyme involved in each pathway, and the concentration of the drug/inhibitor available to the enzyme must all be characterized.[8] This latter point is itself a controversial and difficult topic owing to difficulty in determining the concentration of drug actually available at the CYP active site.[16] The assay conditions utilized *in vitro* also influence our *in vivo* predictions of drug interactions.[17,18] Thus our current ability to predict drug-drug interactions and metabolism has several limitations.[15]

There are many model systems available to the drug metabolism scientist (Figure 15.1). Many of these approaches can be used to study drug-drug interactions prior to administration to humans, and their respective pros and cons have been previously discussed.[7,8,30]

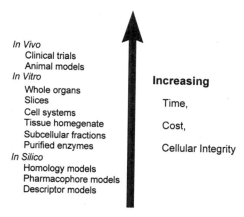

Figure 15.1. Schematic of models available for pharmaceutical research.[43]

Individually expressed enzymes and liver microsomes are the most widely used in vitro models for predicting drug-drug interactions, although they have caveats.[17,31] Despite these drawbacks, *in vitro* systems are being applied as high-throughput screens with the potential for generating large quantities of interaction data.[32] Further additional screens may predict other absorption, distribution, metabolism, and excretion (ADME) properties,[33] such as metabolic stability. The vast databases generated by these high-throughput techniques are potentially useful to generate computational models reflecting the various end-points such as inhibiting a specific P450. We suggest that such computational models, once validated for their predictive power, will play a more prominent role in drug development. In fact, this role would be analogous to that which computational models already play in structure-based drug design.[34]

One computational technique being utilized to predict drug metabolism is homology modeling, in which the sequence of an unknown enzyme is aligned with that of a known crystal structure for a closely related enzyme. Using this technique, one would expect the proteins to fold similarly based on the known crystal structure. However, since no crystal structure for a mammalian membrane bound CYP is available, we are reliant on the crystal structures determined for the soluble bacterial CYPs for homology modeling. Although there is general agreement that the CYP active sites seem to have a high degree of conserved structure,[35-37] the accuracy of homology-built proteins correlates with the degree of aligned pairwise sequence identity. As human CYPs have less than 30% homology with bacterial CYPs, this may be suboptimal. In addition, homology models are not high-throughput, since docking of molecules in the active site model requires considerable computational time in order to define potential sites for inhibitors or substrates.[38] Additionally, docking requires a scoring function, although many of those presently available are also suboptimal. The development of fast docking algorithms for flexible ligands using software such as Hammerhead™ may improve this situation. This would enable more rapid, fully automated screening of very large databases against CYP binding sites derived from homology models.[39] Because the homology models may currently be far from the most favorable approach in terms of accuracy and speed, we have looked at alternative techniques to understand the human CYP active sites. These alternative models may also achieve the desired throughput to match or exceed conventional high-throughput screening obtained *in vitro*.

Starting with the work of Hansch in the early 1970s, there has been an evolution of quantitative structure activity relationships (QSAR) for CYPs.[40] One statement from this seminal 1972 paper predicts a futuristic application: *"As more complete and more precise studies are made we should reach the position where the relative effects of substituents on the metabolism of drugs can be estimated in advance."* Present-day increased computer efficiency and software have allowed development of computational models that describe biological properties, which play a role in binding and inhibition. However, even with the amazing progress in computational software and hardware most would say the goal outlined by Hansch has yet to be attained.[41,42] Ultimately, the user-friendly improvements in software are now allowing a "black box" approach to computer modeling.[42] It is no longer essential to be a computational chemist to generate useful models from software that requires very little knowledge of the algorithms used in model generation. A "black box" approach is not necessarily the ideal, as it is viewed skeptically by some scientists who want to understand the inner workings of the software.

It seems likely that in the future, computational approaches for metabolism and prediction of drug interactions will be another addition to the expanding tool kit of the drug metabolism scientist. This addition will require accessible software in which molecules are easily input and predictions for metabolism and inhibition are generated. In addition, there would need to be superior graphical representation software in order to respond to the large amounts of data which the human brain (the ultimate pattern recognition system) must decipher. Ideally the chemists would have instant access to drug metabolism/inhibition modeling software which would be used to predict affinities and metabolic lability of virtual compounds. This information would then be used to redirect synthesis away from potential substrates and inhibitors of the drug-metabolizing enzymes. The problem with such a hands-on approach for the chemist would be the need for education regarding the value and interpretation of the drug metabolism and biological data produced. Inhibitor pharmacophores for CYPs 1A2,[43,44] 2C9,[45,46] 2D6,[47,48] and 3A4[49] as well as substrate pharmacophores for CYP2B6[50] and CYP3A4[51] have recently been reported. Consequently, there now exists the foundation for an approach to predict the interaction potential of a molecule with these enzymes without recourse to *in vitro* verification. Techniques for extending this methodology to predict affinity and interactions with other enzymes and transporters also exist, as well as approaches to studying experimental variables and their influence on the behavior of an enzyme. Additionally, bioavailability and clearance data may also be modeled using these approaches given enough orders of magnitude in the measured response and chemical structure diversity in the dataset used to create the model. A good example is the comparative molecular field analysis (CoMFA) model that was used to predict CYP2E1/CYP2B1-mediated clearance of chlorinated volatile organic compounds in rat.[52]

Computational approaches are clearly applicable to modeling various aspects likely to influence ADME related properties such as solubility and permeability,[53] although to date there has been only limited success in predicting permeability for large numbers of diverse molecules.[54] Human intestinal absorption has also been successfully predicted using quantitative structure-property relationships.[55] Computational models of ADME-related properties like these would be useful for database mining and commercial library evaluation. Hence, computational approaches would be complimentary to the various scoring efforts underway to distinguish "drugs" and "nondrugs,"[56-58] by enabling computational selection of "drugs" with favorable ADME and drug-drug interaction properties. We would argue that we may now have reached and are surpassing the predictions of Hansch in 1972 as we can predict ADME properties beyond metabolism and in so doing the paradigm for the field of drug metabolism is shifting. As with alterations in paradigms in other fields of science,[59] the present one may reinforce the need to emphasize change in academic programs to include computational chemistry training for graduates of biological sciences intending to go on to the pharmaceutical industry.[60] In addition, this may necessitate biology/metabolism training for chemists in order that they may understand and apply these technologies. Both biologists and chemists should acquire an understanding of the utility of computational modeling, the dependency of the model on the quality of input data and the need for more cross-functional teamwork to maximize the information obtained from this approach.

15.3. Cytochrome P450 Pharmacophore Modeling Methodology

As already introduced, an emerging computational approach that is different to homology modeling of the enzyme active site is the generation of a pharmacophore which describes the features present within the ligand required for the experimentally determined bioactivity. A pharmacophore is essentially a model of the spatial arrangement of structural features for a series of molecules that show activity, and therefore affinity, towards an enzyme/receptor obtained after structure alignment and superimposition.[61] The alignment of structures according to chemical functionality allows structurally unique and diverse molecules to present identical 3D features and be aligned together without atom-by-atom comparison. A generated pharmacophore therefore provides a straightforward way of representing drug-enzyme interactions that does not necessarily represent the active site but instead illustrates the features necessary for the measured response. The prediction of interaction or activity for a new drug candidate is then based on the geometric fit to the chemical features in a generated pharmacophore hypothesis. Thus the resulting pharmacophore hypotheses represent the chemical features important for binding of a molecule to an enzyme active site or measured response. In the case of CYPs, this biological parameter may be enzyme activity (K_m or V_{max}/K_m) or enzyme inhibition (K_i). One method for generating pharmacophores for drug-metabolizing enzymes involves using Catalyst™ (Molecular Simulations Inc., San Diego), an intuitive, integrated software environment that has been used to identify new lead candidates and improve existing drugs. The creation of a model by Catalyst is achieved by integrating diverse software modules into a single interface. These modules include those involved in generating multiple conformers of each molecule (which possess extensive and diverse coverage of conformational space), pharmacophore alignments, automated pharmacophore hypotheses, structure activity relationship data, molecular structures, and pharmacophore or molecular shape-based 3D database searches. Catalyst may also be very useful for deriving simple pharmacophore hypotheses when the number of molecules in the training set is limited but exceeds a minimum number.

Numerous pharmacophores of substrate and inhibitors of CYPs have been reported, some of which are shown in Table 15.1. The following is the generalized procedure we used to generate several different CYP pharmacophores using Catalyst.[44,46,47,49-51] In order to generate CYP pharmacophores from inhibitor (K_i) or substrate (K_m) datasets, the number of conformers generated for each molecule was limited to a maximum of 255, with an energy range of 20 kcal/mol. These parameters were identical for molecules used in generating the pharmacophores (training set) or those left out of the model and then used for prediction (test set). Ten hypotheses were generated for the training set using the conformers for each of the molecules and the K_m or K_i values, after selection of features such as hydrogen-bond donor, hydrogen-bond acceptor, hydrophobic, and negative ionizable. After assessing all 10 hypotheses generated, the lowest energy-cost hypothesis was considered the best, as this possessed features representative of all the hypotheses. The quality of the structure-activity correlations for observed and predicted data generated by Catalyst are estimated by means of a correlation coefficient (r). In order to test the statistical significance of the retrieved hypothesis it can be verified by permuting (randomizing) the response variable, i.e., the activities of the training set compounds are mixed a number of times (so that each value is no longer assigned to the original molecule). The Catalyst hypothesis-generation procedure is then repeated a number of times in order to evaluate whether models can be constructed from this scrambled data. The model is considered significant if the mean correlation coefficient for these scrambled models decreases significantly (and resides closer to zero) below the correlation coefficient for the chosen best model.

In an attempt to further validate the Catalyst pharmacophores, the generated models can be used to predict the K_i or K_m values of a test set of molecules not included in the original training sets. These molecules are fitted by aligning the pharmacophore features of the structures with the hypothesis deduced for each model (an example of this is shown in Plate 15.1). In order to predict a K_i or K_m value, two algorithms are available within Catalyst to perform this alignment, specifically fast fit and best fit. Fast fit refers to the method of finding the optimum fit of the molecule to the hypothesis among all the conformers of the molecule. The optimal fit is the positioning of features on the molecule closest to the centroid of their corresponding pharmacophore features. The best fit procedure starts with fast fit and allows individual conformers to flex over a maximum energy of 20 kcal/mol. This allows examination of more conformational space and minimizes the distance between the hypothesis features and the atoms to which they map onto (Catalyst tutorials release 3.0, MSI, San Diego, CA.) The predictions using best and/or fast fit are generated from the model regression and can then be compared by means of a residual which is calculated from the differ-

Table 15.1. Literature data suitable for pharmacophore modeling human CYPs.

CYP	Kinetic parameter	Number of molecules in data set	Range of activity	Reference
1A1	IC_{50}	10	2 -160 µM	93
1A2	IC_{50}	12	2 -140 µM	93
1A2	IC_{50}	11	29 -1000 µM	94
1A2	K_i	12 + 9 test set	0.22 - 749 µM	44[a,b]
1A2	% remaining	44	18.6 -104.4 %	43[a], 44[b]
1B1	IC_{50}	12	2 -180 µM	93
2A6	K_i	12	0.05 – 100 µM	95
2B6	K_m	16 + 5 test set	1.28 -17700 µM	50[a,b]
2C9	K_i	29	0.1 -50 µM	45[a], 46[b]
2C9	IC_{50}, K_i, K_m	10 (IC50) 5 (Ki) 11 (Km)	13 ->1000 µM 2 - 50 µM 4 -141 µM	96, 46[b]
2C9	K_i	9 + 14 test set	3.5 - 94.3 µM	46[a,b]
2C9	IC_{50}	13	12.9 - 250 µM	97, 46[b]
2C9	IC_{50}, K_m, K_i	24 (IC50) 9 (Km) 8 (Ki)	0.5 - >500 µM 124 - 758 µM 0.22 - 246 µM	98
2C19	IC_{50}	15	23->500 µM	99,100
2D6	K_i	31	0.0046 - >1000 µM	48[a], 47[b]
2D6	K_i	14 + 1 inactive	0.17 - 340 µM	101
2D6	K_i	20 + 15 test set	0.03 - 529.5 µM	47[a,b]
3A4	K_i	22	0.026 - >500 µM	102, 49[b]
3A4	K_i	14 + 8 test set	1.8 - 701.3 µM	49[a,b]
3A4	K_m	38 + 12 test set	0.35 - 5600 µM	51[a,b]
3A4	K_i	32	0.1 - 268 µM	103, 104, 49[b]

[a] *Primary source of data used to generate a QSAR model.*
[b] *Previously published dataset used to build a Catalyst™ pharmacophore*

ence (in log units) between predicted and observed K_i or K_m. In the case of generating preliminary pharmacophores with a limited number of molecules in the training set ($N < 20$), we considered a predicted K_i or K_m value within one log unit of the observed value to be a valid prediction. This relationship appears to be appropriate since the variability in *in vitro* generated CYP K_i or K_m values between different laboratories is often greater than 1 log unit for the same molecule.[47] Although Catalyst has the advantages of not requiring manual molecule alignments like CoMFA and therefore does not impart user bias or expertise in this regard, there are some disadvantages with the software compared with descriptor based methods like MS-WHIM PLS, as described previously (reference[50] and references therein). These disadvantages of Catalyst are mainly focused around testing the models and cross-validation approaches which the software at present does not incorporate but is likely to address in the future.

15.4. Utilizing and Interpreting Data Generated by Computational Models for Enzymes and Transporters Involved in Drug Metabolism

Once predictions are generated using computational models, the problem facing pharmaceutical scientists is evaluating them alongside the overwhelming amount of both pharmacology and drug metabolism data. Presently, there is clearly an unmet need for predictive CYP and ADME models, decision algorithms, and interpretive rationales. We are presently far from being able to provide universal guides as to how drugs will interact or be metabolized from a structure alone. Currently we are only approaching the data collection and initial modeling stages of the paradigm. In order to identify structural factors influencing drug metabolism properties, we need insights into the mechanisms underlying the interrelationships of chemicals and biological systems in this age of drug-metabolizing enzymes. Quantitative structure-activity relationships (QSAR) including pharmacophores clearly have utility in drug discovery as a basis for understanding drug metabolism in which the model is a working hypothesis to be defended or refuted. The predictive power of pharmacophores depends on the range of diversity of chemical structures and physicochemical properties utilized. Further, a wide biological response range is required. Biotransformation and inter-action of chemicals with drug-metabolizing enzymes depends on bind-ing and/or chemical modification and release of metabolite(s). Molecular shape and steric properties of the drugs are therefore impor-tant for enzyme binding. Such QSAR methods would allow determina-tion of locations of groups of biologically similar compounds in chem-ical and physicochemical parameter space. QSAR is clearly limited if there are multiple processes contributing to an activity, hence some models will have limited applicability and may not give a meaningful fit to the data. Therefore, generating data from a purified or expressed CYP or transporter is clearly preferable to a tissue preparation contain-ing multiple competing processes to avoid background "noise" caused by other enzymes or pathways.[32]

Models produced *in silico*[63] could be descriptive, predictive, explica-tive, abstract, or refined. Therefore as indicated by Gerloff,[63] *"the use of an optimal model requires the proper use of both the language and tools where a distinctive feature of science is the model representation of one system by another which simplified is not reality but a facet of it"*. There are many sources of data suitable for building predictive drug metabolism models of human metabolism. However, these models can be essentially reduced to three categories: organ systems, isolated phys-iologic structures (e.g., microsomes), and those computationally derived (see Figure 15.1). One of the initial questions asked during such model construction should be "is the model adequate for the purpose of study?" If the model is to test a hypothesis in early drug discovery, does the computational model save time, conserve resources, and utilize techniques to predict an outcome that could be avoided in the develop-ment phase? It may be imperative to use drug interaction or even metab-olism computational models in discovery as early as possible, as the true value of these techniques is in the redirection of molecule synthe-sis, regardless of whether or not they are 100% predictive. The future of such computational models in drug metabolism may well enable ultra-high throughput screening of compound libraries *in silico*[64] in which CYP, enzyme/transporter interactions, and other metabolism data are encoded in a consistent format. This information will ultimately be used to minimize failure in development by selecting compounds with favorable ADME characteristics. Eventually, drug-drug interaction testing may become obsolete if analysis of inhibitors is correctly predicted. There may be even more important information to be gained by analysis of the ratio of the potency measures for the therapeutic target and for CYPs, which will allow a means to select candidate compounds. Similarly, substrate models may be generated using the apparent Km value even though this a measure of the binding site properties of the enzyme[62] and not necessarily a true representation of substrate affinity for CYPs. Theoretically a dissociation rate constant would be more representative of substrate-enzyme interactions, although we have shown that apparent K_m values are quite useful for producing predictive models of CYP-substrate interactions.[50] The role of QSAR may evolve to enable understanding of important mechanistic aspects of drug metabolism by providing more details on the structure of the active site(s) of metabolizing enzymes using both inhibitor and substrate data. This evolutionary process would naturally require precise data analysis by the detection of small deviations of calculated values compared with those observed. As we gain further insight into the relationship between binding and biological response these models will become more predictive and play an important role in future.[65]

The requirements of such computational models should include validation of internal consistency using the fit of additional data to the model in order to iteratively refine it. The model(s) should provide some true explanatory value and ideally could be able of differentiating enantiomers. To date the scarcity of such enantioselective models is evident from literature searches, but it is likely that the number of these will increase in future. Beyond simple enzyme models for interaction there needs to be a way to explain and simplify complex processes for inhibition types other than competitive, such as mechanism-based inhibitors. This may necessitate a hierarchy of "intelligent" approaches, where structural alerts would identify potential chemical moieties likely to be involved in mechanism-based inhibition before they were fitted to pharmacophore models. It is likely that inhibition mechanisms other than competitive will be poorly predicted by computational models at present. Similarly, CYP inhibitors or substrates that demonstrate allosteric enzyme activation would not be expected to be predicted with these models as activity in this case is not a simple function of binding affinity.[18] Future models will need to assess the chemical features present on these CYP allosteric modulators so that they may be eventually correctly predicted.[51]

When it comes to the published CYP QSAR models, to date there have been few of them and they have rarely been utilized to predict the effects of molecules not in the training set. Other than the numerous substrate or inhibitor templates obtained by manual overlap of molecules, the first models of human CYPs of a more sophisticated nature were the inhibitor pharmacophores produced for CYP1A2,[43] CYP2D6,[48] and CYP2C9.[45] Korzekwa and Jones[66] suggested it might be difficult to develop substrate pharmacophores for CYPs other than CYP1A and CYP2D due to the lack of specific ionic interactions with the enzymes. They also suggested that due to the unique and diverse characteristics of CYPs, predicting metabolism would be a difficult task. These authors did not discuss the applicability of this technique to predicting drug-drug interactions. In general, for enzymes with specific binding requirements, a simple pharmacophore can be of enormous value as a predictive tool. However, it was suggested that if there were no steric binding requirements in the molecules involved, then models would need to be based on electronic characteristics.[66]

The next logical step is to interpret the pharmacophores within the context of the active site homology-modeled on the bacterial CYPs. If the pharmacophore fits realistically in the homology modeled site then the pharmacophore can then be used with more confidence. It would also provide a quicker way to understand the likelihood of binding than requiring the computationally intensive molecular dynamics fit with the protein model. The potential also exists that pharmacophores of CYPs and other drug metabolizing enzymes could be used to search databases for potent and selective inhibitors that might be of therapeutic use. With the increasing number of compounds identified as substrates or inhibitors of the major expressed CYPs (Table 15.1), a meta-analysis of various studies with K_m, K_i or IC_{50} data for any particular CYP could be performed. Theoretically, this would enable QSAR modeling for the substrate and inhibitor binding site(s) for all CYPs if the values encompassed a number of orders of magnitude and if consistent *in vitro* incubation conditions were maintained throughout all studies. In the meantime, the validity of using K_i data derived from human liver, microsomal, or expressed CYP studies for building pharmacophores has been reported.[45,47-49]

Computational modeling approaches could also be applied to other drug metabolizing enzymes beyond the CYPs, as well as to proteins involved in drug transport. There have been some attempts at SAR[67] and QSAR[68-70] modeling for Pgp substrates and modulators. These studies have suggested hydrophobicity is important for Pgp modulators.[70] Similarly, there are few QSAR models for inhibitors or substrates of human and rat sulfotransferases[71] or glutathione S-transferases derived using *in vitro* data,[72,73] and rat glucuronosyltransferases using *in vitro*[74] or *in vivo*[75] data. To date, there have also been no published attempts to build pharmacophores for substrates, inhibitors or inducers of Pgp, sulfotransferases, glucuronosyltransferases, or glutathione S-transferases. This may be in part related to the fact that these have only recently been purified, cloned, or expressed as compared to the CYPs. Another role for 3D QSAR is the prediction of not only the optimal bioactive structures of molecules, but the determination of whether it is the same conformer that is likely to bind the CYP or transporter in question. In these cases we may require more than one model to maximize conformational space and provide a definitive screening approach prior to obtaining predictive, diverse datasets.

15.5. The Challenge Ahead

For models of drug metabolizing enzymes to be of an acceptable standard for the industry and regulatory bodies such as the FDA, they must be rigorously evaluated and scientifically validated. After considerable validation studies, the FDA now suggests that significant negative results in *in vitro* drug-drug interaction studies can negate the need for *in vivo* studies.[76] Perhaps it is not too far-fetched to suppose that after similar rigorous validation of *in silico* methods, negative *in silico* findings will one day remove the need for *in vitro* and *in vivo* studies. However, as it took roughly a decade for regulatory bodies to accept *in vitro* drug metabolism studies, it is likely that the acceptance of *in silico* models will take at least as long. Data for a number of ADME parameters (including CYP inhibition) will need to be generated *in vitro* to test the *in silico* findings. This will require a significant increase in data output to allow some confidence of the predictability. The move towards automation, miniaturizing technologies, higher throughput, and rapid analytical assays will enable the *in vitro* screening of vast numbers of compounds in a pharmaceutical company library,[2,77] e.g., for enzyme inhibition.[78] Thus in the future, orders of magnitude more kinetic parameter data points will be produced although we will have to be sure that it is of high quality if it is to be used for modeling. This higher throughput approach to drug metabolism *in vitro* will require methods for optimizing experimental design[79] and rapid kinetic analysis.[80]

While the screening approach will provide a considerable amount of information for building pharmacophores for CYPs and other enzymes, another challenge will be efficient data organization so that data of significance are highlighted.[81] Techniques to analyze databases for metabolic interaction patterns (regularities or for that matter irregularities) will require clarification of the optimal techniques whether they are knowledge-based,[82] decision trees,[83] neural networks[84] or data classification schemes[85] (like Bayesian[56] or Kohonen[86] networks). These methods or perhaps new or hybrid techniques may enable more efficient prediction of drug interactions if these are descriptors encoded along with the structures in the drug database. Alternatively, such techniques may act as an initial step prior to pharmacophore construction which would be an efficient means of data reduction.[87] The computer will then be used as a simulator in much the same way that engineers have been using them for years, whereby theoretical structures are sketched and the interaction likelihood and metabolism pathways are calculated.

The real challenge facing decision-makers during this paradigm shift is less technological and more psychological in nature. At the very threshold of a new paradigm in biological sciences, will we be willing to accept computational predictions that may shape the very future of medicine? Although genes and their function are becoming known, we really need bioinformatic approaches to be applied to the drug metabolism data to discover new or hidden relationships. Such classification circuits may be used to show that CYPs have relationships with other proteins that may manifest as similar substrate or inhibitor selectivity. An example of this is the suggested positive relationship between CYP2D1 and the dopamine transporter.[88] The field of bioinformatics will assist in the next paradigm shift for drug metabolism in much the same way as it has linked physiology and genetics. In living organisms, the complex interplay of biological systems protects it from adverse influences and environments, with defects in these processes likely to result in disease.[89] We may find that the subtle differences in interindividual expression or catalytic activity of CYPs[16] may be more important when it comes to looking at the metabolism in humans as a complete system of interacting processes. Rather than looking at individual CYPs, we may find that this form of bioinformation will help us appreciate that our individual CYP fingerprint affects how we uniquely respond simultaneously to administered drugs, naturally occurring xenobiotics, and endobiotics at any point in time[89] and in any organ or tissue.

15.6. Concluding Remarks

Pharmacological testing has shifted over the last 20 years from *in vivo* to *in vitro*. However, disadvantages of the *in vitro* approach include that it ultimately neglects the multifactorial nature of diseases and effective therapies. Further ADME parameters are often omitted during structural optimization, there is an inability to identify potential side effects *in vitro*,[90,91] and all the *in vitro* assays are reliant on the incubation conditions. The changing strategies and technologies in drug development represent a significant paradigm shift[92] that once implemented, could potentially limit selection to only "ideal" compounds with better properties as a drug, including fewer side effects. As the pharmaceutical industry utilizes the information from surrogate markers like Caco-2 cells for intestinal absorption, models of blood-brain barrier penetration, microsomes and enzymes for drug metabolism, and cellular models of toxicology, the interdisciplinary behavior of drug research is now clearly focused in industry. The pharmaceutical companies acted quickly to acquire these technologies for metabolism but may have been slower to realize the widening gap between them and academia in terms of using computational approaches as the next paradigm.

The development of computational approaches to model drug metabolism endpoints will allow data mining on a very large scale such that it could be an alternative to synthesis and testing. Computational combinatorial synthesis could generate virtual drugs that either are or are not substrates or inhibitors for any drug-metabolizing enzyme using the rules developed from the pharmacophore models. After validation of predictive computational models it will become possible to screen a database in parallel for both inhibitory and affinity potential for the enzymes involved in human xenobiotic metabolism (Figure 15.2).

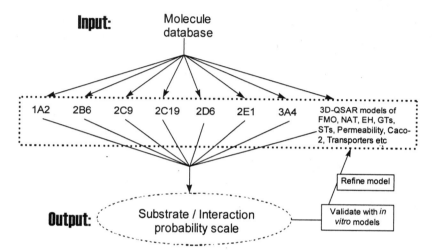

FMO, flavin containing monooxygenase; NAT, N-acetyltransferase; EH, epoxide hydrolase; GTs, uridine diphosphate-glucuronosyltransferases; STs, sulfotransferases.

Figure 15.2. A schematic of an *in silico* parallel screening strategy for drug metabolizing enzyme and transporter 3D QSAR and the steps necessary for model validation and iterative 3D QSAR design.

The outputs from this type of *in silico* analysis will be data-intensive and therefore require reduction or refining using a visualization format such as a matrix (Plate 15.2). This would enable faster recognition of CYP inhibitors and substrates. Increased visual recognition may be particularly advantageous for a series of compounds allowing the visual or computational selection of substrates or inhibitors for one CYP over another and the simultaneous resolution of structural components required to fit a particular CYP. It is feasible that this type of 3D QSAR pharmacophore approach for CYPs could be combined with similar models for other phase I (flavin-containing monooxygenases, or FMO), phase II (glucuronidation and sulfation) enzymes, and transporters such as Pgp. The discipline of drug metabolism is clearly moving to a position of integrating with the discovery process. Eventually, using the strategy described above, *in silico* analysis may preempt the presently accepted discovery process to guide molecular design. This will be particularly obvious if the potential for interaction with a CYP or other drug metabolizing enzyme/transporter is important for a class of compounds. The ultimate goal of this research will be to minimize the potential for drug-drug interactions and pharmacokinetic variability by using this high-throughput method for rational selection of compounds with a low interaction profile for CYPs and ultimately other drug metabolizing enzymes or transporters. These uses of 3D QSAR in combination with other allied modeling techniques will be invaluable as we await the crystallization of membrane bound CYPs, which will improve over homology models.

Will this "paradigm shift" ultimately result in a place for virtual drug discovery companies, where all discovery and drug metabolism is based on computational models? The smaller number of staff required would allow drug discovery companies focused on computational approaches alone. These companies would then contract out the necessary *in vivo* studies for regulatory approval. The future prediction of all ADME and pharmacokinetic parameters *in silico* necessitates that regulatory bodies are aware and kept abreast of developments in the computational modeling field. If this comes to pass, all successful drug companies will need to leverage computational screening, synthesis, and data mining paradigms for all targets and ADME screens at the very earliest stages of drug discovery. This would move the emphasis away from combinatorial chemistry, giving the medicinal chemist the key role producing structures *in silico* that are automatically assessed for *in silico* activity. This activity would not only be focused towards a therapeutic target, but away from or towards certain CYP enzymes and transporters. The *in silico* screening strategy will be dependent on the therapeutic area under study and should take into account other drugs likely to be co-administered and their effect on each enzyme or transporter. The novel concept in this approach will be in obtaining selectivity between pharmacophores for targets that are different (or similar) to those of important human drug-metabolizing enzymes or transporters. In parallel, computing approaches for QSAR for thousands of datasets and data mining will need reliable training sets first as well as test sets for validation before releasing models for widespread use. Future electronic publications describing ADME and other drug metabolism-related QSARs may need to also encode all chemical structures in a universal format with the associated activity values. This would enable a rapid transfer and dissemination of computational models around the world as they are published. Clearly there will be many valuable pharmacophores for predicting drug-drug interactions and pharmacokinetic variability which will be generated in the coming millennium as the data from high-throughput screening becomes available to model.

Acknowledgements

SE gratefully acknowledges the initial encouragement of Dr. Patrick J. Murphy in pursuing this direction and Dr. Richard J. McGowan for his inspirational discussions on paradigm shifts.

References

1.   White RE: **Short- and long-term projections about the use of drug metabolism in drug discovery and development.** *Drug Metab Dispos* 1998, **26**:1213-1216.

2.   Rodrigues AD: **Preclinical drug metabolism in the age of high-throughput screening: An industrial perspective.** *Pharm Res* 1997, **14**:1504-1510.

3.   Bresnick E: Drug metabolism: **Speculations on the future.** *Drug Metab Rev* 1979, **10**:311-313.

4.   Ober RE: **Drug metabolism: An industrial research view of the future.** *Drug Metab Rev* 1979, **10**:315-319.

5.   Leibman KC: **Drug metabolism: Prospects for the future.** *Drug Metab Rev* 1979, **10**:299-309.

6.   Nelson DR, Koymans L, Kamataki T, Stegeman JJ, Feyereisen R, Waxman DJ, Waterman MR., Gotoh O, Coon MJ, Estabrook RW, Gunsalus IC, Nebert, DW: **P450 superfamily: Update on new**

   sequences, gene mapping, accession numbers and nomenclature. *Pharmacogenetics* 1996, **6**:1-42.

7. Ekins S: **Past, present, and future applications of precision-cut liver slices for *in vitro* xenobiotic metabolism.** *Drug Metab Rev* 1996, **28**:591-623.

8. Wrighton SA, Vandenbranden M, Stevens JC, Shipley LA: ***In vitro* methods for assessing human hepatic drug metabolism: their use in drug development.** *Drug Metab Rev* 1993, **25**:453-484.

9. Miwa GT: **Goals, design, timing, and future opportunities for non clinical drug metabolism studies.** *Toxicol Pathol* 1995, **23**:131-135.

10. Campbell DB: **Are we doing too many animal biodisposition investigations before Phase I studies in man? A re-evaluation of the timing and extent of ADME studies.** *Eur J Drug Metab Pharm* 1994, **19**:283-293.

11. FDA: Guidance for industry. Drug metabolism/drug interaction studies in the drug development process: Studies *in vitro.* 1997.

12. Hall SE: **The future of combinatorial chemistry as a drug discovery paradigm.** *Pharm Res* 1997, **14**:1104-1105.

13. Arlington S: **Accelerating drug discovery: Creating the right environment.** *Drug Discovery Today* 1997, **2**:547-553.

14. Heilman RD: **Drug development: history, "overview" and what are GCPs.** *Quality Assurance: Good Practice, Regulation, and Law 1995,* **4**:75-79.

15. Lin JH, Lu AYH: **Inhibition of cytochrome P-450 and implications in drug development.** *Ann Rev Med Chem* 1997, **32**:295-304.

16. Pelkonen O, Maenpaa J, Taavitsainen P, Rautio A, Raunio H: **Inhibition and induction of human cytochrome P450 (CYP) enzymes.** *Xenobiotica* 1998, **28**:1203-1253.

17. Ekins S, Maenpaa J, Wrighton SA: ***In vitro* metabolism: Subcellular fractions.** In: *Handbook of Drug Metabolism.* Woolf TF, ed. New York: Marcel Dekker, Inc. 1999:363-399.

18. Ekins S, Ring BJ, Binkley SN, Hall SD, Wrighton SA: **Autoactivation and activation of cytochrome P450s.** *Int J Clin Pharmacol Ther* 1998, **36**:642-651.

19. McLeod HL: **Clinically relevant drug-drug interactions in oncology.** *Br J Clin Pharmacol* 1998, **45**:539-544.

20. Tucker GT: **The rational selection of drug interaction studies: Implications of recent advances in drug metabolism.** *Int J Clin Pharmacol Thera Toxicol* 1992, **30**:550-553.

21. Schmider J, Greenblatt DJ, Von Moltke LL, Shader RI: **Relationship of *in vitro* data on drug metabolism to *in vivo* pharmacokinetics and drug interactions: Implications for diazepam disposition in man.** *J Clin Psychopharmacol* 1996, **16**:267-272.

22. Ito K, Iwatsubo T, Kanimitsu S, Ueda K, Suzuki H, Sugiyama Y: **Prediction of pharmacokinetic alterations caused by drug-drug interactions: Metabolic interaction in the liver.** *Pharmacol Rev* 1998, **50**:387-411.

23. Zuhlsdorf MT: **Relevance of pheno- and genotyping in clinical drug development.** *Int J Clin Pharmacol Ther* 1998, **36**:607-612.

24. Paine MF, Khalighi M, Fisher JM, Shen DD, Kunze KL, Marsh CL, Perkins JD, Thummel KE: **Characterization of interintestinal and intraintestinal variations in human CYP3A-dependent metabolism.** *J Pharmacol Exp Ther* 1997, **283**:1552-1562.

25. Iatsimiskaia E, Tiulebaev S, Storozhuk E, Utkin I, Smith D, Gerber N, Koudriakova T: **Metabolism of rifabutin in human enterocyte and liver microsomes: Kinetic parameters, identification of enzyme sytems, and drug interactions with macrolides and antifungal agents.** *Clin Pharmacol Thera* 1997, **61**:554-562.

26. Wacher VJ, Wu CY, Benet LZ: **Overlapping substrate specificities and tissue distribution of cytochrome P450 3A and P-glycoprotein: Implications for drug delivery and activity in cancer chemotherapy.** *Mol Carcinogenesis* 1995, **13**:129-134.

27. Scheutz EG, Beck WT, Scheutz JD: **Modulators and substrates of P-glycoprotein and cytochrome P4503A coordinately up-regulate these proteins in human colon carcinoma cells.** *Mol Pharmacol* 1996, **49**:311-318.

28. Zhang Y, Guo X, Lin ET, Benet LZ: **Overlapping substrate specificities of cytochrome P4503A and P-glycoprotein for a novel cysteine protease inhibitor.** *Drug Metab Dispos* 1998, **26**:360-366.

29. Helmeste DM, Tang SW: **Inhibition of platelet serotonin uptake by cytochrome P450 inhibitors miconazole and econazole.** *Life Sci* 1988, **62**:2203-2208.

30. Fuhr U, Weiss M, Kroemer HK, Neugebauer G, Rameis H, Weber W, Woodcock BG: **Systematic screening for pharmacokinetic interactions during drug development.** *Int J Clin Pharmacol Thera* 1996, **34**:139-151.

31. Bertz RJ, Granneman GR: **Use of *in vitro* and *in vivo* data to estimate the likelihood of metabolic pharmacokinetic interactions.** *Clin Pharmacokinet* 1997, **32**:210-258.

32. Moody GC, Griffin SJ, Mather AN, McGinnity DF, Riley RJ: **Fully auto-mated analysis of activities catalyzed by the major human liver cytochrome P450 (CYP) enzymes: Assessment of human CYP inhibition potential.** *Xenobiotica* 1999, **29**:53-75.

33. Tarbit MH, Berman J: **High-throughput approaches for evaluating absorption, distribution, metabolism and excretion properties of lead compounds.** *Curr Opin Chem Biol* 1998, **2**:411-416.

34. Sun E, Cohen FE: **Computer-assisted drug discovery-A review.** *Gene* 1993, **137**:127-132.

35. Szklarz GD, Halpert JR: **Molecular modeling of cytochrome P4503A4.** *J Comput-Aid Mol Des* 1997, **11**:265-272.

36. Szklarz GD, Ornstein RL, Halpert JR: **Application of 3-dimensional homology modeling of cytochrome P450 2B1 for interpretation of site-directed mutagenesis.** *J Biomol Struct Dyn* 1994, **12**:61-78.

37. Chang Y-T, Loew GH: **Construction and evaluation of a three-dimensional structure of cytochrome P450choP enzyme (CYP105C1).** *Prot Engineering* 1996, **9**:755-766.

38. Smith DA, Jones BC, Walker DK: **Design of drugs involving the concepts and theories of drug metabolism and pharmacokinetics.** *Med Res Rev* 1996, **16**:243--266.

39. Welch W, Ruppert J, Jain AN: Hammerhead: **Fast, fully automated docking of flexible ligands to protein binding sites.** *Chem Biol* 1996, **3**:449-462.

40. Hansch C: **Quantitative relationships between lipophilic character and drug metabolism.** *Drug Metab Rev* 1972, **1**:1-14.

41. Hansch C: **The QSAR paradigm in the design of less toxic molecules.** *Drug Metab Rev* 1984, 15:1279-1294.

42. Sansom C: **Extending the boundaries of molecular modeling.** *Nature Biotech* 1998, **16**:917-918.

43. Fuhr U, Strobl G, Manaut F, Anders E-M, Sorgel F, Lopez-de-brinas E, Chu DTW. Pernet AG. Mahr G, Sanz F, Staib AH: **Quinolone antibacterial agents: relationship between structure and** *in vitro* **inhibition of human cytochrome P450 isoform CYP1A2.** *Mol Pharmacol* 1993, **43**:191-199.

44. Ekins S, Bravi G, Binkley S, Wikel JH, Wrighton SA: **Three- and four-dimensional quantitative structure activity relationship (3D/4D QSAR) analyses of CYP1A2 inhibitors.** To be published.

45. Jones JP, He M, Trager WF, Rettie AE: **Three-dimensional quantitative structure-activity relationship for inhibitors of cytochrome P4502C9.** *Drug Metab Dispos* 1996, 24:1-6.

46. Ekins S, Bravi G, Binkley S, Gillespie JS, Ring BJ, Wikel JH, Wrighton SA: **Three- and four- dimensional quantitative structure activity relationship (3D/4D QSAR) analyses of CYP2C9 inhibitors.** To be published.

47. Ekins S, Bravi G, Binkley S, Gillespie JS, Ring BJ, Wikel JH, Wrighton SA: **Three- and four-dimensional quantitative structure-activity relationship (3D/4D QSAR) analyses of CYP2D6 inhibitors.** *Pharmacogenetics* 1999, 9:477-489.

48. Strobl GR, von Kruedener S, Stockigt J, Guengerich FP, Wolff T: **Development of a pharmacophore for inhibition of human liver cytochrome P-450 2D6: Molecular modeling and inhibition studies.** *J Med Chem* 1993, 36:1136-1145.

49. Ekins S, Bravi G, Binkley S, Gillespie JS, Ring BJ, Wikel JH, Wrighton SA: **Three-dimensional quantitative structure-activity relationship (3D QSAR) analyses of inhibitors for CYP3A4.** *J Pharmacol Exp Ther* 1999. 290:429-438.

50. Ekins S, Bravi G, Ring BJ, Gillespie TA, Gillespie JS, VandenBranden M, Wrighton SA, Wikel JH: **Three dimensional-quantitative structure activity relationship (3D-QSAR) analyses of substrates for CYP2B6.** *J Pharmacol Exp Ther* 1999, 288:21-29.

51. Ekins S, Bravi G, Wikel JH, Wrighton SA: **Three-dimensional quantitative structure-activity relationship (3D QSAR) analysis of CYP3A4 substrates.** *J Pharmacol Exp Ther* 1999, 291:424-433.

52. Waller CL, Evans MV, McKinney JD: **Modeling the cytochrome P450-mediated metabolism of chlorinated volatile organic compounds.** *Drug Metab Dispos* 1996, 24:203-210.

53. Lipinski CA, Lombardo F, Dominy BW, Feeney PJ: **Experimental and computational approaches to estimate solubility and permeability in drug discovery and development settings.** *Adv Drug Del Rev* 1997, 23:3-25.

54. Curatolo W: **Physical chemical properties of oral drug candidates in the discovery and exploratory development settings.** *PSTT* 1998, 1:387-393.

55. Wessel MD, Jurs PC, Tolan JW, Muskal SM: **Prediction of human intestinal absorption of drug compounds from molecular structure.** *J Chem Inf Comput Sci* 1998, 38:726-735.

56. Ajay, Walters WP, Murcko MA: **Can we learn to distinguish between "drug-like" and "nondrug-like" molecules?** *J Med Chem* 1998, **41**:3314-3324.

57. Gillet VJ, Willett P, Bradshaw J: **Identification of biological activity profiles using substructural analysis and genetic algorithms.** *J Chem Inf Comput Sci* 1998, **38**:165-179.

58. Sadowski J, Kubinyi H: **A scoring scheme for discriminating between drugs and nondrugs.** *J Med Chem* 1998, **41**:3325-3329.

59. Ekins S, McGowan RJ: **The limits of reductionism: The shifting genomic paradigm's impact on industry and academia.** To be published.

60. EUFEPS: **An assessment of the future training needs for PhD graduates for Eurpoean pharmaceutical companies.** *Eur J Pharm Sci* 1999, **7**:iii-v.

61. Langer T, Hoffman RD: **On the use of chemical function-based alignments as input for 3D-QSAR.** *J Chem Inf Comput* Sci 1998, **38**:325-330.

62. Nelsestuen GL, Martinez MB: **Steady state enzyme velocities that are independent of [enzyme]: An important behavior in many membrane and particle-bound states.** *Biochemistry* 1997, **36**:9081-9086.

63. Gerloff J: **Optimization of methods and models in clinical pharmacology.** *J Clin Pharmacol* 1997, **37**:4S-7S.

64. Spencer RW: **High-throughput screening of historic collections: Observations on file size, biological targets and file diversity.** *Biotechnol Bioeng* 1998, **61**:61-67.

65. Hopfinger AJ, Tokarski JS: **Three-dimensional quantitative structure-activity relationship analysis.** In: *Practical Application Of Computer-Aided Drug Design.* Charifson PS, ed. New York: Marcel Dekker. 1997:105-164.

66. Korzekwa KR, Jones JP: **Predicting the cytochrome P450-mediated metabolism of xenobiotics.** *Pharmacogenetics* 1993, **3**:1-18.

67. Chiba P, Ecker G, Schmid D, Drach J, Tell B, Goldenberg S, Gekeler V: **Structural requirements for activty of propafenone-type modulators in P-glycoprotein-mediated multidrug resistance.** *Mol Pharmacol* 1996, **49**:1122-1130.

68. Pajeva IK, Wiese M: **A comparitive molecular field analysis of propafenone-type modulators of cancer multidrug resistance.** *QSAR* 1998, **17**:301-312.

69. Pajeva IK, Wiese M: **QSAR and molecular modelling of cataphilic drugs able to modulate multidrug resistance in tumors.** *QSAR* 1997, **16**:1-10.

70. Pajeva I, Wiese M: **Molecular modeling of phenothiazines and related drugs as multidrug resistance modifiers: A comparative molecular field analysis study.** *J Med Chem* 1998, **41**:1815-1826.

71. Campbell NCR, van Loon JA, Sundaram RS, Ames MM, Hansch C, Weinshilboum R: **Human and rat liver phenol sulfotransferase: Structure-activity relationships for phenolic substrates.** *Mol Pharmacol* 1987, **32**:813-819.

72. Soffers AEMF, Ploeman JHTM, Moonen MJH, Wobbes T, van Ommen B, Vervoort J, van Bladeren PJ, Rietjens IMCM: **Regioselectivity and quantitative structure-activity relationships for the conjugation of a series of fluoronitrobenzenes by purified glutathione S-transferase enzymes from rat and man.** *Chem Res Toxicol* 1996, **9**:638-646.

73. Rietjens IMCM, Soffers AEMF, Hooiveld GJEJ, Veegar C, Vervoort J: **Quantitative structure-activity relationships based on computer calculated parameters for the overall rate of glutathione S-transferase catalyzed conjugation of a series of fluoronitrobenzenes.** *Chem Res Toxicol* 1995, **8**:481-488.

74. Naydenova ZG, Grancharov KC, Algarov DK, Golovinsky E.V, Stanoeva IM, Shalamanova LD, Pajeva IK: **Inhibition of UDP-glucuronylsyltransferase by 5'-O-amino acid and oligopeptide derivatives of uridine: Structure-activity relationships.** *Z Naturforsch* 1998, **53c**:173-181.

75. Cupid BC, Holmes E, Wilson ID, Lindon JC, Nicholson JK: **Quantitative structure-metabolism relationships (QSMR) using computational chemistry: pattern recognition analysis and statistical prediction of phase II conjugation reactions of substituted benzoic acids in the rat.** *Xenobiotica* 1999, **29**:27-42.

76. FDA: Guidance for industry. *In vivo* drug metabolism/drug interaction studies—Study design, data analysis, and recommendations for dosing and labeling. 1998.

77. Hook D: **Ultra high-throughput screening—A journey into nanoland with Gulliver and Alice.** *Drug Discovery Today* 1996, **1**:267-268.

78. Singh J, Soloweij J, Allen M, Killar L, Ator M: **Lead development: validation and application of high throughput screening for determination of pharmcokinetic parameters for enzyme inhibitors.** *Bioorg Med Chem* 1996, **4**:639-643.

79. Lutz MW, Menius JA, Choi TD, Laskody RG, Domanico PL, Goetz AS, Saussy DL: **Experimental design for high-throughput screening.** *Drug Discovery Today* 1996, **1**:277-286.

80. Bronson DD, Daniels DM, Dixon JT, Redick CC, Haaland PD: **Virtual kinetics: Using statistical experimental design for rapid analysis of enzyme inhibitor mechanisms.** *Biochem Pharmacol* 1995, **50**:823-831.

81. Palsson :O. **What lies beyond bioinformatics?** *Nature Biotech* 1997, **15**:3-4.

82. Klopman G, Tu M, Talafous J: META. 3. **A genetic algorithm for metabolic transform priorities optimization.** *J Chem Inf Comput Sci* 1997, **37**:329-334.

83. Lewis DFV, Eddershaw PJ, Dickins M, Tarbit MH, Goldfarb PS: **Structural determinants of cytochrome P450 substrate specificity, binding affinity and catalytic rate.** *Chem Biol Interact* 1998, **115**:175-199; *Erratum Chem Biol Interact* 1998, **115**:186.

84. Erb RJ: **The backpropagation neural network—A Bayesian classifier.** *Clinical Pharmacokinetics* 1995, **29**:69-79.

85. Bemis GW, Murcko MA: **The properties of known drugs 1. Molecular frameworks.** *J Med Chem* 1996, **39**:2887-2893.

86. Zupan J, Gasteiger J: *Neural networks for chemists* Weinheim: VCH, 1993.

87. Chen X, Rusinko III A, Young SS: **Recursive partitioning analysis of a large structure-activity dataset using three-dimensional descriptors.** *J Chem Inf Comput Sci* 1998, **38**:1054-1062.

88. Niznik HB, Tyndale RF, Sallee FR, Gonzalez FJ, Hardwick JP, Inaba T, Kalow W: **The dopamine transporter and cytochrome P450IID1 (debrisoquine 4-hydroxylase) in brain: resolution and identification of two distinct [3H]GBR-12935 binding proteins.** *Arch Biochem Biophys* 1990, **276**:424-432.

89. Austel V, Kutter E: **Absorption, distribution, and metabolism of drugs.** In: *Quantitative Structure-Activity Relationships of Drugs.* New York: Academic Press. 1983:437-496.

90. Kubinyi H: **Structure-based design of enzyme inhibitors and receptor ligands.** *Drug Disc Dev* 1998, 1:4-15.

91. Kubinyi H: **Combinatorial and computational approaches in structure-based drug design.** *Drug Disc Dev* 1998, 1:16-27.

92. Kubinyi H: **Stratergies and recent technologies in drug discovery.** *Pharmazie* 1995, **50**:647-662.

93. Shimada T, Yamazaki H, Foroozesh M, Hopkins NE, Alworth WL, Guengerich FP: **Selectivity of polycyclic inhibitors for human cytochrome P450s 1A1, 1A2 and 1B1.** *Chem Res Toxicol* 1998, **11**:1048-1056.

94. Kobayashi K, Nakajima M, Chiba K, Yamamoto T, Tani M, Ishizaki T, Kuroiwa Y: **Inhibitory effects of antiarrhythmic drugs on phenacetin**

O-deethylation catalyzed by human CYP1A2. *Br J Clin Pharmacol* 1998, **45**:361-368.

95. Draper AJ, Madan A, Parkinson A: **Inhibition of coumarin 7-hydroxylase activity in human liver microsomes.** *Arch Biochem Biophys* 1997, **341**:47-61.

96. Mancy A, Broto P, Dijols S, Dansette PM, Mansuy D: **The substrate binding site of human liver cytochrome P4502C9: An approach using designed tienilic acid derivatives and molecular modeling.** *Biochemistry* 1995, **34**:10365-10375.

97. Morsman JM, Smith DA, Jones BC, Hawksworth GM: **Role of hydrogen-bonding in substrate structure-activity relationships for CYP2C9.** *ISSX Proceedings* 1995, **8**:259.

98. Back DJ, Tjia JF, Karbwang J, Colbert J: **In vitro inhibition studies of tolbutamide hydroxylase activity of human liver microsomes by azoles, sulphonamides and quinolines.** *Br J Clin Pharmacol* 1988, **26**:23-29.

99. Lock RE, Jones BC, Smith DA, Hawksworth GM: **Substrate structure-activity relationships (SSAR) of benzodiazepines for cytochrome P450 2C19.** *Human Exp Toxicol* 1998, **17**:514.

100. Lock RE, Jones BC, Smith DA., Hawksworth GM: **Investigation of substrate structure-activity relationships (SSAR) for cytochrome P450 2C19.** *Br J Clin Pharmacol* 1998, **45**:511P.

101. Wu D, Otton SV, Inaba T, Kalo, W. Sellers EM: **Interactions of amphetamine analogs with human liver CYP2D6.** *Biochem Pharmacol* 1997, **53**:1605-1612.

102. Zhao X-J, Ishizaki T: **Metabolic interactions of selected antimalarial and non-antimalarial drugs with the major pathway (3-hydroxylation) of quinine in human liver microsomes.** *Br J Clin Pharmacol* 1997, **44**:505-511.

103. Pichard L, Fabre I, Fabre G, Domergue J, Aubert BS, Mourad G, Maurel P: **Screening for inducers and inhibitors of cytochrome P-450 (cyclosporin A oxidase) in primary cultures of human hepatocytes and in liver microsomes.** *Drug Metab Disp* 1990, **18**:595-606.

104. Pichard L, Domerergue J, Fourtanier G, Koch P, Schran HF, Maurel P: **Metabolism of the new immunosuppressor cyclosporin G by human liver cytochromes P450.** *Biochem Pharmacol* 1996, **51**:591-598.

16

Feature-Based Pharmacophores: Application to Some Biological Systems

Rémy Hoffmann, Hong Li, and Thierry Langer

Abstract

Pharmacophore generation has been widely used over the past 20 years in drug design. Among all the available methods, feature-based pharmacophore generation is the most recent one. In this approach, chemical features (H-bond donors, H-bond acceptors, hydrophobic points, etc) represent the pharmacophoric points. This chapter is not intended to describe the underlying methodology, but illustrate its use in several situations. In the two first examples, feature-based pharmacophore is applied to ligands to: (a) derive chemically reasonable alignments of molecules as input for 3D-QSAR (thromboxane) or (b) analyze receptor sub-type selectivity (retinoids). The last example illustrates the use of this method using the chemical-feature-based information derived from a protein active site (DHFR/Methotrexate) to derive the pharmacophore models.

16

Feature-Based Pharmacophores: Application to Some Biological Systems

Rémy Hoffmann,[†] Hong Li,[‡] and Thierry Langer[▽]

†Molecular Simulations SARL,
Parc Club Orsay Université, Orsay Cedex, France
‡ChemInnovation Software, Inc., San Diego California
▽University of Innsbruck, Institute of Pharmaceutical
Chemistry, Innsbruck, Austria

16.1. Introduction

For almost 20 years, pharmacophore generation has been a widely used approach to derive models that are intended 1) to explain the SAR within series of molecules, and 2) to serve as a design tool to identify new ligands for a given biological target. Pharmacophore models are of special interest when the 3D structure of a biological target has not be resolved (eg., G-coupled protein receptors). The generation of pharmacophores uses the information derived from the ligands. A pharmacophore can be defined as the characteristic three-dimensional set of structural elements that are responsible for the activity of these ligands.[1] Many different pharmacophore generation methods have been published since then.[2] In most of these methods, pharmacophoric points are represented by atoms.

Inclusion of chemical features in pharmacophores has appeared only recently,[3] although it constitutes a logical concept used by chemists for years in the drug discovery process. The originality of this type of pharmacophores resides mostly in the fact that their definition is general and represents the different types of interactions between organic molecules and proteins. In organic molecules, different structural motifs can express the similar chemical behavior.

Feature-based pharmacophores can be generated automatically using DISCO,[4] GASP,[5] APEX-3D,[6] or the Catalyst[7] software. They can be at a quantitative (HypoGen) or a qualitative level (HipHop™).[8,9] They can also be built manually, using a manual chemical function mapping procedure on a molecule represented in a given conformation (hopefully the bioactive conformation, Catalyst). Other approaches allow users to build feature-based models from a ligand-protein complex.[10]

Our goal in this chapter is not to make an exhaustive comparison of the different pharmacophore generation methods, but to give the potential user some insight about feature-based pharmacophores and their use in the drug discovery process. This chapter will focus on feature-based pharmacophores generated with the program Catalyst.

16.2. First Case: TXSI-TXRA

16.2.1. Introduction

This section will focus on the use of feature-based pharmacophores as alignment tools for 3D QSAR, and show how the nature of the dataset can guide the user for the choice of an appropriate pharmacophore generation method.

The hypothesis that thromboxane A_2 (TXA_2), an unstable arachidonic acid metabolite, may be involved in the pathogenesis of cardiovascular disease is generally accepted. Clinical trials of TXA_2 receptor antagonists (TXRA) or TXA_2 synthase inhibitors (TXSI) for these indications have given equivocal results and it has been postulated that dual-acting (TXRA/TXSI) compounds might show positive clinical results. A set of 24 thromboxane A_2 receptor antagonists (TXRA), also described as thromboxane synthase inhibitors (TXSI), was used. Activities of these molecules ranged from 3 nm to 53 μM against the thromboxane receptor and from 3.5 nM to 6 μM against the enzyme. However, the TXSI dataset showed an unbalanced distribution of activity data, with 23 out of the 24 compounds having an activity value lower than 1 μM. Therefore, one can estimate that the activity scale for this set covers only 2 orders of magnitude. This observation is an important guideline to help us selecting the method to use for the pharmacophore generation.

16.2.2. Methods

All molecular structures were sketched within the Catalyst software and minimized to their closest local energy minimum. Poled conformations[11] were generated using an energy cutoff of 15 kcal/mol.

The TXRA and TXSI datasets were submitted to pharmacophore generation using the HypoGen procedure.[9] This process uses the activity data as part of the pharmacophore building process. The resulting models can be related to QSAR models.

Both datasets were handled under similar experimental conditions. The H-bond acceptor, donor, hydrophobe, negative ionizable (acidic), and aromatic ring functions[3] were considered, and because of the relatively high flexibility of the molecules, only hypotheses containing five features were retained. Since all molecules had a carboxylic acid function in their structure, the presence of this feature in all the pharmacophore models was required. All the remaining parameters were kept to their default value. Two runs were done in each series of molecules by varying the location tolerance of point features (1.6 Å and 1.8 Å).* Results are shown in Table 16.1.

Table 16.1. Numerical results of the HypoGen runs for the TXRA and TXSI datasets.

	TXRA		TXSI	
	Tolerance=1.6 Å	Tolerance=1.8 Å	Tolerance=1.6 Å	Tolerance=1.8 Å
Fixed Cost	97.99	97.99	94.43	94.43
Null Cost	150.92	150.92	110.53	110.53
Cost range	119.22–122.93	114.94–120.10	106.66–119.01	110.31–114.02
RMS range	1.32–1.44	1.13–1.35	1.00–1.35	1.15–1.28
Correlation range	0.84–0.80	0.89–0.83	0.77–0.53	0.69–0.59
Error Cost Fixed Hypo	80.73	80.73	80.73	80.73
Error Cost Null Hypo	150.92	150.92	110.53	110.53
Error Cost range	101.65–105.64	96.14–102.78	92.96–110.53	96.50–110.53

* This is obtained by changing the TOLERANCE parameter in the $CATALYST_CONF/hypo.data file.

This pharmacophore generation method is based on Occam's razor principle. Pharmacophores are ranked by a cost factor which is an indicator of their complexity.[9] An important component of the cost function (*Error*) measures the deviation between experimental and predicted activities among the molecules in the dataset. The goal of the method is to generate the simplest hypotheses (with a cost as close as possible from the cost of an ideal hypothesis that shows the minimum deviation between experimental and predicted activities—fixed hypothesis/fixed cost) that can predict correctly the activity of the molecules in the dataset.

16.2.3. Results and Discussion

The results obtained with the TXRA dataset were satisfactory. The hypotheses costs (total cost and error cost), as well as the correlation coefficients and RMS values, indicate good quality models. Increasing the tolerance of the pharmacophoric spheres from 1.6 Å to 1.8 Å results in an overall improvement of all the parameters described in Table 16.1. Increasing the feature location tolerance has a direct effect on the calculated fit value that is used to estimate activities,[*] for a similar mapping within a pharmacophoric feature, the Dist/Tol component of the fit equation decreases, which results in an increase of the fit value. Plate 16.1 shows compound 16-11 aligned on the best pharmacophore model generated for TXRA antagonists.

This pharmacophore model is characterized by one acidic function (blue), two hydrophobic areas (cyan), one ring aromatic function (gold), and a hydrogen-bond acceptor function (green).

Unfortunately, none of the pharmacophores generated for the TXSI dataset showed a good balance between the cost, correlation, and RMS components. Thus, the selection of a good hypothesis to align the molecules as the starting point for the 3D QSAR analysis is nearly impossible. The poor results obtained for this dataset can be interpreted as the consequence of the combined effect of using a dataset with a limited structural diversity associated to a narrow spread of activities.

---

[*] Fit = $\Sigma W [1 - \Sigma$ blobs (Disp/Tol)2], w = weight of the hypothesis function—adaptively determined.

It has to be noted that the reduction of the feature tolerance improved the results, probably due to pharmacophores presenting a greater selectivity (given the smaller spread of activities, making the feature location tighter allows a better discrimination between molecules of different activity classes).

This observation, combined with the one made for the TXRA dataset, leads us to conclude that pharmacophore generation using variable feature tolerance would certainly constitute an improvement in feature-based pharmacophore generation. Datasets could be analyzed in a more thorough way.

The TXSI dataset has then been submitted to common-feature pharmacophore generation, using only the top order activity compounds.[8] The dataset consists of nine compounds. As opposed to HypoGen, this method does not use activity values in the pharmacophore generation process. The same chemical features are used (negative ionizable, hydrophobes and H-bond acceptor function, ring aromatic) and a minimum of 5 features is requested for the generated pharmacophores. Plate 16.2 shows some of the compounds aligned on the highest score pharmacophore. All the generated pharmacophores contain more features which allows to constrain the alignment of molecules.

All 24 molecules were aligned on the generated pharmacophore models (allowing partial mapping on the pharmacophore features), and the final alignment was used for the 3D QSAR study. Preliminary results have shown the potential of using these feature-based alignments as a starting point for 3D QSAR.[12]

16.3. Second Case: Retinoic Acid Receptor Ligands

16.3.1. Introduction

Vitamin A and its biologically active derivatives, retinal and retinoic acid (RA), are essential for human health and survival. The natural compounds, together with a large repertoire of synthetic analogs, are collectively referred as retinoids. In addition to their well-known role in vision, retinoids act as morphogenic agents during embryonic development, and regulate the growth and differentiation of a wide variety of cells throughout life of the organism.[13] Retinoid receptors comprise two distinct groups of nuclear receptors, namely the RARs and RXRs, consisting each of three members, namely alpha, beta, and gamma.[14] These receptors function as transcriptional activators by binding to specific sequences in the genome's response elements and activating the expression of the adjacent genes. The 3D structure of the different RAR subtypes is not known.

Feature-based pharmacophore generation has been applied to a set of 32 retinoids for which activity data on the three known subtypes of RARs was available. The structure of the molecules in the dataset is described elsewhere.[15] Different pharmacophore generation experiments were performed in order to explain RAR subtype selectivity.

16.3.2. Training Set and Methods

Figure 16.1 shows the activity and selectivity profiles for the 32 retinoids used in this study. The activities are spread over 3-4 orders of magnitude which should make this dataset a good set for HypoGen. A more precise analysis of the activity data based on the selectivity profile of the molecules allows us to group them in different families: Selectivity has been assessed on the basis of a 10-fold activity difference between the different subclasses of receptors. The resulting classification is shown in Table 16.2. From this table, it appears that different types of pharmacophore generation experiments can be performed based on which type of selectivity profile one wants to consider. More molecules in each family would probably help to better study subtype selectivity of RARs.

Table 16.2. Classification of the retinoids based on their selectivity profiles for the three subtypes of retinoic acid receptors.

Selectivity profile	Compounds
Active BUT NOT selective	Retinoic Acid (RA), 9-cis RA, Comp4, 11
Selectivity for the alpha subtype	Comp5, 17, 18
Selectivity for the beta subtype	Comp7, 23
Selectivity for the gamma subtype	Comp3, 9, 29
Selectivity for the beta/gamma subtypes	Comp6, 8, 12, 13, 14, 16, 22, 23, 27, 28, 30
Selectivity for the alpha/gamma subtypes	Comp15
Low activity AND NO selectivity	Comp1, 2, 10, 19, 20, 21, 24, 25, 26

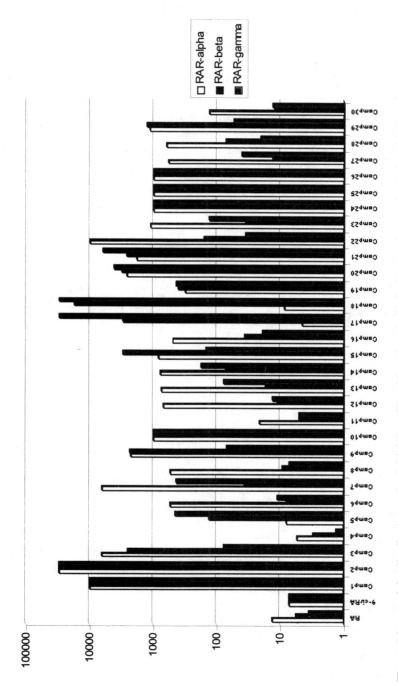

Figure 16.1. Activity distribution and selectivity profile of the 32 retinoids for the 3 subtypes of retinoic acid receptors.

All the compounds were sketched in Catalyst and poled conformations were generated in a 15 kcal/mol energy window above the computed global minimum energy conformation.

An initial series of runs using HypoGen were done using the entire dataset. These runs pointed out the importance of an acidic group (Negative Ionizable) and of hydrophobic areas. The presence of other chemical features led to partial mappings of active molecules (beside its carboxyl group, Comp4 does not contain any hydrogen bond donor or acceptor group). As a result, new runs were performed considering only these two feature types. Because of the size of the molecules, the inter-feature spacing penalty was reduced from its default value to 2 Å. The results of these runs are illustrated in Table 16.3.

Table 16.3. Results of the HypoGen runs for the 3 subtypes of retinoid
receptors.

	Fixed Cost	Null Cost	Cost range	RMS range	Correl Range	Feature definition	Observations
RAR-alpha	109.77	188.44	136.23–169.36	1.30–1.99	0.84–0.56	H H H H NI *	3 first hypotheses with r>0.80
RAR-beta	109.13	211.26	152.13–177.14	1.62–2.19	0.80–0.62	H H H H NI *	2nd hypothesis is the best
RAR-gamma	109.84	221.20	158.58–195.26	1.66–2.38	0.81–0.54	H H H H NI *	1st hypothesis has r>0.80

H: Hydrophobic group   *NI: Negative Ionizable*

16.3.3. Results and Discussion

Although the cost terms indicate a low overall predictivity[9] (this may be due to the relative structural homogeneity of the training set), each run produces at least one or two hypotheses with r values greater than 0.80. For the RAR-beta subtype, the second lowest cost hypothesis produces the best results in estimating activities of the dataset molecules.

Plate 16.3 shows Comp4 (Comp4 is a very active but nonselective molecule) mapped on the best hypothesis selected for each run (lowest cost hypothesis for RAR-alpha and RAR-gamma runs, and second lowest cost hypothesis for the RAR-beta run). It has to be noted that the same low energy conformation (ΔE=2.16 kcal/mol) of Comp4 is used to map all of these hypotheses.

In an attempt to characterize the regions of the molecules responsible for selectivity, these hypotheses were compared using the Negative

Ionizable and the distal hydrophobic features (two features that seem to be conserved in all the pharmacophores). The pharmacophore comparison is shown in Plate 16.4. Based on these observations, subtype selectivity can be explained by a different 3D distribution of hydrophobic areas.

Using the subtype classification shown in Table 16.2, RAR subtype selectivity can also be analyzed by deriving common-feature pharmacophores for each class of molecules. The class of compounds with low activity and no selectivity will not be considered. Although some classes only contain as few as three compounds, this approach constitutes an interesting starting point, since all molecules within a class show a similar selectivity profile. In order to constrain the common-feature pharmacophore generation as much as possible, all the molecules were forced to map to all the features of the generated pharmacophores (for all molecules: Principal=2 and MaxOmitFeat=0; Misses, FeatureMisses and CompleteMisses parameters set to 0).[16] Hydrogen-bond Donors, Acceptors, and Hydrophobic and Negative Ionizable features were selected from the Feature Dictionary. The presence of one Negative Ionizable feature per generated pharmacophore was requested. Comparison of the pharmacophores was based on the best pharmacophores generated for each class. Because of the small number of molecules used in each run, the pharmacophore comparison analysis is purely qualitative and is not intended to predict quantitatively the selectivity ratio of any candidate molecule.

Characteristics of the best pharmacophores of each run are reported in Table 16.4. They all present more pharmacophoric features than the pharmacophores generated with the HypoGen procedure. This allows a more precise differentiation analysis between the different subtypes of RARs. Plate 16.5 shows that the presence of hydrogen-bond donor and acceptor functions as well as an extension of the distal hydrophobic region (red) will differentiate the alpha subtype from the beta one. In the beta subtype model, a hydrophobic interaction (yellow) replaces the hydrogen-bonding donor interaction The remaining features are common to both models.

Considering the alpha/gamma subtype selectivity, differentiation is based on the same donor and acceptor features as well as on some hydrophobic features (in red for the alpha subtype, in yellow for the gamma one). Among the 32 compounds, the beta/gamma selective molecules constitute the most populated class of compounds. The pharmacophore model consists of four features only (one Negative Ionizable and three hydrophobes) and can easily be compared to the alpha subtype pharmacophore (see Plate 16.6). Common areas are colored in green, yellow areas are specific to the alpha subtype pharmacophore, and red areas are specific to the beta/gamma subtype.

Table 16.4. Characteristics of the common feature pharmacophores generated from different classes of subtype selective molecules.

Subtype Selectivity Class	Feature Definition	Score[8]
Active BUT NOT selective	NI H H H H H	59.68
Selectivity for the alpha subtype	NI H H H H H D A	62.08
Selectivity for the beta subtype	NI H H H H H	45.37
Selectivity for the gamma subtype	NI H H H H	38.81
Selectivity for the beta/gamma subtypes	NI H H H	123.99

NI: Negative Ionizable   *H: Hydrophobe*   *D: HB Donor*   *A: HB Acceptor*

16.4. Third Case: Feature-Based Pharmacophores Derived from Structural Information

16.4.1. Introduction

Feature-based pharmacophores can also be built by using the structural information derived from the protein active site. More and more protein structures and protein-ligand complexes are resolved by means of X-ray crystallography and NMR spectroscopy (as of November 9, 1999, there are 9041 structures determined by X-ray diffraction, 1747 structures determined by NMR spectroscopy, and 237 structures proposed by modeling in the Brookhaven database). One can consider the protein alone or, when available, use a protein-ligand complex as the starting point, since the residues involved in binding are identified. It is also possible to start from the active conformation of the ligand and manually map chemical features on this specific conformation in order to build the feature based-pharmacophore. Pharmacophores derived from structural information constitute interesting tools to focus libraries. In this chapter, we will illustrate the building of feature-based queries derived from protein information using a well-known system: DHFR/Methotrexate.

Dihydrofolate reductase (DHFR; EC 1.5.1.3) is ubiquitous, essential enzyme which catalyzes the reduction of dihydrofolate to tetrahydrofolate, an important carrier of one-carbon units essential for the biosynthesis of purines, pyrimidines, and some amino acids. The bacterial enzyme, which can be inhibited with great specificity with respect to human DHFR, has been established clinically as a target for chemotherapy. Trimethoprim (TMP), although marketed in many countries in combination with sulfamethoxazole as Bactrim®, itself shows good clinical activity against a broad range of pathogens.[17,18]

A DHFR/MTX complex (1rh3.pdb—resolution: 2.4 Å)[19] was used as our starting point. Careful examination of this complex shows the following key interactions. These interactions will be used later in the text (see Table 16.5) and will help us to define the key features in the pharmacophores.

- **Interaction1**: Hydrogen bond donor interaction between NH37 of MTX and O of Ile94
- **Interaction2**: Hydrogen bond donor interaction between NH36 of MTX and O of Ile5
- **Interaction3**: Hydrogen bond donor interaction between NH34 of MTX and OD1 of Asp27
  Hydrogen bond donor interaction between NH35 of MTX and O of HOH242
- **Interaction4,5**: Hydrogen bond acceptor interaction between O of MTX and HH22 of Arg52
  Hydrogen bond acceptor interaction between O of MTX and HH22 of Arg52
- **Interaction6**: Hydrogen bond acceptor interaction between O2 of MTX and Hz2 of Lys32
- **Interaction7**: Hydrogen bond acceptor interaction between O2 of MTX and HH21 of Arg57
- **Interaction8**: Hydrogen bond acceptor interaction between O1 of MTX and HH11 of Arg57
- **Interaction9**: Lipophilic interaction between the aromatic ring of MTX and Phe31, Leu28 and Leu50

Interaction7 and **Interaction8** are interacting with the same residue of the protein (Arg57 of DHFR) in an anion-cation type interaction.

16.4.2. Methods

- ### *Deriving the Pharmacophore from the Protein Active Site*

The pdb file was read into Cerius[2], and the structure-based focusing module was used.[20] This module uses a combination of a) Ludi[21] to define an interaction map within a sphere centered on a given atom characterized by its x, y, and z coordinates, b) editing and clustering of the interaction map and calculation of exclusion spheres to delimit the active site pocket, and c) the Catalyst hypoedit script to derive single or multiple feature-based hypotheses from the feature clusters and exclusion spheres.

The center of the sphere used for the Ludi search was located on atom C14 of MTX (x=23.315, y=20.617, z=34.013), and the radius of the sphere was set to 10 Å in order to include all the residues of DHFR involved in the binding with MTX (see text above). Clustering was performed using the complete linkage method (threshold set to 0.7 Å) and 3 HBA, 4 HBD, and 3 Hydrophobic clusters were requested. Excluded regions were defined using the closest atoms method within a sphere of 12 Å (to consider all the atoms of the selected residues within the 10 Å radius). Their radius was set to 1.0 Å.[22] Hydrogen atoms were not considered in the building of the exclusion model. The hydrophobic features found by the Structure-Based Focusing module that map the N-Me group and the purine rings were not considered. Multiple queries that represent multiple-feature combinations have been built. The resulting hypotheses were used as queries to search the Derwent WDI (see Table 16.5: Hypo1-Hypo8).[23]

Table 16.5. Multiple feature-based pharmacophores built for DHFR and results of database mining experiments.

	Int1	Int2	Int3	Int4,5	Int6	Int with Arg57 Int7	Int8	Int9	*Hits*[a]
Hypo1		v	v	v				v	551
Hypo2	v		v	v				v	445
Hypo3		v	v	v		v	v	v	3
Hypo4	v		v	v		v	v	v	1
Hypo5		v	v	v	v			v	41
Hypo6	v		v	v	v			v	30
Hypo7		v	v			v	v	v	29
Hypo8	v		v			v	v	v	27
Hypo9[b]	v		v	v		v [c]	v [c]	v	19
Hypo10		v	v	v		v [c]	v [c]	v	21

a: Number of hits from Derwent WDI   b: Manually built pharmacophore (no exclusion sphere), c: the two HB Acceptor features have been replaced by a single Negative Ionizable one.

- *Manual mapping on the active conformation of MTX*

The active conformation of MTX was saved as a mol file and exported to Catalyst. Two hypotheses were built by mapping manually the features on MTX. Five feature pharmacophores were constructed, each one consisting of two HBD, one hydrophobe, one HBA, and one Negative Ionizable function. The only difference between the two pharmacophores was the orientation of one hydrogen-bond donor. The resulting hypotheses were also used as queries to search the Derwent WDI (see Table 16.5: Hypo9-Hypo10).[23]

16.4.3. Results and Discussion

The Ludi procedure has identified 53 possible HB Acceptor, 85 HB Donor, and 42 Hydrophobic interaction sites within the 10 Å search sphere. Some interaction sites were located outside the binding pocket. Since we were only looking for interaction sites that could map MTX, manual editing of the interaction map was used. Clustering on the remaining features returned the feature map shown in Plate 16.7, a. Plate 16.7, b, shows the same interaction map combined with the 239 excluded volume spheres. Exclusion spheres map the protein backbone atoms and describe the 3D shape and size of the active site pocket. It constitutes a way to delimit the space accessible to ligands in an active site since each exclusion sphere acts as a hard sphere in which no mapping is possible.

The feature definition of all the hypotheses we have built, as well as the number of hits retrieved from the Derwent WDI database, are reported in Table 16.5. In case a query is too restrictive and returns no hits, the constraints on the exclusion spheres can be loosened (their size can be reduced). Table 16.5 clearly shows the selective nature of all the pharmacophores. Information reported in this table is only descriptive and no analysis of the hit list was performed (see Chapter 11).

All these hypotheses resulted in the extraction of known DHFR ligands, as well as other interesting molecules from the Derwent database. Plate 16.8 shows Methotrexate (Plate 16.8, a) and AG-2032 (Plate 16.8, b) mapped on Hypo7.

Further studies can be carried on these hits (docking/scoring in the active site of DHFR) in order to prioritize them and find the most promising candidate(s).

16.4.4. Mapping the Chemical Features on the Active Conformation of Methotrexate

The lower complexity of the hypotheses built from the active conformation of allows to return significantly more hits from the database (compare Hypos 3 and 4 with Hypos 9 and 10). The danger of getting more hits resides in the fact that more false positive can be retrieved from the database. Plate 16.9 shows Fluorasquin, a methotrexate analog extracted from Derwent-WDI, mapped on Hypo3 and Hypo10. The same conformer of this molecule is used to map to both hypotheses.

16.5. Conclusion

In this chapter, we have shown the interest of feature-based pharmacophores. Their main originality resides in their nature—the pharmacophoric points are described by chemical features. As illustrated in the different examples, they can be used as alignment tools for 3D QSAR analyses, can constitute powerful tools to analyze subtype selectivity. One of the most exiting approaches resides in deriving these pharmacophores from protein information. These pharmacophores can be used to screen libraries (combinatorial libraries, for example.)

References

1. Humblet C, Marshall GR: **Pharmacophore identification and receptor mapping.** *Annu Rep Med Chem* 1980, **15**:267-276.

2. Golender VE, Vorpagel ER: **Computer-assisted pharmacophore identification.** In: *3D QSAR in Drug Design: Theory, Methods and Applications.* Kubinyi H, ed. Leiden: Escom, 1993:137-149.

3. Greene J, Kahn S, Savoj H,. Sprague P, Teig S: **Chemical function queries for 3D database search.** *J Chem Inf Comput Sci* 1994, **34**:1297-1308.

4. Martin YC, Bures MG, Danaher EA, DeLazzer J, Lico I, Pavlik PA: **A fast new approach to pharmacophore mapping and its application to dopamineric and benzodiazepine agonists.** *J Comput-Aided Mol Des* 1993, **7**:83-102.

5. Beusen D: **Alignment of Angiotensin II Receptor Antagonists Using GASP.** *Tripos Technical Notes* Nov 1996, 1(4).

6. Golender V, Vesterman B, Eliyahu O, Kardash A, Kletzin M, Shokhen M, Vorpagel E: **Knowledge-engineering approach to drug design and its implementation in the Apex-3D expert system.** In: *10th European Symposium on Structure-Activity Relationships.* Barcelona: Prous Science, 1994:246-251.

7. *Catalyst* version 4.0, Molecular Simulations Inc, San Diego, CA, USA

8. Barnum D, Greene J., Smellie A, Sprague P: **Identification of common functional configurations among molecules.** *J Chem Inf. Comput Sci* 1996, **36**:563-571.

9. For more information on *HypoGen*, see: http://www.msi.com/support/catalyst/hypogen.html.

10. *Structure-Based Design Module in Cerius²*, version 4.0, Molecular Simulations Inc., San Diego, CA, USA

11. Smellie A, Teig SL, Towbin P: **Poling: Promoting conformational variation.** *J Comp Chem* 1995, **16**:171-187.

12. Hoffmann RD, Langer T, Lukavsky P, Winger M: **Chemical-function based alignment generation for 3D QSAR of highly flexible platelet aggregation.** In: *Molecular Modeling and Prediction of Bioactivity.* Gundertofte K, Jørgensen FS, eds. Copenhagen: Plenum Press, 1999. In press.

13. Evans RM: **The steroid and thyroid hormone receptor superfamily.** *Science* 1988, **240**(4854):889-895.

14. Giguère V: **Retinoic acid receptors and cellular retinoid binding proteins: Complex interplay in retinoid signaling.** *Endocrine Reviews* 1994, **15**(1):61-79.

15. Bachmair F, Hoffmann R, Daxenbichler G, Langer T: **Studies on Structure activity relationships of retinoic acid receptor ligands by means of molecular modeling.** In: *Vitamins and Hormones,* Vol.59. Litwack GE, ed.New York: Academic Press, 1999:159-215.

16. *HipHop Manual*, Molecular Simulations, Inc, San Diego, CA, USA

17. Hitchings GH: **Mechanism of action of Trimethoprim-Sulfamethoxazole. I.** *J Infect Diseases* 1973, **128**:S433-S436.

18. Burchall JJ: **Mechanism of action of Trimethoprim-Sulfamethoxazole. II.** *J Infect Diseases* 1973, **128**:S437-S441.

19. Sawaya MR, Kraut J: **1rh3.pdb: Dihydrofolate reductase complexed with methotrexate and nicotinamide adenine dinucleotide phosphate (reduced form), resolution: 2.4 Å.** Nov 27, 1996; http://www.pdb.bnl.gov/pdb-bin/opdbshort.

20. *Cerius²*, Version 4.0, Molecular Simulations, San Diego, CA, Structure-Based focusing module.

21. Böhm HJ: **The computer program LUDI: A new method for the *de novo* design of enzyme inhibitors.** *J Comput-Aided Mol Des* 1992, **6**:61-78.

22. Greenidge P, Carlsson B, Bladh LG, Gillner M: **Pharmacophores incorporating numerous excluded volumes defined by X-ray crystallographic structure in three-dimensional database searching: application to the thyroid hormone receptor.** *J Med Chem* 1998, **41**:2503-2512.

23. Derwent World Drug Index, Version 96.2 Derwent Ltd, London, UK.

17

The Design and Pharmacophore Definition of Retinoid X Receptor Specific Ligands

Steven K. White

Abstract

The retinoid X receptors (RXRs) are homodimer and heterodimeric partners with a variety of nuclear receptors (NRs), including PPAR, TR, and Vitamin D. While high-affinity binding to the RXRs is important, a functional cotransfection assay is required to delineate the role of the RXR ligand. The criteria for structure-activity correlation depends on proper choice of ligands according to biological function, pharmacophore space sampling, and 2D similarity. By using 2D keys to bin compounds with dissimilar RXR activity, a number of RXR specific ligand series were designed.

17

The Design and Pharmacophore Definition of Retinoid X Receptor Specific Ligands

Steven K. White

Ligand Pharmaceuticals, San Diego, California

17.1. Introduction

The retinoid receptors belong to a superfamily of nuclear receptors (NRs), which include steroid, thyroid, Vitamin D hormone receptors, and other "orphan" receptors without known ligands.[1] The NRs are thought to act as ligand-dependent transcription factors directly interacting, as homodimers or heterodimers, with response elements in target gene promoters. What is unusual is that the hormone ligand forms an integral part of the protein complex involved in DNA binding and transcriptional activation.[2] Recent structural solutions of several different NR binding domains have shown a common canonical fold consisting of 12 helices that bind the ligand entirely within the protein.[3]

There are two subfamilies of retinoid NRs: the retinoic acid receptors (RARα, RARβ, RARγ) and the retinoid X receptors (RXRα, RXRβ, RXRγ). The natural ligand for the RARs is all-*trans*-retinoic acid (ATRA, **1a**), while 9-*cis*-retinoic acid (9-*cis*-RA, **1b**) was identified as the natural hormone for the RXRs.[4] The classification of the subfamilies is based upon differences in amino acid sequence, response to synthetic retinoids, and the ability to modulate expression of different gene targets. There have been a number of publications on RAR subtype selective retinoids[5] but no RXR subtype specific retinoids have been reported. Retinoids have been shown to regulate cellular processes such as development, reproduction, cellular proliferation and differentiation, bone formation, programmed cell death (apoptosis), and vision. Clinical trials have evaluated the usefulness of these compounds in head and neck, skin, and cervix cancer,[6] as well as dermatological disease.[7] A selective RXR agonist (LGD1069, **2**) is under development for use in the treatment of various cancers and diabetes. Recent studies reported that LGD1069 induces fat cell differentiation and reduces growth of cancer cells in a rat breast cancer model, resulting in regression of the tumors.[8] Selective RXR agonists are of interest because they may elicit the beneficial pharmacological activities of retinoids without toxic side effects common to retinoids such as teratogenicity and hyperlipidicity.

The RXRs form homodimers with RXR response elements, as well as heterodimers with RARs, the thyroid hormone receptor (TR), Vitamin D receptor (VDR) and the peroxisome proliferator-activated receptors (PPARs),[9] among other NRs. As part of our studies to develop novel retinoids with increased affinity and selectivity for the RXR family, we have synthesized a number of chemical series with conformational restriction relative to the natural hormone 9-*cis*-RA (Chart 17.1). Despite the abundance of literature surrounding the retinoids and their biological effects, there have been few publications able to quantify a structure-activity relationship.[10] We have likewise been unable to generate meaningful relationships using standard QSAR techniques such as Hansch analysis or CoMFA. Those techniques that rely heavily on 2D descriptors fail in the retinoid series because they cannot distinguish between stereo isomers such as ATRA and 9-*cis*-RA, which are distinct toward the retinoid receptors. The use of 3D descriptors and QSAR models dependent on conformation similarity fail due the importance of intermolecular alignment and the many conformations accessible to molecules with high degrees of torsional freedom. During our investigation of homologous series, we were unable to identify any significant heteroatom ligand-receptor interactions and found the significant changes in receptor activity associated with changes in local lipophilicity and conformation.

Chart 17.1.

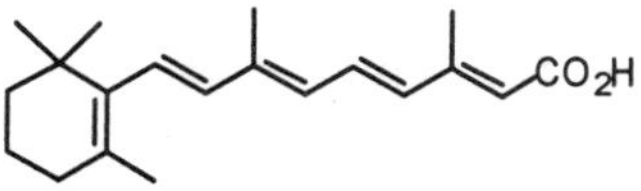

1a ATRA RAR Activity
1b 9-cis-RA RAR/RXR Activity
2 LGD1069 RXR Activity
3 LG0100351 RAR/RXR Activity

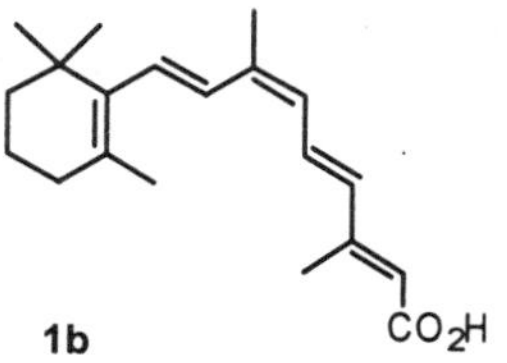

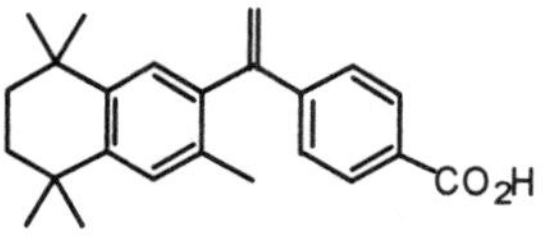

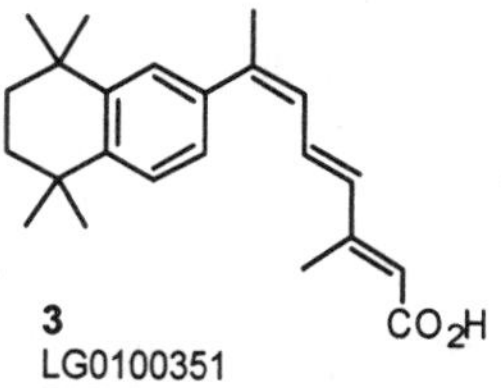

17.2. Pharmacophore Definition

The activity of each retinoid was measured with a 9-*cis*-RA ^{3}H-labeled ligand binding assay and a cotransfection assay.[11] The ability of retinoids to induce gene transcription was determined using CV-1 cells transfected with individual RXR holoreceptors and a luciferase reporter. The advantage of collecting both activity scores assures that the principal assumption of QSAR is followed; ligands bind in the same receptor pocket in a similar and effective manner. The initiation of biological effect begins with the binding of the retinoid to the RXR and despite various effects of homodimerization, recruitment of co-factors, and other transcriptional responses, the quantification of gene expression by measurement of luminescence confirmed a uniform biological mechanism. We have found numerous cases of high-affinity RXR-binding compounds which do not activate the gene expression regulated by a RXR homodimer. These RXR antagonists, the first ever reported,[12] have been labeled "rexinoids" as some have been shown to have agonist effects on gene expression characterized as regulated by other

NRs.[13] Only those compounds which demonstrated RXR-binding affinity and functional activity in the cotransfection assay were used to build training sets for pharmacophore analysis.

The pharmacophore model is defined as the essential geometric arrangement of atoms or functional groups necessary to produce a given biological response. The technique of developing a pharmacophore is based upon identification of bioisosteric functional groups in each molecule, common to all highly potent ligands. For automated pharmacophore hypothesis generation, the Molecular Simulations Inc. application Catalyst HypoGen[14] v4.0 was used. We used the feature selection tool to restrict the tracking of distance geometry to hydrophobes, aromatic ring centroids, and the acid function (a negative ionizable group). Following the general considerations of the Catalyst product we used the "best" conformation generation algorithm[15] with a 20 kcal energy range to define conformation sampling to be used in the training sets. In general, we find that the "best" conformer method generates nearly double the number of conformations stored within a Catalyst database constructed using the default "fast" conformation algorithm. In those cases where there are more torsions to be sampled, a smaller energy range with adjustment of various operations (e.g., increase MaxSuccessiveFailures) were examined and found to sample a larger conformational space.

Because the training set selection was deemed critical to a successful application of the CatHypo analysis, a number of alternative methods for the selection of training sets were tested. Care was exercised to avoid feature set redundancy. An example of this can be demonstrated by the comparison of compound **2** to **4** (Chart 17.2).

Chart 17.2.

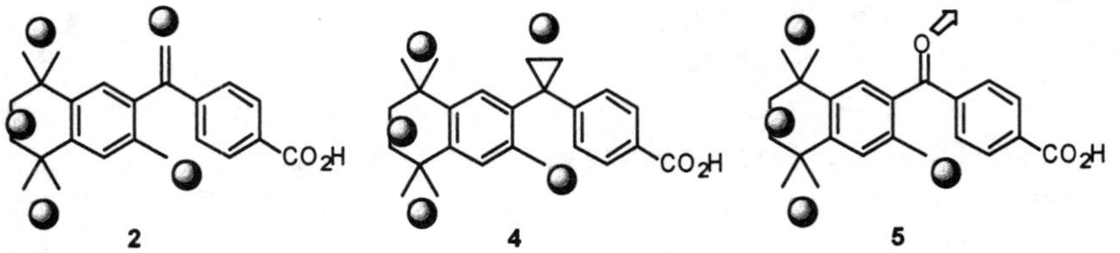

2	**4**	**5**
RXR α Ki = 36 nM	RXR α Ki = 46 nM	RXR α Ki = 349 nM

The only difference between these two compounds is the replacement of an external olefin with a spiro cyclopropane. The feature query does not change, with a nearly identical placement of a hydrophobe between the two aryl rings, and there is essentially no change in RXRα-binding affinity. These two compounds are therefore redundant and only one can be chosen for a training set. The compound **5** is included in the test set as it creates a hydrogen bond acceptor in place of a hydrophobe and there is 10-fold decrease in affinity.

Another method of compound selection for inclusion into a training set is to compare molecular pharmacophore fingerprints. The application Chem-X[16] from Oxford Molecular has the ability to consider three-center pharmacophores and compare compound pharmacophore keys against each other. These triplets store the interatomic feature distances across a conformational space and attempt to quantify the pharmacophore space for each compound. The key is built from a conformational search and is a collection of bits where each bit (Chart 17.3) corresponds to a specific selection of 3 features from a selection of 7 (e.g., hydrophobe, aromatic ring centroid, Hbond donor) and a bined geometry for each edge of the triangle (e.g., 5.5-6.5 Å, 3.0-3.5 Å, 10.0-15.0 Å). Compounds with diverse pharmacophore keys or subsets of actives are chosen to help define the pharmacophore of a series. The important rule in building a training set is to avoid as much redundancy as possible, both in terms of structure and activity.

Chart 17.3.

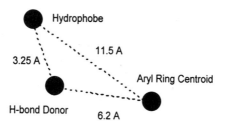

One final consideration before embarking on a pharmacophore analysis of any set of compounds is that a pharmacophore is a 3D definition of activity. The majority of computational tools that differentiate chemical structure are focused upon 2D descriptors for speed and efficiency.[17] There are a number of references which define chemical similarity with the expectation of similarity in biological response.[18] This is a simplistic explanation of an often complex event and the reasons for activity can change on subtle electrostatic and/or steric effects. Some of the most meaningful 3D information can be derived from compounds which are similar in 2D descriptor chemical space, yet distinct in activity. We review our compounds with the use of the MDL ISIS keys[19] by listing the most "similar" structures to the observed compound and viewing the difference in activity (Figure 17.1). This is an important tool for the selection of compounds to include in a Catalyst HypoGen training set.

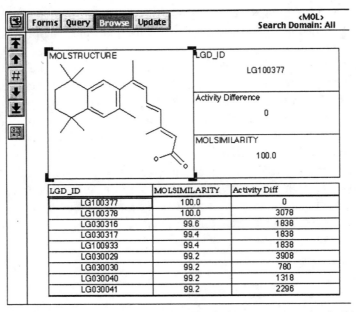

Figure 17.1. The ISIS database can display chemical structures associated with ORA-CLE activity tables. In this view the chemist can identify compounds of similar structure as scored by the ISIS keys and make note of how well similar compounds track a particular activity.

Finally, the assumption of pharmacophore-defining software is that those compounds with a larger number of binding interactions with the receptor will bind with greater affinity. Adverse steric interactions are not considered during the Catalyst automatic pharmacophore generation and thus, those compounds with a greater number of features will often be overestimated. They are best left out of the training set and a volume or size constraint should be applied to results from database searching with hypotheses.

17.3. Retinoid Series 1

For our study of the retinoic acid series 1 (Chart 17.4), the replacement of methyl groups R_1-R_3 with steric alkyl functions (Me, i-Pr/t-But, Ph) resulted in a measurable decrease in energetically assessable conformations. A systematic search of 9-*cis*-RA conformations (R_2=Me) versus the 9-t-butyl analog (R_2=t-Butyl) revealed a 64% decrease in conformations within an energy range of 10 kcal/mol of the lowest energy conformer.[*] Likewise, the substitution of the C-7 or C-11 olefin bonds with an alkyne bond resulted in a sharp reduction in the population of accessible pharmacophore space.

Chart 16.4.

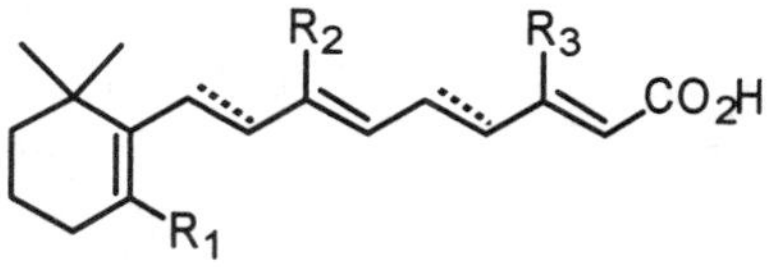

R_1, R_2, R_3 = Me, i-Pr, t-But, Ph
--- = Single, Double, Triple bond

The test set consisted of 21 compounds with a range of RXRα-binding affinity from 23 nM for the t-butyl-9-*cis*-isomer to 10 μM for two compounds. The average binding affinity was 2 μM and the average number of conformations registered per compound was 65. The first five hypotheses from HypoGen are summarized in Table 17.1.

The hypotheses are sorted according to an increasing cost function of the hypotheses, as scored within Catalyst. The definition of the cost function is not explicitly defined but three values are described to guide the end user:

- Fixed Cost (Ideal)—Cost of the simplest possible hypothesis that fits the data perfectly.

- Null Hypothesis Cost (Random)—The null hypothesis has a regression line whose slope is zero. It acts as a hypothesis without features.

---

[*] A grid search of each molecule was run (15° torsion increments) using MSI Cerius² software and an adopted-basis Newton-Raphson method used to minimize the torsion constrained conformers.

Table 17.1. Features, correlation coefficients, and cost factors for the first five HypoGen hypotheses for the retinoid series based on compounds **1a** and **1b**.

Hypo	Feature 1	Feature 2	Feature 3	Feature 4	Feature 5	r^2	Cost
RXRa1.1	Hydrophobe	Hydrophobe	Hydrophobe	---	Neg Ion	0.8541	87.67
RXRa1.2	Hydrophobe	Hydrophobe	Hydrophobe	---	Neg Ion	0.8587	87.80
RXRa1.3	Hydrophobe	Hydrophobe	Hydrophobe	---	Neg Ion	0.8451	87.87
RXRa1.4	Hydrophobe	Hydrophobe	Hydrophobe	Hydrophobe	Neg Ion	0.8432	87.96
RXRa1.5	Hydrophobe	Hydrophobe	Hydrophobe	---	Neg Ion	0.8621	88.27

- Hypothesis Cost—A sum of three cost factors: weight costs for the features, error cost proportional to the RMS difference between estimated and measured response, and a configuration cost which depends on the complexity of the considered hypothesis.

While the correlations ranged from 0.860 to 0.843, there is not much to separate the ideal hypothesis (Fixed Cost = 80.2) from a random fitting of the data (Null Cost = 101.2). Catalyst documentation suggests that a range of cost from the ideal situation (fixed cost) to a random fitting should be at least 50 bits and that the larger the difference in a hypothesis cost from the null hypothesis, the more likely the model represents a true correlation. The statistical "insignificance" of these hypotheses may reflect the underrepresentation of the pharmacophore detection problem and/or the fact that some of the larger group replacements create steric collision interactions between the ligand and receptor which are not considered in hypothesis generation.

17.4. Retinoid Series 2

For this study of RXR-selective agonists[20] (Chart 17.5) we evaluated the effects of the positioning of alkyl groups on the left aromatic ring and various bridgehead groups. The right hand ring was very specific toward unsubstituted aryl and heteroaryl rings, with near complete loss of activity with any modifications. The test set consisted of 27 compounds with a range of activity for RXRα binding from 30 nM for compound **2** to 30 μM for two compounds. The average activity for the training set was 3.2 μM with 23 conformers representing the average compound. The most active compound **2** was represented by only

18 conformations. The first five hypotheses are summarized in Table 17.2. The fixed cost for this series was 102.5 bits and the null cost was 132.3 bits. Again we found that the costs were scored without a large difference between the perfect and random hypotheses. This may have been a factor of the limited solutions available from such rigid models because of an underrepresentation of conformer space.

Chart 17.5.

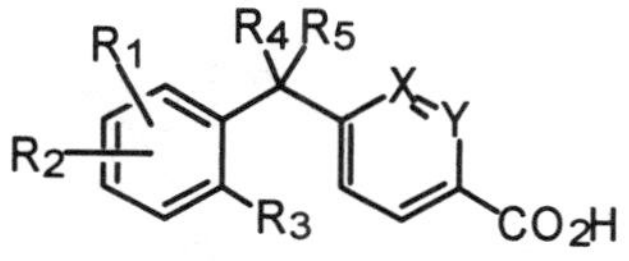

X = C H, N
$R_{1,2}$ = Me, Et, i-Pr, n-Pr, F, c-C$_5$, c-C$_6$
R_3 = Me, Et, i-Pr, n-Pr, F, Br, Cl, OH, OMe
$R_{4,5}$ = H, Me, =O, =CH$_2$, c-C$_3$, c-C$_5$

Table 17.2. Features, correlation coefficients, and cost factors for the first five HypoGen hypotheses for the retinoid series based upon compound **2**.

Hypo	Feature 1	Feature 2	Feature 3	Feature 4	Feature 5	r^2	Cost
RXRa2.1	Hydrophobe	Hydrophobe	---	Ar Ring	Neg Ion	0.887	109.2
RXRa2.2	Hydrophobe	Hydrophobe	---	Ar Ring	Neg Ion	0.826	112.9
RXRa2.3	Hydrophobe	Hydrophobe	---	Ar Ring	Neg Ion	0.797	114.1
RXRa2.4	Hydrophobe	Hydrophobe	---	Ar Ring	Neg Ion	0.791	114.3
RXRa2.5	Hydrophobe	Hydrophobe	Ar Ring	Ar Ring	Neg Ion	0.781	115.1

17.5. Retinoid Series 3

The arotinoid series[21] (Chart 17.6), based upon compound **3**, was a hybrid of the first two-retinoid series. These compounds have a conformationally defined left-hand portion and a flexible acid chain, which allows for spatially addressing many possible areas. This series was designed upon a test series of 30 compounds with a range in RXRα-binding activity from 1.4 nM to 30 µM, with an average affinity of 1.1 µM. There were eight compounds with single digit nM affinities. The most potent compound was represented by 58 conformations and the average compound was represented by 83 conformations.

Chart 17.6.

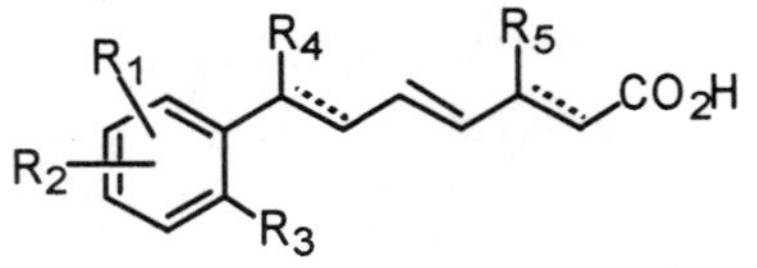

$R_{1,2}$ = Me, Et, i-Pr, n-Pr, t-But, F, c-C_5, c-C_6
R_3 = Me, Et, iPr, n-Pr, F, Br, Cl, OMe
$R_{4,5}$ = H, Me, =CH_2, c-C_3, c-C_5
=== = Single, Double Bond

Table 17.3. Features, correlation coefficients, and cost factors for the first five HypoGen hypotheses for the retinoid series based upon compound 3.

Hypo	Feature 1	Feature 2	Feature 3	Feature 4	Feature 5	r^2	Cost
RXRa3.1	Hydrophobe	Hydrophobe	Hydrophobe	Ar Ring	Neg Ion	0.937	128.5
RXRa3.2	Hydrophobe	Hydrophobe	Hydrophobe	Ar Ring	Neg Ion	0.935	129.3
RXRa3.3	Hydrophobe	Hydrophobe	Hydrophobe	Ar Ring	Neg Ion	0.931	129.5
RXRa3.4	Hydrophobe	Hydrophobe	Hydrophobe	Ar Ring	Neg Ion	0.910	132.0
RXRa3.5	Hydrophobe	Hydrophobe	---	Ar Ring	Neg Ion	0.891	137.5

In this study, the fixed cost of 113.0 bits was well separated from the null hypothesis cost score of 215.5 bits. There were a number of high-affinity models in the dataset and the number of conformers per compound was significantly better represented. The test set also had an increased number of systematic changes with groupings of four or more examples of similar compounds as scored with ISIS keys. As an analogy one could consider the "cluster" size of each lesson for Catalyst to be trained upon as larger than in previous training sets.

One of the significant capabilities to review the hypothesis generation step is the visualization of the models. The first hypothesis (RXRa3.1) shows how one compound can map different groups to features and provide the user with alternative ideas for structure modification. In this example (Plate 17.1), the high-affinity compound **6** can use alternative methyl groups to fill feature space without appreciable loss of fit. One can also see from the fitting capabilities that the γ-*trans* olefin compounds prefer mapping the C-3' methyl group of the naphthyl ring system to a hydrophobic feature, rather than the C-7 methyl group on the olefin chain. If there is no methyl group at the C-3' position, then the C-7 methyl group is used, resulting in the inability of the C-3 olefin methyl group to fit. Plate 17.2, b, shows the all-*trans* olefin compound in blue and the γ-*cis* olefin compound 3 in red.

By comparison of all models one can see that the first (RXRa3.1) and sixth (RXRa3.6) hypotheses share four features. The red-colored centroids of Plate 17.3, b, show the five features of the sixth hypothesis, while the blue-feature centroids belong to the first hypothesis. These two hypotheses can be merged into one hypothesis to form a six-feature query.

17.6. Pharmacophore Validation

The end goal of the generation of various hypotheses is the validation of the models. As with any search technique, there are a number of query properties that can be adjusted. There is a fast search, which uses the precomputed conformations of each model in the database (rigid fitting), and there is a best flexible search, which allows the model to flex versus the stored conformation within an energy restriction. There are also 1D properties that can be defined, including a minimum fit criteria (mf) which can be set relative to the maximum possible fit, defined is the sum of the weights of all features. The 2D constraints include interfeature distances and feature tolerances. There are 3D constraints such as excluded volumes that can be added to a hypothesis. There are many variations because the circumstances surrounding each hypothesis generation are also numerous. In general, we find value in applying a minimum fit score (mf) to the hypothesis to produce a more discriminating search. We also reduce the default interfeature distance constraint variance (d) from the default value of ± 1 Å to $\pm 10\%$ of the distance. After the hypothesis has been generated from the training set, the searching of the test set proves invaluable for adding additional constraints.

An additional problem exists in how to interpret the test set search results. We tend to review a number of parameters simultaneously, including the percent yield (%Y), the percent of actives (%A), the percentage of the database that was found as hits (%Db), the percent enrichment (%E), and something we call the hit efficiency (H_{eff}). These values are defined in Chart 17.7 and are calculated for a number of queries in Table 17.4.

Chart 17.7.

$$\%Y = \left(\frac{Ha}{Ht}\right)\times100 \qquad \%A = \left(\frac{Ha}{A}\right)\times100 \qquad \%Db = \left(\frac{Ht}{D}\right)\times100$$

$$\%E = \left[\left(\frac{Ha/Ht}{A/D}\right)\right] = \frac{Ha\times D}{Ht\times A}$$

$$Heff = \left(\frac{Ha}{Ht}\right)\times\left[1-\left(\frac{Ht}{D}\right)\right] = Y(1-Db)$$

where:
    Ht is the number of hits returned by the query;
    Ha is the number of active compounds in the hit list;
    A is the total number of active compounds in the database;
    D is the number of compounds in the database.

Table 17.4. Queries with resultant percent yields, percent actives, percent of database returned as hits, percent enrichment, and the hit efficiency for various HypoGen hypotheses and an ISIS Subsimilar search set with a criteria of >85.

	Query	%Y	%A	%Db	E	H_{eff}
1	RXRa3.1(mf+d)	77.2	14.4	1.7	8.31	0.759
2	RXRa3.10(mf+d)	79.5	41.8	4.9	8.55	0.756
3	RXRa1.1(mf+d)	76.2	16.6	2.0	8.20	0.747
4	RXRa1.10(mf+d)	70.6	16.4	2.2	7.59	0.691
5	RXRa1.5(mf+d)	68.5	16.9	2.3	7.37	0.669
6	RXRa3.2(mf+d)	68.4	19.5	2.6	7.36	0.666
7	RXRa3.2(mf)	61.9	37.1	5.6	6.66	0.585
8	RXRa3.6(mf+d)	56.1	10.5	1.7	6.03	0.551
9	RXRa2.1(mf)	53.0	14.6	2.6	5.70	0.517
10	Cmpd 2 Sub 85	53.6	32.8	5.7	5.76	0.505
11	Cmpd 1a Sub 85	51.1	14.4	2.6	5.49	0.497
12	Cmpd 1b Sub 85	51.1	14.4	2.6	5.49	0.497
13	RXRa3.1(mf)	51.1	69.3	12.6	5.5	0.447
14	RXRa3.10(mf)	49.0	63.4	12.0	5.27	0.431
15	RXRa3.6(mf)	40.4	54.7	12.6	4.35	0.354
16	Cmpd 3 Sub 85	36.1	36.9	9.5	3.88	0.326

What can be seen from Table 17.4 is that for a hypothesis query, there is a better yield in searching a test set when there are both minimum fit (mf) and distance constraints (d) applied (1, 2, 8 vs. 13, 14, 15). There is little difference between the best hypothesis and the worst hypothesis, as defined by the cost function in Catalyst (1 vs. 2, 3 vs. 4); however, this does not always hold true as the complexity of the query is important. The more statistically significant hypotheses, defined by the difference in hypothesis cost versus the null hypothesis (Series **3**), return more actives found in the database search (*%A*). There may not be much advantage to a statistically weak hypothesis, derived from a set of compounds as in Series **2**, versus a similarity search based upon 2D ISIS keys (9 vs. 10) with information derived from a single compound **2**.

However, for the Series **1** compounds, one can see the redundancy of ISIS key information for compounds **1a** and **1b** (11 vs. 12) and that information from a series can extend into a database (3, 4, 5 vs. 11, 12). The most important advantage of the hypothesis query over a 2D ISIS key query is that the hypothesis query returns hits from all series in the database, or test set. This is a typical advantage of 3D searching versus 2D searching.

17.7. Conclusions

The training of a hypothesis test set leads to visual interpretation for the medicinal chemist and suggests chemical modifications for future exploration. The degree of statistical relevance of a test set suggests the extent of experimental testing and can be interpreted as one measure of completeness. If there are statistically poor correlations, then the extent of conformational exploration or pharmacophore space may need to be increased or restricted. There are a number of critical tools which can aid in the experimental design, including the cost function scores and a comparison of pharmacophore keys. Finally, the resulting hypotheses can lead to a pharmacophore definition and 3D database searching can find new and useful templates.[22]

References

1. Rosen J, Day A, Jones TK, Jones ETT, Nadzan AM, Stein RB: **Intracellular receptors and signal transducers and activators of transcription superfamilies: Novel targets for small-molecule drug discovery.** *J Med Chem* 1995, **38**:4855-4874.

2. Resche-Rigon M, Gronemeyer H: **Therapeutic potential of selective modulators of nuclear receptor action.** *Curr Opin Chem Biol* 1998, **2**:501-507.

3. Bogan AA, Cohen FE, Scanlon TS: **Natural ligands of nuclear receptors have conserved volumes.** *Nature Struc Biol* 1998, **5**:679-681.

4. Heyman RA, Mangelsdorf DS, Dyck JA, Stein RB, Eichele G, Evans RM, Thaller C: **9-*cis*-retinoic acid is a high affinity ligand for the retinoid X receptor.** *Cell* 1992, **68**:397-406.

5. (a) Vuligonda V, Lin Y, Thacher SM, Standeven AM, Kochar DM, Chandraratna RAS: **A new class of RAR subtype selective retinoids: Correlation of pharmacological effects with receptor activity.** *Bioorg Med Chem* 1999, **7**:263-270. (b) Benbrook DH, Subramanian S, Gale JB, Liu S, Brown CW, Boehm MF, Berlin KD: **Synthesis and characterization of heteroarotinoids demonstrate structure specificity relationships.** *J Med Chem* 1998, **41**:3753-3757. (c) Yu K-L, Spinazze P, Ostrowski J, Currier SJ, Pack EJ, Hammer L, Roalsvig T, Honeyman JA, Tortolani DR, Reczek PR, Mansuri MM, Starrett JE: **Retinoic acid receptor b,γ-selective ligands: Synthesis and biological activity of 6-substituted 2-naphthoic acid retinoids.** *J Med Chem* 1996, **39**:2411-2421.

6. Miller WH: **The emerging role of retinoids and retinoic acid metabolism blocking agents in the treatment of cancer.** *Cancer* 1998, **83**:1471-1482.

7. Boehm MF, Heyman RA, Patel S, Stein RB, Nagpal S: **Retinoids: Biological function and use in the treatment of dermatological diseases.** *Exp Opin Invest Drugs* 1995, **4**:593-612.

8. Agarwal VR, Bischoff ED, Prudente R, Cooke TA, Love DL, Heyman RA, Lamph WW: **Targretin causes complete regression of mammary carcinoma by inducing adipocyte differentiation in mammary glands.** *Program & Abstracts, The Endrocine Society's 81ˢᵗ Annual Meeting*, San Diego, CA, June 12-15, 1999. OR28-4.

9. (a) Apriletti JW, Ribeiro RC, Wagner RL, Feng W, Weebb P, Kushner PJ, West BL, Nilsson S, Scanlan TS, Fletterick RJ, Baxter JD: **Molecular and**

structural biology of thyroid hormone receptor. *Clin Exp Pharmacol Physiol* 1998, **25**:S2-S11; (b) Zou A, Elgort MG, Allegretto EA: **Retinoid X receptor (RXR) ligands activate the human 25-hydroxyvitamin D3-24-hydroxylase promoter via RXR heterodimer binding to two vitamin D-responsive elements and elicit additive effects with 1,25-dihydroxyvitamin D3.** *J Biol Chem* 1997, **272**:19027-19034; (c) Mukherjee R, Strasser J, Jow L, Hoener P, Paterniti J.R Heyman RA: **RXR agonists activate PPARa-inducible genes, lower triglycerides, and raise HDL levels *in vivo.*** *Arterioscler Thromb Vasc Biol* 1998, **18**:272-276.

10. Borodina Y, Filimonov D, Poroikov V: **Computer-aided estimation of synthetic compounds similarity with endogenous bioregulations.** *Quant Struct-Act Relat* 1998, **17**:459-464.

11. (a) Boehm M.F, McClurg M.R, Pathirana C, Mangelsdorf D, White S.K, Hebert J, Winn D, Goldman ME, Heyman RA: **Synthesis of high specific activity tritium-labeled [3H]-9-*cis*-retinoid acid andits application for identifying retinoids with unusual binding properties.** *J Med Chem* 1994, **37**:408-414; (b) Allegretto EA, Heyman RA: **Intracellular receptor characterization and ligand screening by transactivation and hormone-binding assays.** *Methods Mol Genet* 1996, **8**:405-420.

12. Canan Koch SS, Dardashti LJ, Hebert JH, White SK, Croston GE, Flatten KS, Heyman RA, Nadzan AM: **Identification of the first retinoid X receptor homodimer antagonist.** *J Med Chem* 1996, **39**:3229-3234.

13. Schulman IG, Shao G, Heyman RA: **Transactivation by retinoid X receptor-peroxisome proliferator-activated receptor γ (PPARγ) heterodimers: Intermolecular synergy requires only the PPARg hormone-dependent activation function.** *Mol Cell Biol* 1998, **18**:3482-3494.

14. *Catalyst*, Release 4.0, September 1998, Molecular Simulations Inc., San Diego, CA.

15. Smellie A, Teig, S.L, Towbin P: **Poling: Promoting conformational variation.** *J Comp Chem* 1995, **16**:171-187.

16. Davies K: **Using pharmacophore diversity to select molecules to test from commercial catalogs.** In: *Molecular Diversity and Combinatorial Chemistry.* Chaiken IM, Janda KD, eds. Washington, DC: American Chemical Society, 1996:309-316.

17. Willet P: **Using computational tools to analyze molecular diversity.** In: *A Practical Guide to Combinatorial Chemistry.* Czarnick AW, DeWitt SH, eds. Washington, DC: American Chemical Society, 1997:17-48.

18. Cramer RD, Clark RD, Patterson DE, Ferguson AM: **Bioisosterism as a molecular diversity descriptor: Steric fields of single "topomeric" conformers.** *J Med Chem* 1996, **39**:3060-3069.

19. *ISIS*; Molecular Design Ltd.; 14600 Catalina Street, San Leandro, CA 94577.

20. (a) Boehm MF, Zhang L, Zhi L, McClurg MR, Berger E, Wagoner M, Mais DE, Suto CM, Davies PJA, Heyman RA, Nadzan AM: **Design and synthesis of potent retinoid X receptor selective ligands that induce apoptosis in leukemia cells.** *J Med Chem* 1995, 38:3146-3155; (b) Nadzan AM, Boehm MF, Zhang L, Badea BA, Zhi L, White SK, Mais DE, Berger E, Suto CM, McClurg MR, Davies PJA, Heyman RA: **Design of novel RXR selective retinoids.** *Eur J Med Chem* 1995, **30**:520s-533s.

21. (a) Farmer LF, Jeong SE, Kallel EA, Canan Koch SS, Croston GE, Flatten KS, Heyman RA, Nadzan AM: **Synthesis and structure-activity relationships of potent retinoid X receptor ligands.** *Bio Med Chem Lett* 1997, **7**:2393-2398; (b) Farmer LF, Zhi L. Jeong SE, Kallel EA, Croston GE, Flatten KS, Heyman RA, Nadzan AM: **Synthesis and structure-activity relationships of potent conformationally restricted retinoid X receptor ligands.** *Bio Med Chem Lett* 1997, **7**:2747-2752.

22. Kaminski JK, Rane DF, Snow ME Weber L, Rothofsky ML, Anderson SD, Lin SL: **Identification novel farnesyl protein transferase inhibitors using three-dimensional database searching methods.** *J Med Chem* 1997, **40**:4103-4112.

PART III

Receptor-Based Pharmacophores

- **Receptor-Based Pharmacophore Perception and Modeling**

- **Pharmacophore-Based Molecular Docking**

- **Applications in Drug Design**

18

Receptor-Based Pharmacophore Perception and Modeling

C. M. Venkatachalam, Paul Kirchhoff, and Marvin Waldman

Abstract

Considerable information on three-dimensional structure of receptors is available from X-ray studies of receptors with bound complexes. This information is valuable in designing compounds to bind to a given receptor. In this article, we describe our recent efforts to recognize pharmacophores from a three-dimensional structure of a receptor. The method involves analyzing the active site to generate an interaction map of desirable features that a ligand should satisfy to adequately interact with the receptor. These features include hydrogen-bond donors, hydrogen-bond acceptors, and lipophilic sites. A set of 3D queries is derived from the interaction map of the active site. These queries are employed in searching a multi-conformational database of compounds with known activities. An analysis of the set of queries that "hit" or "reject" highly active compounds can help in understanding the 3D features essential for activity. We present a new software program called SBF (Structure-Based Focusing) developed within the Cerius^2 environment that automates the process of pharmacophore exploration. We illustrate the workings of this method using the example of ligands binding to the estrogen receptor.

18

Receptor-Based Pharmacophore Perception and Modeling

C. M. Venkatachalam, Paul Kirchhoff, and Marvin Waldman

Molecular Simulations Inc., San Diego, California

18.1. Introduction

The general problem of designing compounds that can successfully bind to a receptor is a challenging one. It is generally believed that if the three-dimensional structure of a given receptor is experimentally known, the complexity of such a task is considerably reduced. From known three-dimensional structures of receptors and/or of receptor-bound ligands, it should be possible, in principle, to design compounds that can bind to receptors. Methods that have been employed fall broadly into two categories: (i) *de novo* design of compounds in an active site, and (ii) development of a pharmacophore model and use of derived pharmacophores in ligand design. When elements of a pharmacophore can be correctly elucidated from the receptor active site, then molecules that are likely to bind adequately to the receptor can be identified by fitting a variety of molecules to pharmacophoric features. This approach is different than the more traditional approaches, like analog-based design, where a pharmacophore is derived by aligning 3D structures of highly active compounds without explicit knowledge of the receptor structure. The availability of the 3D structure of a receptor active site provides invaluable information that can be utilized in developing pharmacophore models.

By examining the nature of interactions of experimentally determined receptor-bound ligands, one can deduce the key residues of the receptor involved in ligand interactions. One may employ such information to generate a pharmacophore. In practice, however, the active site of a receptor often displays a large number of complex features. Deriving the 3D requirements that a ligand has to satisfy can, therefore, be quite complicated. Thus, there is a need for an automated method that can consider various pharmacophoric features systematically and identify the features that are consistent with highly active compounds. With this in mind, we have developed a new application called Structure-Based Focusing (SBF) within the Cerius[2] software environment.[1] The principles behind this application are described in the following section.

18.2. Cerius[2] Structure-Based Focusing Method

Assuming that the three-dimensional structure of a receptor is available and a set of molecules has been identified whose likelihood for binding to the active site is to be evaluated, the Cerius[2] application—Structure-Based Focusing—works as follows. For the given set of compounds, a multi-conformation Catalyst[1] database is first generated. The active site of the receptor protein is analyzed using Ludi[2-4] to obtain the set of desirable features that a ligand may need to adequately interact with the receptor. The resulting interaction map consists of hydrogen-bond donor, hydrogen-bond acceptor, and lipophilic features. These features, along with excluded volume regions based on the positions of receptor atoms, are used to generate three-dimensional Catalyst queries. The generated queries are then used to rapidly screen Catalyst databases to obtain hits for ligands that are likely to bind to the receptor site.

The Structure-Based Focusing (SBF) application is designed such that the requisite Ludi and Catalyst programs are automatically invoked from within Cerius[2]. A flowchart for the Cerius[2] SBF method is displayed in Figure 18.1. Each step is further illustrated here by an application of ligand binding to the estrogen receptor. This receptor is capable of binding a variety of ligands and has a number of different binding modes.[5-7] We employ the 1ERE PDB structure for the receptor. Queries produced from the 1ERE structure are expected to be more selective toward agonists as opposed to antagonist ligands. A database of 31 ligands with known relative binding affinities was generated and is used as a training set. Complete details of the application of SBF to estrogen binding are being presented elsewhere.[8]

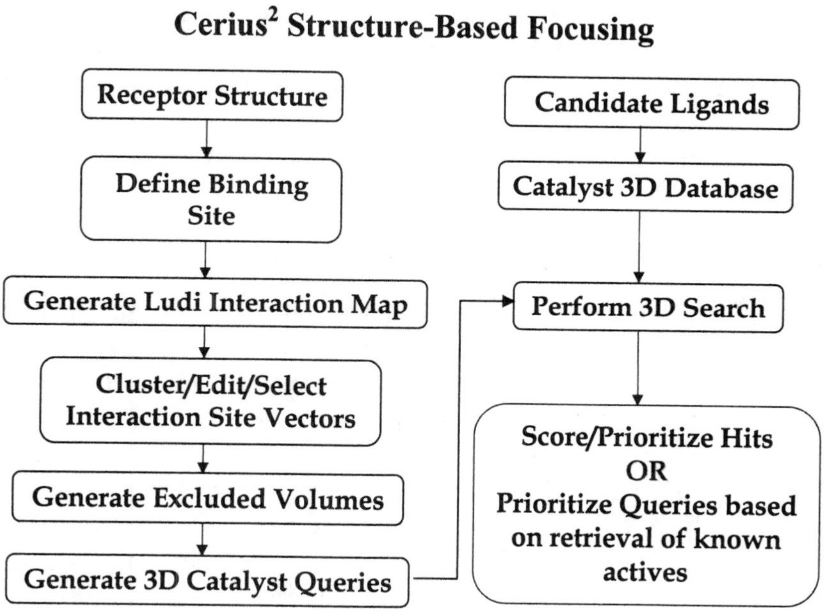

Cerius^2 Structure-Based Focusing

Figure 18.1. Flowchart for Cerius² Structure-Based Focusing.

18.2.1. Active Site

A three-dimensional receptor structure is usually obtained from the pdb file (1ERE). The active site region is identified using a sphere. The location and the size of the sphere are adjusted so as to include the active site and the key residues of the protein involved in interacting with ligands. Tools are available to specify the center and the radius of the sphere—for example, the sphere center may be specified as the geometric center of selected atoms. Plate 18.1, a shows the active site region used in defining the sphere for the estrogen receptor.

18.2.2. Ludi Interaction Map

With the binding site defined, Ludi is employed to generate an interaction model. The interaction model describes desirable interactions that
a potential ligand is expected to have in the defined binding site. The
interaction model consists of three types of features: hydrogen-bond
donor, hydrogen-bond acceptor, and lipophilic features. Features of the
interaction model are generated at a user-defined density and represent
features that complement the binding site. The method employed by
Ludi to generate the interaction map is described elsewhere.[4] Plate 18.1, b
shows the interaction map obtained for the estrogen receptor.

18.2.3. Cluster Analysis of the Interaction Map

As can be seen from Plate 18.1, b the interaction map generated by Ludi
can, in general, consist of several dozens of features. The map is usually so rich in detail that it is impractical to extract a single query from it.
Often features will appear in *clusters* of donors, acceptors, and
lipophilic centers. Obviously, a ligand is not expected to contain all the
features in the map. The complexity of the interaction map is reduced in
two steps. First, cluster analysis is employed to identify clusters of features of each type. Plates 18.2, a-c, illustrate the cluster analysis of the
interaction map for the estrogen receptor. Here, donor features are
grouped into 4 clusters, acceptors into 2 clusters, and lipophilic features
into 4 clusters. A complete linkage hierarchical clustering method was
employed. Second, for each cluster, the feature closest to the geometric
center of the cluster is retained while discarding the other features in the
cluster. Even though this step can considerably reduce the number of
features, one still may have a dozen or so features in the interaction map.

The resulting interaction model overlaid with one of the active ligands, E2, is displayed in Plate 18.3. The features have been labeled in
Plate 18.3 with their assigned numbers to allow for comparison with
Plate 18.4. The numbers are colored by feature type: blue for donor, red
for acceptor, and gray for lipophilic feature. Each hydrogen-bond donor
and acceptor is labeled with the receptor residue number that produced
that feature. Residue labels are given the complementary color of the
feature that they generated to graphically illustrate that the interaction
model is the complement of the binding site.

18.2.4. Multiple Queries

A query developed from an interaction map, reduced in complexity as described in the previous section might still be too complicated to retrieve any hits from a database. For example, cluster analysis of the interaction map resulted in a map with 10 features for the estrogen receptor (see Plate 18.3). Experience shows that queries with about 3 to 7 features are likely to retrieve valid hits. The approach we have adopted here is to generate multiple queries from the interaction map. For instance, if there are N hydrogen-bond acceptors in the map, assuming one constructs queries with n acceptors (n < N), then there are N! / [n! (N-n)!] combinations to be considered. This must be done for each feature type. In practice, it may be necessary to avoid placing features too close or too far away. As an inter-feature distance increases, the resulting queries can only retrieve large molecules. Therefore, while considering all combinations of queries, limits are placed on inter-feature distances. In general, this can still lead to hundreds of queries. Using a minimum distance of 1.5 Angstroms, in the estrogen example, we obtained 112 3-feature queries, 182 4-feature queries, 196 5-feature queries and 140 6-feature queries.

18.2.5. Volume Exclusions

Volume exclusions must be added to each of the queries in order to prevent hits from overlapping with receptor atoms. The excluded regions may be defined by identifying the receptor atoms lining the active site. An algorithm is available in SBF with which one can quickly identify the receptor atoms lining the active site. From the center of the Ludi sphere already defined, one can search in various directions for atoms of the receptor closest to the center. Only non-hydrogen atoms were considered for the volume exclusions. The resulting exclusion volumes are added to each of the queries. A total of 228 exclusion spheres were employed in the estrogen example with a radius of 1.3 Å.

18.2.6. Catalyst Database Search

A multi-conformation Catalyst 3D database is generated from prospective candidate ligand molecules within the Cerius^2 SBF application.

Queries generated from the interaction and exclusion models are used to search the Catalyst 3D databases for compounds that are likely to bind to the receptor.

Since one deals with hundreds of queries, it may be impractical to search a large database with this many queries. The ideal application for these queries, however, is for a small database of ligands with known activities. In such a case, hits obtained with the queries may be analyzed to identify the queries that are most selective for finding very active compounds.

18.3. Results and Discussion for the Estrogen Binding

In the case of estrogen, all of the queries generated were used to screen the 3D Catalyst database generated from the 31 estrogen ligands. In general, queries consisting of more features are less likely to produce hits than queries consisting of fewer features. For the 4-feature queries, 60 of the 182 queries or 33 percent of the queries generated produced hits. Only 13 and 3 percent of the 5- and 6-feature queries produced hits. Similarly, the number of ligands for which hits were obtained decreases as the number of features present in the queries increases.

Examples of hits obtained for individual queries and totals for the complete sets of 4-, 5-, and 6-feature combinations are tabulated in Plate 18.4. This table shows the general nature of the results that one can obtain with SBF. Ligands are listed here in decreasing activity from left to right based on relative binding affinity (RBA) values and have been colored by group. Here, a value of "0" indicates that no hits were obtained for the particular ligand with that particular query. A value of "1" indicates that there were hits for 1 or more conformations of the particular ligand with that particular query.

It is clear from the table in Plate 18.4 that individual queries can be found which are more selective for certain ligands. One can use this information to identify a number of queries that possess the desired selectivity and use these queries to search larger databases. Information contained in the complete listing of the hits (not shown) can also be used to determine which features are more important for the binding of a ligand or group of ligands for the purpose of further developing and refining queries for this system.

In order to consider each set of queries generated as a whole, hit totals for each set are listed in Table 18.1. Here the highly active and less active ligands are divided by a vertical line. Highly active ligands are considered to be ligands with a RBA of 50 or greater. Percentages of hits for the highly and less active ligands are tabulated for each set of queries. Clearly, each set of queries shows greater selectivity toward the more active ligands even when each set is viewed as a whole.

Table 18.1. Analysis of Queries by Group (*Division at a RBA value of 50.*)

Queries	Diethylstilbestrol	Hexestrol	Dienestrol	E2	Coumestrol	Estrone	17α-estradiol	Moxestrol	β-zearalanol	Estriol	4-hydroxy-E2	2-hydroxy-E2	5-androstenediol	Genistein	3β-androstanediol	Norethynodrel	4-androstanediol	3α-androstanediol	Norethindrone	BisphenolA	5α-dihydrotestosterone	Dehydroepiandosteron	Nandrolone	Methoxychlor	Testosterone	Progesterone
4 Feature Totals	5	21	4	15	1	2	7	0	0	11	11	7	6	3	8	1	7	6	0	18	0	2	0	0	0	0
5 Feature Totals	1	11	3	6	0	1	2	0	0	3	3	0	1	0	2	0	2	2	0	5	0	0	0	0	0	0
6 Feature Totals	0	3	1	0	0	0	0	0	0	0	0	0	0	0	0	0	0	0	0	0	0	0	0	0	0	0

(The first seven data columns — Diethylstilbestrol through 17α-estradiol — are **Highly Active**; the remaining columns are **Less Active**.)

Queries	Percentage of Highly Actives Hit	Percentage of Less Actives Hit	GH	E
4 Feature Totals	100	58	0.293	1.7
5 Feature Totals	86	37	0.397	2.0
6 Feature Totals	29	0	0.821	4.4

There are a number of ways in which the quality of a hit list can be evaluated in addition to calculating the percentages of hits for the highly and less active ligands. The enrichment, E (see Chapter 11), of the highly active ligands in the hit list compared to the original database can be calculated using Equation 18.1:

$$E = \frac{H_a / H_t}{A / D} = \frac{H_a \times D}{H_t \times A} \qquad (18.1)$$

where H_t is the total number of ligands for which hits were obtained, H_a is the number of highly active ligands for which hits were obtained, A is the number of highly active ligands in the database, and D is the total number of ligands in the database.

Values for E, as well as the GH-score (see chapter 11), are also listed in Table 18.1 for each set of queries. A value of E greater than 1.0 indicates the hit list has been enriched with a greater percentage of highly active ligands relative to the original database. As can be seen in Table 18.1, each set of queries has an E value greater than 1.0, indicating that these queries as a whole have a greater selectivity toward the highly active ligands. The 4-feature queries retrieve all of the highly active compounds, as well as 58% of the less active compounds in the training set. On the other hand, 6-feature queries retrieve 29% of the highly active compounds and none of the less active ones. The increase in the number of features, while reducing the number of hits, increases the selectivity of the query. GH-scores corroborate these results.

An example of hits obtained for a 4-feature query is illustrated in Plate 18.5. Docked conformations of the three most active ligands examined in this study are shown with the features of the 4-feature query feat4_159 that retrieved them. As can be seen in Plate 18.4 or by comparing Plates 18.3 and 18.5, this query consists of 1 donor (number 4), 1 acceptor (number 2), and 2 lipophilic features (numbers 1 and 3). (Excluded volumes in the feat4_159 query are not displayed.) As calculated by Cerius^2, hydrogen bonds between hexestrol and several of the estrogen receptor residues are displayed by dashed yellow lines. The hydrogen-bond pattern closely matches the donor and acceptor features of the query and the expected hydrogen-bonding pattern for the E2 ligand.

Detailed analysis of the hits showed that the 4-feature query, feat4_159 (consisting of Donor 4, Acceptor 2, and Lipophiles 1 and 3— see Plate 18.3 for numbering scheme) extracted highly active hits from the database. Also, a 3-feature query consisting of Donor 2 and Lipophiles 1 and 2 and a 3-feature query consisting of Donor 2, Acceptor 2, and Lipophile 2 retrieved moderately active compounds.

18.4. Conclusions

The SBF method automates the process of constructing 3D queries from receptor interaction maps and performs database searches to find hits in an efficient manner. SBF avoids alignment and superimposition of ligands with one another based on shapes. It also makes no assumptions about specific binding modes. Though hundreds of queries have to be considered, the procedure is automatic and is quite practical when dealing with a training set of a small number of molecules with known activity. For the case of the estrogen receptor, using a training set of 31 compounds, several hundred queries were employed in the database search. The hits obtained from the training set helped in identifying the queries (and features) that are consistent with highly active compounds. The pharmacophore so identified may be employed to search large databases.

Acknowledgements

The authors wish to thank Scott Kahn for extensive discussions that lead to the formulation of the workings of the SBF application. Also, we acknowledge valuable assistance received from D. Ann Giammona, Guy del Mistro, Jeff Jiang, Hong Li, Bernard Chang, Jan Bielawski, Daniel McDonald, and Rob Brown during the development of this application.

References

1. *Cerius² and Catalyst* are software packages available from Molecular Simulations Inc., 9685 Scranton Rd., San Diego, CA 92121-3752.

2. Bohm HJ: Prediction of binding constants of protein ligands: **A fast method for the prioritization of hits obtained from *de novo* design or 3D database search programs.** *J Comput-Aided Mol Des* 1998, **12**:309-323.

3. Bohm HJ: **The development of a simple empirical scoring function to estimate the binding constant for a protein ligand complex of known three-dimensional structure.** *J Comput-Aided Mol Des* 1994, **8**:243-256.

4. Bohm HJ: **Ludi-rule-based automatic design of new substituents for enzyme inhibitor leads.** *J Comput-Aided Mol Des* 1992, **6**:593-606.

5. Gould JC, Leonard LS, Maness SC, Wagner BL, Conner K, Zacharewski T, Safe S, McDonnell DP, Gaido KW: **Bisphenol A interacts with the estrogen receptor Alpha in a distinct manner from estradiol.** *Molecular and Cellular Endocrinology* 1998, **142**:203-214.

6. Sun J, Meyers MJ, Fink BE, Rajendran R, Katzenellenbogen JA, Katzenellenbogen BS: **Novel ligands that function as selective estrogens or antiestrogens for estrogen receptor-alpha or estrogen receptor-beta.** *Endocrinology* 1999, **140**:800-804.

7. Kuiper GGJM, Lemmen JG, Carlsson B, Corton JC, Safe, SH, van der Saag PT, van der Burg P, Gustafsson JA: **Interaction of estrogenic chemicals and phytoestrogens with estrogen receptor beta.** *Endocrinology* 1998, **139**:4252-4263.

8. Paul Kirchhoff et al. Unpublished results.

19

Pharmacophore-Based Molecular Docking

Bert E. Thomas IV, Diane Joseph-McCarthy, and Juan C. Alvarez

Abstract

Rapid computational mining of large three-dimensional molecular databases is central to generating new drug leads. To virtually screen a database accurately conformational flexibility of the ligand molecules must be considered. Ligand flexibility can be included without prohibitively increasing the search time by docking pre-computed conformers from a conformationally expanded database. To further decrease the time required, ensembles of conformations can be simultaneously docked. A pharmacophore-based docking method whereby conformers of the same or different molecules are overlayed and simultaneously docked by their largest three-dimensional pharmacophore is presented. The method, as implemented in DOCK4.0.1, is described in detail and the use of an automated script to generate chemically labeled site points with the program MCSS is discussed.

19

Pharmacophore-Based Molecular Docking

Bert E. Thomas IV, Diane Joseph-McCarthy, and Juan C. Alvarez

Wyeth Research, Cambridge, Massachusetts

19.1. Introduction

Small molecule drugs exert their biological action by binding to a macromolecular target, thereby modulating its activity. Computational mining of 3D molecular databases has proven to be extremely valuable in the identification of novel biologically active compounds as drug leads.[1,2] Database searches fall into two major classes: ligand-based (pharmacophore) and target-based (molecular docking). Pharmacophore searches consist of finding molecules that match a set of distances between specific types of atoms or functional groups which interact favorably with the target, whereas docking methods search for electronic and steric complementarity between the putative ligands and the macromolecular target.

Over the last several years there have been great advances in pharmacophore-based searching.[3,4] Users have the capability to define queries incorporating complex geometric relationships, as well as inclusion and exclusion volumes. In the absence of structural information for the target, queries can be generated from the structure-activity relationships of known ligands.[5-8] If the structure of the target is known, queries can be extracted from experimentally determined interactions, such as protein-ligand complexes and bound water molecules, or computationally determined interactions (e.g., modeled complexes, GRID[9] maps, and MCSS[10,11] minima).

Pharmacophore-based searching, however, suffers from some significant limitations, particularly in cases where the target structure is available. Even with the recent advent of partial matching, there is a limited subset of key interactions (typically 4-6) which must be extracted from a target site with dozens of potential interactions. Furthermore, complex queries, particularly those allowing for partial matching and/or containing large number of exclusion spheres, are extremely slow, taking as long as several weeks on an average-sized database. Finally, and most importantly, the majority of the information contained in the target structure is not considered during the database search. Thus, there is no scoring function beyond the binary readout of "hit" (matches the query) or "not hit" (doesn't match). Any steric or electronic constraints imposed by the target, but not defined in the query, are ignored.

Molecular docking algorithms aim to predict the conformation and orientation of a ligand bound to a macromolecular target. In contrast to pharmacophore-based searching, a three-dimensional structure of the target is required. Although a variety of docking algorithms have been described in the literature, in general the methodology involves sampling, scoring, and ranking multiple conformations and orientations (rotations and translations) of the ligand within the target site.[1,2,12] Some of the challenges in the development of an effective docking algorithm include: incorporation of ligand and target conformational flexibility, efficient sampling of orientational space, and reliable scoring functions. Additionally, if the docking method is to be used for the virtual screening of large compound databases, it must be fast.

Early docking algorithms treated both the ligand and target molecules as conformationally rigid.[13,14] Nonetheless, these algorithms have been effective in reproducing crystallographic complexes[1,2] as well as identifying novel inhibitors.[15-17] Ligand flexibility has more recently been explored during the docking stage using Monte Carlo methods,[18,19] genetic algorithms,[20-23] simulated annealing,[24] tabu searches,[25] and fragment build-up procedures,[26-30] and during the database generations stage using conformationally expanded databases[31,32] and conformational ensembles.[33]

The rapid growth of small molecule databases available for virtual screening, both commercial and proprietary, necessitates that molecular docking algorithms should be minimally able to handle hundreds of thousands of molecules, thus placing an upper limit for evaluation of seconds, rather than minutes, on a per molecule basis. One approach aimed at satisfying this requirement is to address conformational flexibility at the database generation step, and not during the docking procedure.[31-33] Although conformational expansion of a large database is a time-consuming effort requiring significant amounts of disk space, once completed the database can be more rapidly screened against a multitude of targets.

19.2. The Dock Algorithm

There are two essential steps in the DOCK[14] algorithm when run in rigid ligand mode: orienting the putative candidate molecule in the site and scoring the resulting orientation (Figure 19.1). Orientation of the putative ligand is guided by matching distances, within a defined tolerance, between pre-defined "site points" on the target to interatomic distances of the ligand. When four distance matches are identified, a rotation-translation matrix is used to transform the ligand coordinates, thus placing the molecule in the site. Each orientation is scored for its quality of fit and the process is repeated until either a user-defined maximum number of orientations has been examined or all possible matches have been exhausted.

Site points are typically generated with the DOCK utility SPHGEN,[14] although atoms from known ligands or crystallographic waters can also be used. The matching portion of the algorithm can be directed through the use of chemical matching and critical clusters. Chemical matching involves the labeling of site points such that only particular atom types are allowed to be matched to them.[15,31,34] Additionally, if there are subsites of interest in the target binding site, the site points in those regions can be defined as part of a critical cluster, which requires that at least one member of the critical cluster be part of any accepted ligand "match".[15,31] A further advantage of chemical matching and critical clusters is an increase in the matching efficiency and speed due to the elimination of potentially less promising orientations.

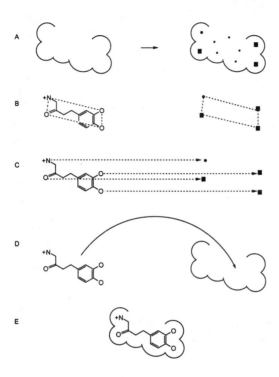

Figure 19.1. Schematic of DOCK methodology. In the first step (A), the target binding site is filled with site points which may be colored. Then (B) distances between pairs of atoms in a database molecule (or points in a pharmacophore in the case of pharmacophore docking) are matched to distances between pairs of site points. A transformation matrix is calculated for the orientation (C), the molecule is docked into the binding site (D), and the fit of the molecule is scored (E).

19.2.1. Conformational Ensemble Docking

Conformational expansion of the ligand database results in a linear increase in the search time—a prohibitive increase for large databases containing a significant number of ligand conformers. One method that has been used to decrease the search time is that of docking conformational ensembles.[33] Conformational ensembles are generated by overlaying all conformations of a given molecule onto its largest rigid fragment. Only atoms within this largest rigid fragment are used during the distance matching step in DOCK. Once the rotation-translation matrix is determined for the ensemble, each of the conformers is oriented into the site and scored. Thus, a single successful matching step, or selection of a particular orientation, results in all the conformers being docked and evaluated in that orientation. Lorber et al. generated an ensemble version of the Available Chemicals Directory (ACD)[35] with an average of 297 conformers per molecule.[33] They achieved a 100-fold speed increase by docking this database rather than one containing individual conformations. An additional contribution to the increase in speed comes from the fact that the largest rigid fragment of the molecule generally has fewer atoms than the entire molecule, which reduces the number of potential matches that must be examined.

There are limitations to the ensemble docking method, however. As Lorber et al. point out, there is a loss of information when the orientations are guided only by a subset of the atoms in a molecule (as is also the case in algorithms treating flexibility using the fragment build-up procedures). Alternative orientations may be missed because potential distance matches from non-rigid portions of the molecule are not considered. Furthermore, the use of chemical matching and critical clusters is limited since any molecule whose rigid fragment alone does not meet these more restrictive criteria will be eliminated from consideration. Our goal has been to develop a method which takes advantage of the speed of docking ensembles of molecules without limiting the potential for chemical matching and critical clusters, and does not suffer as greatly from a loss of information.

19.3. Pharmacophore-Based Docking

Pharmacophore searching is based on the idea that the appropriate spatial disposition of a small number of functional groups in a molecule is sufficient for achieving a desired biological effect. At the atomic level, it is these groups which provide the primary interactions between the small molecule ligand and the macromolecular target. Therefore, it is desirable for these groups to guide the ensemble formation (or overlay of molecular conformers) and the subsequent docking events.

Typical pharmacophore features include: hydrogen-bond donors and acceptors, positive and negative ionizables, hydrophobes, and ring centroids. Each conformer of a molecule has a pharmacophore fingerprint—a set of pharmacophore features and their relative positions.

Bond rotations which do not change the relative position of any such feature within a molecule would result in different conformers with the same pharmacophore fingerprint. Likewise, different molecules may have identical pharmacophore fingerprints; the trivial case is a congeneric series where the differences do not involve pharmacophore features, while the non-trivial case is unrelated molecules that can identically orient the same features in space.

Our implementation of pharmacophore-based docking, like the conformational ensemble docking methodology of Lorber et al., is built on the DOCK framework. Conceptually, pharmacophore-based docking works as follows (Figure 19.2). A pharmacophore fingerprint is selected from the database and the standard DOCK steps are carried out. The pharmacophore fingerprint contains no atoms, only the features and their corresponding coordinates. These pharmacophore points are matched to the pre-defined, chemically labeled target site points. When a transformation matrix is determined which can overlay at least four pharmacophore features with a corresponding set of site points, it is applied to all conformers (of all molecules) in the database that have that pharmacophore fingerprint. These conformers are then scored in that orientation. The process is repeated until all possible orientations, or a user-defined maximum number of orientations, have been examined.

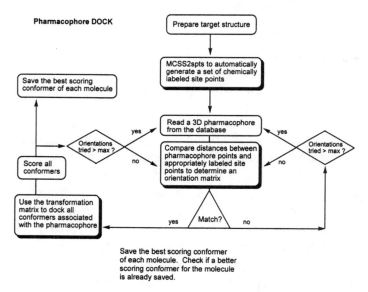

Figure 19.2. Overview of pharmacophore-based DOCK methodology.

In essence, a series of rigid pharmacophore-based searches are carried out on a conformationally expanded database with a molecular docking scoring function used to evaluate the fitness of the "hits." The combinatorial matching of sets of pharmacophore feature points to chemically labeled site points enables the rapid, simultaneous searching of thousands of potential four-center (or more) pharmacophores capable of interacting with the target. Evaluation of the hits docked into the target site allows: 1) for the identification of ligands that have shapes complementary to the binding site and are capable of making additional favorable interactions and 2) for rapid elimination of those containing functional groups which would interfere with binding.

Currently, the features which define the pharmacophore fingerprint are: a hydrogen-bond donor, a hydrogen-bond acceptor, a dual hydrogen-bond donor and acceptor (e.g., hydroxyl), and a five or six-membered ring centroid. The definitions were limited to four types to allow substantial numbers of molecules to be represented by each pharmacophore fingerprint. The process of evaluating the oriented molecules with a scoring function resolves potential issues such as the lack of differentiation between ionizable groups and hydrogen-bond donors/acceptors, the absence of formally defined hydrophobes, and the lack of distinction between saturated and unsaturated rings.

As with the docking of conformational ensembles, a significant speed increase is achieved over the docking of individual molecules. One source of the gain in speed is the fact that multiple molecules get oriented and scored from a single distance matching event. In the case of conformational ensembles, this degeneracy is equal to the average number of conformers per molecule in the database, which was 297 in the case of Lorber et al.[33] For pharmacophore docking the degeneracy is equal to the average number of conformers per pharmacophore, which appears to be on the order of 50-100 for a similar database. However, this value is database dependent. A second source of the speed increase is the reduced number of ligand points considered during distance matching, which ranges from four to twenty for pharmacophore docking. On average, for conformational ensemble docking, the number of ligand points considered (all the heavy atoms in the rigid fragment) is probably significantly higher, although no formal estimate has been made.

In contrast to conformational ensemble docking, however, more information pertaining to the entire molecule is retained in pharmacophore docking. Pharmacophore atoms from both the rigid and flexible portions of the molecule are used to guide the docking orientations. Chemical matching is not only fully functional, but strongly encouraged (within the context of pharmacophoric features). Furthermore, the dimensions of the molecule are more closely preserved, thus allowing the user to preferentially select molecules spanning the site of interest through the use of critical clusters.

19.3.1. Database Preparation

Database preparation is key to pharmacophore-based docking. The preparation of a database involves generating molecular conformations, and overlaying the molecular conformers onto pharmacophores. The database is exported as 3D SD files clustered by the number of ionizable functional groups per molecule so that the current lack of a solvation correction does not arbitrarily bias the ordering of charged molecules when using a force-field scoring function.[36] That is, during the docking steps, only force field scores for hits with the same number of ionizables will be directly compared. Furthermore, the molecules are grouped by their one-dimensional pharmacophore, defined as the number and type of features present, sin order to speed up the subsequent overlay process. The SD files are processed using the DOCK utilities sdf2mol2 and sybdb, which convert the molecules to SYBYL mol2 format and assign SYBYL atom types so that the molecules are protonated appropriately at physiological pH.

Conformational expansion of the database is carried out using the systematic search method in SYBYL with an upper limit of 500 conformations per molecule. The bond rotation increments are set to 120° as a default value and are adjusted to 180° where the bond has sp[2] character (e.g., for an amide bond). Bonds that produce degenerate conformations due to symmetry (e.g., an attached methyl group) are not allowed to rotate. No minimization is performed on the resulting conformers, but a 30 kcal/mol relative conformational energy limit is imposed.

The overlay process is achieved using various scripts in conjunction with SYBYL and UNITY.[37] A three-dimensional pharmacophore is extracted from the first molecule of a cluster and is used to perform a rigid 3D UNITY search of the rest of that cluster to find matches. The pharmacophore query and its associated molecules are saved (Plate

19.1); those molecules are deleted from the cluster and the process continues until all molecules are associated with a pharmacophore.

19.3.2. Site Point Generation

Chemically labeled site points are generated in an automated fashion using the script MSCSS2SPTS. The script runs a series of multiple copy simultaneous searches (MCSS) calculations on the macromolecular structure and extracts the chemically labeled site points from the resulting functional group maps. The MCSS program[10,11] determines energetically favorable positions for various functional group types in the binding site of a target macromolecular structure. MCSS simultaneously energy minimizes thousands of copies of a given chemical group in the binding site region using the CHARMM potential energy function[38] to determine the preferred locations or potential energy minima. The MSCSS2SPTS script calculates maps for acetic acid, methyl ammonium, N-methyl acetamide, methanol, water, cyclohexane, oxazole, and benzene and then clusters minima based on type, position, and energy to generate a set of chemically labeled site points.

19.3.3. Validation

Pharmacophore DOCK has been implemented in DOCK4.0.1.[28] As an initial test case, pharmacophore DOCK was used to dock methotrexate (MTX) into the dihydrofolate reductase (DHFR) binding site. Starting from the X-ray crystal structure conformation of MTX bound to DHFR (pdb accession number 3dfr[39]) MTX was translated away from the protein and conformationally expanded; a database was created that consists of 500 pharmacophores each with one associated molecular conformer. The calculations were done using chemical matching and contact scoring with the manual matching option selected. The definitions for the chemical matching are summarized in Table 19.1. The contact scoring involves summing over all ligand atoms the number of macromolecular target atoms within 4.0 Å and adding a contact clash penalty of 50 for any target atom closer than 0.75 of its van der Waals radius. An upper limit of 5000 orientations was tried for each pharmacophore.

Table 19.1. Chemical Matching.

Receptor Site Point Label	Allowed Ligand Atom Type Match
null	all
centroid	centroid
donor	donor, dual
acceptor	acceptor, dual
dual	acceptor, donor, dual

Test calculations were run using two different sets of site points. The first set of site points consists of all pharmacophore points from the bound X-ray conformation of MTX; this set contains 3 centroid, 9 acceptor, and 3 donor sites. With this site set of points and a distance tolerance of 0.25Å, only 23 of the 500 MTX conformers satisfied the matching (pharmacophore) criteria and were docked into the site. The contact scores of the docked conformers ranged from -111 to -3. The best scoring conformer was the one extracted from the X-ray complex. The root-mean-square difference (RMSD) between MTX in the X-ray structure and the docked conformation is 0.38 Å for all heavy atoms, and 0.087 Å excluding the oxygens from one of the carboxylates that is slightly rotated.

The second set of site points (Plate 19.2) used was generated with the MCSS2SPTS script, described above. This set consists of 23 centroid, 19 acceptor, 28 donor, and 31 dual site points. When the calculation is carried out with a distance tolerance of 0.5 Å, the scores for the top 100 hits ranged from -121 to -60 and the best scoring hit was the X-ray conformation. The docked X-ray conformation overlaid very closely with the bound structure (heavy atom RMSD of 0.79 Å) and had a slightly better score (-121 versus -111). Full validation using a large database of diverse molecules is currently underway.

19.4. Discussion

In its current implementation, pharmacophore docking is a rigid body method requiring a conformationally expanded database. Consequently, one limitation is the amount of conformational space that is covered for each molecule in the database. The combinatorial nature of conformational expansion results in rapid growth in database size. For example, a molecule containing 6 rotatable bonds would yield 729 conformers for three positions per bond (a 120° rotation) versus 4096 conformers for four positions per bond (a 90° rotation). We chose torsional increments expected to generate conformers close to local minima and afford substantial coverage of conformational space, while keeping the total number of conformers in the database to a manageable number. Nonetheless, if the appropriate conformation for a ligand is not explicitly represented in the database, that "best" orientation will not be found, and the ligand may be missed entirely. In a recent comparison, however, the rigid docking of a diverse, multiple conformer database performed similarly to flexible docking methods when reproducing X-ray complexes.[40] The combination of docking ensembles based on pharmacophores and chemically labeled site points enables the rapid screening of databases for molecules which are competent to binding a target site.

Various improvements to the pharmacophore docking algorithms are currently underway. Optimization of the database processing, currently the most tedious and time-consuming portion of the process, is necessary. Implementation of the additional scoring functions available within DOCK 4.0, grid scoring and chemical scoring, is in progress as contact scoring is the only one presently supported. Future plans include the addition of a solvation correction and energy minimization. Shoichet et al. have shown that the addition of a solvation correction, which is a calculated ΔG of solvation for the ligand, reorders the list of hits such that less interesting highly charged ligands are lower priority.[36]

In addition to the top scoring molecules, the pharmacophoric fingerprint is included in the output. It is anticipated that a database search will result in the enrichment of fingerprints capable of matching either site points making the most favorable interactions or simply a greater number of site points. These enriched pharmacophores present an ideal starting point for further database searches. One can envision searching for hits from various commercial databases as well as prioritizing virtual combinatorial libraries for synthesis. We believe this extension of the methodology will prove particularly useful.

Acknowledgements

We would like to thank Demetri Moustakas and Mike Belmarsh for their contribution to the development of pharmacophore DOCK, Brian Shoichet and Dave Lorber for valuable insights and discussions, and John Swanson for help with SYBYL SPL and UNITY.

References

1. Kuntz ID, Meng EC, Shoichet BK: **Structure-based molecular design.** *Acc Chem Res* 1994, **27**(5):117-123.

2. Kuntz ID: **Structure-based strategies for drug design and discovery.** *Science* 1992, **257**:1078-1082.

3. Dammkoehler RA, Karasek SF, Shands EF, Marshall GR: **Constrained search of conformational hyperspace.** *J Comput-Aided Mol Des* 1989, **3**:3-21.

4. Hurst T: **Flexible 3D searching: The directed tweak technique.** *J Chem Inf Comput Sci* 1994, **34**:190-196.

5. Green J, Kahn S, Savoj H, Sprague P, Teig S: **Chemical function queries for 3D database search.** *J Chem Inf Comp Sci* 1994, **34**:1297-1308.

6. Cramer RD, Patterson DE, Bunce JD: **Comparative molecular field analysis (CoMFA): 1. Effect of shape on binding of steroids to carrier proteins.** *J Am. Chem Soc* 1988, **110**:5959-5967.

7. Martin YC, Bures MG, Danahar EA, DeLazzar J, Lico I, and Pavlik PA: **A fast new approach to pharmacophore mapping and its application to dopaminergic and benzodiazepine agents.** *J Comput-Aided Mol Des* 1993, **7**:83102.

8. Jones G, Willet P, Glen RC: **A genetic algorithm for flexible molecular overlay and pharmacophoric elucidation.** *J Comput-Aided Mol Des* 1995, **9**:532-549.

9. Goodford P: **A computational procedure for determining energetically favorable binding sites on biologically important macromolecules.** *J Med Chem* 1985, **28**:849-857.

10. Miranker A, Karplus M: **Functionality maps of binding sites: A multiple copy simultaneous search method.** *Proteins* 1991, **11**:29-34.

11. Evensen E, Joseph-McCarthy D, Karplus M: *MCSS version 2.1.* Cambridge, Massachusetts: Harvard University, 1997.

12. Lengauer T, Rarey M: **Computational methods for biomolecular docking.** *Curr Opin Struct Biol* 1996, **6**:402-406.

13. Lawerence MC, Davis PC: CLIX: **A search algorithm for finding novel ligands capable of binding proteins of known three-dimensional structure.** *Proteins* 1992, **12**:31-41.

14. Kuntz ID, Blaney JM, Oarley SJ, Langridge R, Ferrin TE: **A geometric approach to macromolecule-ligand interactions.** *J Mol Biol* 1982, **161**:269-288.

15. DesJarlais RL, Dixon JS: **A shape- and chemistry-based docking method and its use in the design of HIV-1 protease inhibitors.** *J Comput-Aided Mol Des* 1994, **8**:231-242.

16. Grootenhuis PDJ, Roe DC, Kollman PA, Kuntz ID: **Finding potential DNA-binding compounds by using molecular shape.** *J Comput-Aided Mol Des* 1994, **8**(6):731-750.

17. Shoichet B.K, Stroud RM, Santi DV, Kuntz ID, Perry KM: **Structure-based discovery of inhibitors of thymidylate synthase.** *Science* 1993, **259**(5100):1445-1450.

18. McMartin C, Bohacek RS: QXP: **Powerful, rapid computer algorithms for structure-based drug design.** *J Comput-Aided Mol Des* 1997, **11**(4):333-344.

19. Guida WC, Bohacek RS, Erion MD: **Probing the conformational space available to inhibitors in the thermolysin active site using monte carlo/energy minimization techniques.** *J Comput Chem* 1992, **13**:214-228.

20. Clark KP, Ajay: **Flexible ligand docking without parameter adjustment across four ligand-receptor complexes.** *J Comput Chem* 1995, **16**:1210-1226.

21. Judson RS, Jaeger EP, Treasurywala AM: **A genetic algorithm method for molecular docking flexible molecules.** *J Mol Struct* 1994, **308**:191-206.

22. Jones G, Willett P, Glen RC, Leach AR, and Taylor R: **Development and validation of a genetic algorithm for flexible docking.** *J Mol Biol* 1997, **267**(3):727-748.

23. Oshiro CM, Kuntz ID, Dixon JS: **Flexible ligand docking using a genetic algorithm.** *J Comput-Aided Mol Des* 1995, **9**(2):113-130.

24. Morris GM, Goodsell DS, Huey R, Olson AJ: **Distributed automated docking of flexible ligands to proteins: Parallel applications of AutoDock 2.4.** *J Comput-Aided Mol Des* 1996, **10**(4):293-304.

25. Baxter CA, Murray CW, Clark DE, Westhead DR, Eldridge MD: **Flexible docking using tabu search and an empirical estimate of binding affinity.** *Proteins* 1998, **33**:367-382.

26. Welch W, Ruppert, J, Jain AN: Hammerhead: **Fast, fully automated docking of flexible ligands to protein binding sites.** *Chem Biol* 1996, **3**(6):449-462.

27. Rarey M, Kramer B, Lengauer T, Klebe G: **Predicting receptor-ligand interactions by an incremental construction algorithm.** *J Mol Biol* 1996, **261**:470-489.

28. Ewing TJA, Kuntz ID: **Critical evaluation of search algorithmns for automated molecular docking and database screening.** *J Comput Chem* 1997, **18**:1175-1189.

29. Leach AR, Kuntz ID: **Conformational analysis of flexible ligands in macromolecular receptor sites.** *J Comput Chem* 1992, **13**:730-748.

30. Makino S, Kuntz ID: **Automated flexible ligand docking method and its application for database search.** *J Comput Chem* 1997, **18**(14):1812-1825.

31. Miller MD, Kearsley SK, Underwood DJ, Sheridan RP: FLOG: **A system to select "quasi-flexible" ligands complementary to a receptor of known three-dimensional structure.** *J Comput-Aided Mol Des* 1994, **8**:153-174.

32. Kearsley SK, Underwood DJ, Sheridan RP, Miller MD: Flexibases: **A way to enhance the use of molecular docking methods.** *J Comput-Aided Mol Des* 1994, **8**:565-582.

33. Lorber DM, Shoichet BK: **Flexible ligand docking using conformational ensembles.** *Protein Sci* 1998, **7**(4):938-950.

34. Shoichet BK, Kuntz I.D: **Matching chemistry and shape in molecular docking.** *Protein Eng* 1993, **6**:223-232.

35. *ACD: Available Chemicals Directory.* San Leandro, California: MDL Information Systems, Inc.

36. Shoichet BK, Leach AR, Kuntz ID: **Ligand solvation in molecular docking.** *Proteins* 1999, **34**:4-16.

37. *Tripos*, St. Louis, Missouri: Tripos Associates.

38. Brooks BR, Bruccoleri RE, Olafson BD, States DJ, Swaminathan S, Karplus M: **CHARMM: A program for macromolecular energy, minimization, and dynamics calculations.** *J Comput Chem* 1983, **4**:187-217.

39. Bolin JT, Filman DJ, Matthews DA, Hamlin RC, Kraut J: **Crystal structures of** *E. Coli* **and** *L. Casei* **DHFR refined to 1.7 Angstrom resolution. 1. General features and binding of Methotrexate.** *J Biol Chem* 1982, **257**:13650-13662.

40. Knegtel RMA, Bayada DM, Engh RA. von der Saal W, van Geerestein VJ, Grootenhuis PDJ: **Comparison of two implementations of the incremental construction algorithm in flexible docking of thrombin inhibitors.** *J Comput-Aided Mol Des* 1999, **13**(2):167-183.

Applications in Drug Design

20

The Use of Multiple Excluded Volumes Derived from X-Ray Crystallographic Structures in 3D Database Searching and 3D QSAR

Mikael Gillner and Paulette Greenidge

Abstract

We have used the Catalyst software to construct and assess pharmacophores for nuclear receptor ligands. Pharmacophore features essential for ligand binding were extracted from both the receptor and the ligand. The pharmacophores were also supplemented with many (100-300) excluded volumes (spheres that can not be penetrated by the ligand) to describe the shape of the binding pocket. The excluded volumes were defined by the receptor atoms delineating the binding cavity and scaled down to 50% of their respective atomic van der Waals radii to account for ligand binding flexibility. It was found that excluded volumes can improve pruning of database hit lists by 30-75% for stringent (5-7 feature) pharmacophores. In this manner 50k-compound multiconformer databases can be searched in 1-2h. After such pruning, hit lists were shown to contain relevant new target ligands. For 3D QSAR using Catalyst it was found that excluded volumes may not be necessary for scoring of pre-filtered datasets using structure-based pharmacophores. However, if ligands with substituents challenging rigid parts of the receptor-binding cavity are included in the dataset, excluded volumes may improve the correlation between observed and predicted affinities.

20

The Use of Multiple Excluded Volumes Derived from X-Ray Crystallographic Structures in 3D Database Searching and 3D QSAR

Mikael Gillner and Paulette Greenidge

Karo Bio AB, Huddinge, Sweden

20.1. Introduction

The increasing number of three-dimensional structures of target proteins of pharmaceutical interest, obtained by X-ray crystallography or NMR, is followed by an increased interest in how these structures can be exploited to enhance drug discovery. To this end we have used the Catalyst software to build and evaluate pharmacophores for nuclear receptor ligands [In line with the definition by Gund,[1] a pharmacophore is here to be interpreted as a collection of chemical features located in three-dimensional space that accounts for the binding of ligands to a common receptor; in the Catalyst software such a collection is referred to as a hypothesis].

The basic strategy followed was to utilize features from both the ligand and the receptor for construction of the pharmacophores, and also to include a description of the shape of the binding cavity. Thus the atomic X-ray crystallographic coordinates of the ligand-protein complex was used to spatially locate the pharmacophoric features (such as hydrogen-bond donor/acceptor pairs and hydrophobic spots) as well as numerous excluded volumes (not penetrable by the ligands) delineating the binding cavity.

In one study this methodology was applied to the thyroid hormone receptor to construct and assess the utility of such pharmacophores for electronic database mining.[2] More recently the same methodology of using structure-based pharmacophores supplemented with numerous excluded volumes was also applied to try to assess its utility for 3D QSAR as exemplified with the binding of ligands to the estrogen receptor.[3]

20.2. Background

Excluded volumes have been used in database searching with structure-based pharmacophores for some time. For example, the database queries of the program 3D search[4] consisted of pharmacophore models supplemented by steric (ligand-inaccessible) constraints defined from protein crystallographic coordinates, but ligand flexibility was not considered.

In our earlier study[2] where we applied this methodology to the thyroid hormone receptor by the use of the Catalyst software, 5-7 feature pharmacophores were supplemented with 100-300 excluded volumes (6-8 Å from the ligand) scaled to 25-50% of the atomic van der Waals radii (Plate 20.1). The pharmacophores were used to search the Maybridge database as supplied by MSI (47K compounds stored as multi-conformer structures). The most stringent pharmacophore produced 1 hit that was subsequently purchased and subjected to binding assay and thus shown to have an IC_{50} of 69 μM. One of the more productive pharmacophores yielded 52 hits, of which 12 were experimentally validated and 4 of those hits bound with IC_{50}s ranging from 0.9 to 39 μm. Timings for the above searches were 0.7 h and 2.5 h respectively on an SGI R4000 series workstation, which compares very favorable to those of other software for database searching.

We have thus previously demonstrated the advantages, with respect to specificity, of including numerous excluded volumes in structure-based pharmacophores used for database searching. More recently we have investigated the effect of including excluded volumes in structure based pharmacophores used for the purpose of 3D QSAR.[3] We also compared the performance of structure-based pharmacophores (with and without excluded volumes) with pharmacophores automatically generated by Catalyst. To this end we used the X-ray crystallographic structure of the human estrogen receptor-α solved at 3.1 Å resolution[5] as an example. In this receptor the binding cavity is completely partitioned from the external environment.

In the crystal structure complex of estradiol and human estrogen receptor-a (ER-α), the A-ring phenolic hydroxyl group forms direct hydrogen bonds to the carboxylate of Glu-353, the guanadinium group of Arg-394, and a water molecule. The D-ring's 17β-hydroxyl forms a hydrogen bond with His-524. The other main interactions of the ligand with the protein are nonpolar. The A-ring of E2 is sandwiched between the side chains of hydrophobic residues on its α- and β- faces, and the D ring has nonpolar contacts with hydrophobic residues. Whether the estrogen receptor acts a hydrogen-bond donor or acceptor with the 17β-hydroxyl group of estradiol is not clear from the crystal structure. The 17β-oxygen atom of estradiol is located 3.0 Å from the His-324 ND1 atom. However, the backbone carbonyl of Glu-419 is located so that it can function as a hydrogen-bond acceptor for the NE2 atom of His-524 (O···NE2 separation of 2.7 Å), which indicates that the ND1 atom acts as a hydrogen-bond acceptor with the 17β-hydroxyl group of E2. The estrogen receptor is able to bind a broad spectrum of chemical structures,[6] and for training and test of pharmacophores we used a diverse dataset of 57 estrogen agonists from 8 structurally different chemical classes previously used for a CoMFA study of estrogen receptor ligand binding.[7] This dataset consists of both environmental, pharmacological and physiological estrogens. The environmental estrogens are represented by plant estrogens as well as environmental contaminants of industrial origins with diverse chemical structures. Specifically, the dataset contained 16 PCBs, 6 phenols, 2 pthalates, 3 phytoestrogens, 6 and 7 molecules structurally related to DDT and diethylstilbesterol (DES), respectively, 8 other pesticides, one androgen inhibitor, 3 plant estrogens, and 9 steroids, of which one, ICI 182 780, was excluded because it is an antagonist and cannot be accommodated in the binding site of the agonist structure.

20.3. Methods

20.3.1. Catalyst Pharmacophore Construction and 3D QSAR

A training set of molecules and their binding affinities may be used by the program to automatically generate a number of pharmacophore models which specify the relative alignments and active conformations of the ligands consistent with their binding to a common receptor site. Catalyst 3.1 was used to automatically generate a set of 10 alternative hypotheses with a maximum of 10 features 0-5 hydrogen-bond acceptors/donors or hydrophobic features from our training set of 16 molecules.

Alternatively, the features of the pharmacophore may be placed manually, guided by a receptor X-ray structure as also done in the present study. These models may in turn be used to perform 3D QSAR analyses or as database queries to search 3D coordinate databases for structurally novel ligands. A pharmacophore model (in Catalyst called a hypothesis) consists of a collection of features necessary for the biological activity of the ligands arranged in 3D-space, the common ones being hydrogen-bond acceptor, hydrogen-bond donor and hydrophobic features.[8] Hydrogen-bond donors are characterized by the availability of an electropositive hydrogen atom (e.g., -OH, -SH and NH).[8] Any nitrogen, oxygen or sulfur atom with at least one available lone pair of electrons is considered to be an acceptor atom. Within the program, hydrogen-bond donors are defined as vectors from the donor atom of the ligand to the corresponding acceptor atom in the receptor. Hydrogen-bond acceptors are analogously defined.[8] Hydrophobic features are located at centroids of hydrophobic ligand atoms.[8] The location of features in the structure based pharmacophore were defined by the crystallographic coordinates of atoms in the complex. Hydrophobic features were placed at the centroids of the rings of the steroid nucleus of estrogen in its receptor bound conformation. The carboxylate of Glu-353 and the A-ring phenolic hydroxyl of estradiol were used to define the end points of a hydrogen-bonding donor vector. Similarly the 17β-oxygen atom of estradiol and the ND1 atom of His-324 were utilized to define hydrogen-bond accepting features. The remaining atoms delineating the binding cavity of the human ER-α were represented as excluded volumes (space which the ligand is not allowed to occupy). For the present study, we have used an order of magnitude more (~10^2) excluded volumes than usually used in Catalyst pharmacophores. The excluded volumes were defined within a spherical based cut off of 6 Å from estradiol which corresponds to the atoms, delineating the binding cavity of ER-α. The spherical excluded volumes were scaled to a given percentage (50%) of the van der Waals radii of the corresponding atom so as to increase the effective size of the binding cavity in order to partially compensate for the flexibility of both the receptor protein and ligand and to adjust the hit rate. The values for the van der Waals radii were taken from Pauling[9] (i.e., 1.4, 1.5, 1.7, and 1.85 Å for O, N, C, and S, respectively).

Catalyst "features" are associated with position constraints which consist of the ideal location of a particular feature in 3D space surrounded by a spherical tolerance.[8] In order to map to the pharmacophore, a ligand must not possess all the appropriate functional groups which can simultaneously reside within the respective tolerance spheres of the pharmacophoric features. However, the fewer features of the ligand that maps to the pharmacophore, the less will its predicted affinity be. Each feature is associated with a weight (a measure of its proposed importance to the pharmacophore as a whole). It is possible to interactively view the fit of the molecules to pharmacophores in Catalyst. Default parameters were used throughout unless otherwise stated. In a Catalyst formatted spreadsheet, compounds are stored as multiple conformers which are representative of their available conformational space. For the training and test datasets consisting of a total of 57 molecules, conformers were generated with the "best quality" option, a maximum of 250 conformers were allowed, and a maximum conformational energy of 10 kcal/mol above the lowest-energy conformation was permitted. The training set contained 16 molecules that included 6 halogenated and/or hydroxylated biphenyls, two indenestrols, diethylstilbestrol, estrogen, estrone, progesterone, genistein, bisphenol, metoxychlor, and PPDDE. These ligands were selected to have a spread of 6 orders of magnitude in binding affinity and to represent each chemical subclass of the whole Waller dataset.[7] The training set was used to regress (calibrate) the pharmacophores for 3D QSAR.

20.4. Results and Discussion

To autogenerate pharmacophores to be used for prediction of ER ligand binding affinities we selected 16 representative ligands of the 57 ligands in the Waller dataset. By default, Catalyst produced 10 suggestions with two hydrogen-bond donor acceptor-pairs (Table 20.1). Of these 6 contained also one hydrophobic feature and one contained two hydrophobic features. We also regressed the pharmacophores with the training set receptor affinities and scored the remainder of the 57 compounds in the Waller dataset, which was then used a test set for the suggestions (Table 20.1). In general it can be said that the autogenerated and regressed hypotheses are somewhat biased to the training set as compared to the test set (as can be seen from Table 20.1 that the correlation coefficients for training set are better than for the test set ligands) which emphasizes the importance of having a well-selected training set.

Table 20.1. Autogenerated Catalyst hypotheses for test and training sets of ligands which bind to the estrogen receptor.

Hypo	Hypo Features		Cost	Training set		Test set	
				r_{train}	RMS	r_{test}	RMS
1	2 HBD	1 HPHOB	108.2	0.84	2.24	0.46	3.9
2	2 HBD	1 HPHOB	111.0	0.83	2.30	0.48	4.0
3	2 HBD	1 HPHOB	118.7	0.78	2.56	0.57	3.4
4	2 HBD	1 HPHOB	119.3	0.78	2.57	0.44	3.9
5	2 HBD		119.3	0.77	2.61	0.53	3.7
6	2 HBD	1 HPHOB	119.6	0.78	2.56	0.43	4.2
7	2 HBD	1 HPHOB	120.2	0.77	2.62	0.53	3.5
8	2 HBD		120.2	0.77	2.63	0.54	3.7
9	2 HBD		129.0	0.72	2.85	0.54	3.6
10	2 HBD	2 HPHOB	130.4	0.72	2.84	0.48	3.5
	Null		189.0				

Thus, the inclusion a feature for estimation of a cross-validated correlation coefficient as measure of how well test data will be predicted, instead of simply how well the data is fitted, may enhance the quality of the use of the Catalyst software for 3D QSAR. Visual inspection of the Catalyst autogenerated suggestions (e. g., hypothesis 3) showed that the hydrophobic feature was located at one of the ethyl substituents of diethylstilbestrol and the indenestrones. Since these ligands have higher affinities than estradiol, and since estradiol does not map to the hydrophobic feature, the regression/scoring is solved by not mapping estradiol properly to the pharmacophore.

To make sure that all ligands would map to the pharmacophores that can do so we constructed structure-based pharmacophores with hydrophobic features corresponding to the A-D rings of estradiol in addition to two pairs of hydrogen-bond donor acceptor features. These pharmacophores were supplemented with excluded volumes, regressed with the training set, and used to score the test set ligands. The pharmacophores based on crystal structure yield improved correlation coefficients for the test set (as can be seen in Table 20.2) as compared to the autogenerated ones (in Table 20.1). The correlation coefficients also differ by a lesser extent for training and test sets for the structure-based, as compared to the autogenerated hypotheses. This indicates that the regression is less overfitted to the training set for the structure-based pharmacophores.

Table 20.2. Structure-based Catalyst hypotheses with excluded volumes for test and training sets of ligands which bind to the estrogen receptor. Hydrophobic features are located at the centroids of A- to D-rings of estradiol, and hydrogen bonds correspond to coordinates of Glu-353 and His-524.

Hypo	Hypo Features		Training set		Test set	
			r_{train}	RMS	r_{test}	RMS
1	2 HBD	A,D	0.67	3.1	0.58	3.5
2	2 HBD	A	0.66	3.1	0.57	4.5
3	2 HBD	A,B,D	0.63	3.2	0.55	3.7
4	2 HBD	A,C,D	0.74	2.7	0.61	3.9
5	2 HBD	D	0.67	3.1	0.47	3.8
6	2 HBD	C	0.53	3.5	0.38	4.1
7	2 HBD	B	0.57	3.4	0.32	4.3

In order to compare the automatically generated pharmacophores to the structure-based pharmacophores with excluded volumes we selected the ones with the lowest RMS difference for the predicted versus experimental binding affinities for the test set (from Tables 20.1 and 20.2). We also regressed the structure-based pharmacophore without excluded volumes against the training set and scored the test set with it (Table 20.3). Although the structure-based pharmacophore with excluded volumes fared less well on the training set, it performed as well as the autogenerated pharmacophore on the test set (r_{test} = 0.58 and 0.57, respectively). When the excluded volumes were removed from the structure-based pharmacophore it fared even worse with the training set, but performed much better with the test set (r_{test} = 0.75).

Table 20.3. A comparison of automatically generated and structure-based Catalyst hypotheses with and without excluded volumes for test and training sets of ligands which bind to the estrogen receptor.

Hypo Features			Training set		Test set	
			r_{train}	RMS	r_{test}	RMS
auto	2 HBD	1HPHOB	0.78	2.6	0.57	3.4
structure-based						
with excl. vols.						
	2 HBD	A,D	0.67	3.1	0.58	3.5
without excl. vols.						
	2 HBD	A,D	0.58	3.3	0.75	3.1

Thus, the structure-based pharmacophores appear less biased towards the training set than the autogenerated ones. That the correlation of the predicted versus experimental binding affinities for the test set improved when the excluded volumes were removed was somewhat surprising. This could be due to the fact that some ligands in the test set clash with excluded volumes in regions of the binding site that are relatively flexible in the receptor. The excluded volumes are, in Catalyst, relatively hard and cannot be dislocated, and thus may force the ligand into energetically unfavorable mappings when clashes occur. Alternatively, the high interaction energy with the excluded volumes could make ligands occupy space different from the X-ray ligand in regions where the binding site flexibility is underestimated in the 3D QSAR.

It is known that the receptor-bound conformation of ligands frequently differ from the minimum energy conformation of ligands. In the liganded RAR structures the 9-*cis*-retinoic acid is more bent than the binding cavity whereas the 9-*trans*-retinoic acid is flatter than the binding cavity. It was thus concluded that ligand binding to a nuclear receptor is a complex process where both the ligand and the binding site have to adjust for binding.[10] The rigid unpenetrable excluded volumes as implemented in Catalyst may not be able to reflect the induced fit of the ligand binding cavity to the ligand. In order to overcome this problem the excluded volumes may be made smaller, or the offending ones could be identified and selectively removed. We have used scaling of the size of the excluded volumes according to the van der Waals radii of the atoms to somewhat account for flexibility, but scaling according to the crystallographic temperature factors would be another option. A suggestion for program improvement would be to implement penetrable excluded volumes with adjustable individual force constants so that ligands penetrating them would pay an energy penalty relative to the differing flexibility of the binding site in its various regions. The force constants could then for this purpose be scaled according to atom type, temperature factors, or by regression to the training set. As yet another alternative, it has been shown for some HIV protease inhibitors that moving features relative to the excluded volumes using simplex optimization and use of the CI test program distributed with Catalyst[11] may improve the correlation of the predicted versus experimental binding affinities.

From our results presented so far it does not appear necessary, or even advantageous to supplement structure-based pharmacophores with excluded volumes for 3D QSAR when they are applied to prefiltered datasets. The prefiltering can be done by database searching with structure-based pharmacophores supplemented with excluded volumes, or by a knowledge-based selection procedure (such as use of the Waller dataset which contains primarily known estrogens).

That the use of excluded volumes appear less successful for 3D QSAR than for database searching may be due to that what fits a rigid binding site will also fit a flexible site (i.e., a ligand mapping to a rigid pharmacophore will bind to a flexible receptor), whereas the opposite is not true (a ligand that challenges impenetrable parts of the pharmacophore but could be accommodated by a flexible binding site gets underestimated).

In order to illustrate that the use of excluded volumes can be of advantage in 3D QSAR in some situations, we selected estrogen receptor ligands that have small substituents in positions that are not tolerated by the receptor for a test set. In Table 20.4 it can be seen that these ligands are scored in reverse order by the structure-based pharmacophore without excluded volumes, whereas the scoring by the structure-based pharmacophore with excluded volumes produces the correct rank-order between the experimental and predicted affinities. Thus our structure-based pharmacophore is not able to correctly rank estrogen analogues possessing substituents which challenge rigid parts of the receptor, unless it is supplemented with excluded volumes.

Table 20.4. Advantage of excluded volumes for 3D QSAR. An ER-α structure based pharmacophore with many excluded volumes discriminates against unfavorable E2-substitutuents.

Ligand	IC_{50} (nM)		Experimental
	Predicted		
	with	without	
	excluded volumes		
E2	25	31	2.4[*]
C9-methyl-E2	25	30	6.8
6a-methyl-E2	32	28	7.7
6b-methyl-E2	42	24	65.8

[*] Recalculated from reference[6]

20.5 Conclusion

The conclusions from the studies regarding the use of multiple excluded volumes in pharmacophores used with the Catalyst software may be summarized as follows:

   i) Excluded volumes can improve pruning of database hit lists by 30-75% for stringent (5-7 feature) pharmacophores. After such pruning, hit lists were shown to contain relevant new target ligands.[2]

ii) Timings showed, that it is now feasible to search medium-sized (50 k) databases in 1-2 h with stringent (7-feature) pharmacophores including many (~200) excluded volumes.[2] These timings compare very favorably with those of earlier published studies where commercially available software were used to search databases with 3D queries.

iii) Excluded volumes may not be necessary for 3D QSAR/scoring of pre-filtered datasets using 3D pharmacophores. However, if ligands with substituents challenging rigid parts of the receptor-binding cavity are included in the dataset, excluded volumes may improve the correlation between observed and predicted affinities.

References

1. Gund P: **Three-dimensional pharmacophoric pattern searching.** In: *Progress in Molecular and Subcellular Biology*, Vol. 5. Hahn FE, ed. New York: Springer Verlag, 1977:117-143.

2. Greenidge PA, Carlsson B, Bladh L-G, Gillner M: **Pharmacophores incorporating numerous excluded volumes defined by X-ray crystallographic structure in three-dimensional database searching: Application to the thyroid hormone receptor.** *J Med Chem* 1998, **41**:2503-2512.

3. Gillner M, Greenidge P: **Pharmacophores including Multiple Excluded Volumes derived from X-ray crystallographic Target Structures to be used in 3D-database searching.** Technical program abstracts, 62. Division of Chemical Information. 217th ACS National Meeting, Anaheim, CA, March 21-25 1999. http://www.lib.uchicago.edu/~atbrooks/CINF/abstracts_217.html.

4. Sheridan RP, Rusinko A, Nilakantan R, Venkataraghavan R: **Searching for pharmacophores in large coordinate data bases and its use in drug design.** *Proc Natl Acad Sci U.S.A.* 1989, **86**:8165-8169.

5. Brzozowski AM, Pike ACW, Dauter Z, Hubbard RE, Bonn T, Engström O, Öhman L, Greene GL, Gustafsson J-Å, Carlquist M: **Molecular basis of agonism and antagonism in the oestrogen receptor.** *Nature* 1997, **389**:753-758.

6. Anstead GM, Carlson KE, Katzenellenbogen JA: **The estradiol pharmacophore: ligand structure-estrogen receptor binding affinity relationships and a model for the receptor binding site.** *Steroids* 1997, **62**:268-303.

7. Waller CL, Oprea T, Chae K, Park HK, Korach KS, Laws SC, Wiese TE, Kelce WR, Gray LE: **Ligand-based identification of environmental estrogens.** *Chem Res Toxicol* 1996, **9**:1240-1248.

8. Greene J, Kahn S, Savoy H, Sprague P, Teig S: **Chemical function queries for 3D database search.** *J Chem Inf Comput Sci* 1994, **34**:1297-1308.

9. Pauling L: *The Nature of the Chemical Bond.* 3 ed. Ithaca, NY: Cornell University Press, 1960.

10. Klaholz BP, Renaud J-P, Mitschler A, Zusi C, Chambon P, Gronemeyer H, Moras D: **Conformational adaptation of agonists to the human nuclear receptor RARg.** *Nature Struct Biol* 1998, **5**:199-202.

11. Ulf Norinder, personal communication, http://www.msi.com/user/groups/catalyst/CITEST.doc.

21

Docking-Derived Pharmacophores from Models of Receptor-Ligand Complexes

Renate Griffith, John B. Bremner, and Burak Coban

Abstract

In the absence of any detailed three-dimensional structure of adrenergic receptors, models have been constructed for the α_{1A} and α_{1B} subtypes of these important members of the G-protein coupled family of membrane-bound receptors. Docking of the endogenous ligand, adrenaline, and also of a rigid, α_{1A} selective antagonist (IQC) (developed in our laboratory) into these models has been performed. For the agonist, known interactions between the receptor and the ligand have been reproduced successfully and a new interaction has been proposed between adrenaline and the α_{1B} model, which would help explain the higher affinity of the natural (R) enantiomer. From the models of the complexes between the receptors and the antagonist we have constructed what we have termed "docking-derived pharmacophores." This has been achieved by analyzing the observed receptor-ligand interactions and placing appropriate chemical features onto the structural template of the antagonist. The steric demands of the receptor proteins have also been incorporated into these pharmacophores *via* excluded volume features. This new approach offers further opportunities for tailored ligand design and for database searching for new lead compounds.

21

Docking-Derived Pharmacophores from Models of Receptor-Ligand Complexes

Renate Griffith,[†] John B. Bremner,[†] and Burak Coban[‡]

[†]*University of Wollongong, Wollongong, Australia*
[‡]*Zonguldak Karaelmas University, Zonguldak, Turkey*

21.1. Introduction

The previous chapter has treated the case where one is fortunate enough to have available a detailed three-dimensional structure of the biological target. Unfortunately, for a large group of targets for drug design—the superfamily of G-protein coupled receptors (GPCRs)—no such structure is available. Within this superfamily, molecular cloning has revealed substantial structural similarity among the receptor proteins, despite the great diversity of their ligands. They all contain seven hydrophobic, membrane-spanning regions, which are almost certainly α-helical and where most of the sequence homology is located. The N-terminus of the receptors is located extracellularly and the C-terminus intracellularly. Helices adjacent in sequence are antiparallel to each other and are connected via loops which are located alternately inter- and intracellularly. The third intracellular loop has been shown to be responsible for coupling to the G-proteins.[1]

Models of the G-protein coupled receptors as membrane-spanning helical bundles can be built on the basis of a crystal structure of bacteriorhodopsin[2] and low resolution electron diffraction structures of rhodopsin.[3,4] Bacteriorhodopsin is not a member of the GPCR family. However, experimental evidence has shown that it has a three-dimensional fold similar to the GPCR family and has a functional resemblance to rhodopsin.[5] Rhodopsin is a GPCR and its comparison with bacteriorhodopsin is very important to assess the three-dimensional structure of the GPCRs. Although the structures of rhodopsin indicate the presence of seven transmembrane α-helices, their arrangement appears to be different from the one in bacteriorhodopsin. The structural information derived from the analysis of roughly 500 sequences of the GPCRs has been used in conjunction with the electron diffraction structure to derive a model for the three-dimensional arrangement of the seven transmembrane helices and a model for the α-carbon positions in the helices in the rhodopsin family of GPCRs has been published.[6]

We have built models for the α_{1A} and α_{1B} subtypes of the adrenergic receptor (AR), a member of the GPCR superfamily, based on the above template. We have then constructed models of the complex between a rigid ligand and these two proteins by "docking" the ligand into the receptor models manually and minimizing the resulting complexes. The nature of the interactions between the ligand and the receptor proteins was studied in detail. Within the pharmacophore development software Catalyst™ (MSI), a pharmacophore can be constructed by placing features describing these interactions onto the ligand in its docked conformation. The locations of receptor atoms in contact with the ligand can also be determined from the ligand-receptor complexes and these can be added to the pharmacophore to define excluded volumes.

The α_1-adrenoceptors have three subtypes (α_{1A}, α_{1B} and α_{1D})[7] and numerous α_1-adrenoceptor antagonists are available but the ideal selective ligand, which recognizes only one among the others, is not available yet for the α_{1B} and α_{1D} subtypes.

Recently, a QSAR study investigated antagonist selectivity towards three subtypes of the α_1-AR using docking techniques on the computer models of these subtypes.[8] Molecular dynamics simulations were used to analyze the ligand-receptor interactions, and binding energies of ligands were calculated and compared with the experimental binding affinities. The results showed that the transmembrane domains of these subtypes have different dynamic behaviors and different topographies at the binding sites. In particular, the α_{1A}-AR binding site was found to be more flexible and topographically different from the other two subtypes.[8] Nonselective antagonists gave similar binding energies for different subtypes, whereas antagonists showing selectivity towards one subtype gave higher stabilization for this subtype over the other two subtypes. This shows that binding, as well as selectivity, is guided by the dynamic complementarity between ligand and receptor and this point will need to be addressed in the future for any structure-based drug design effort (see also below). Higher flexibility of the α_{1A} subtype over the other two subtypes was also suggested in that study[8] because docking the antagonists into the α_{1A} subtype model was much easier than for the other two subtypes. However, no structural details on interacting residues of the receptor or details about the binding sites for the antagonists, or on the selective binding interactions, were discussed.

21.2. Agonist and Antagonist Binding Site(s) on the Adrenergic Receptors

The adrenoceptors, like other G-protein coupled biogenic amine receptors, have a conserved aspartic acid residue in the third transmembrane (TM) helix, which is essential for activity and is assumed to bind a protonated amine counter-ion present in the ligands for these receptors. For example, the direct binding of adrenaline to the conserved aspartate in TM3 of β_2-ARs was identified by site-directed mutagenesis.[9] The catechol ring of adrenaline interacts with serine residues at the top of TM5 of the same receptor and also interacts *via* a π–π interaction with a phenylalanine in TM7.[9] The α_1-ARs share a similar structure, but it is clear from the different affinities of ligands of different structural classes for the subtypes,[7] that the ligand binding sites may differ in each subtype and that the binding sites of different classes of ligands may involve different helices. Therefore, to get a better understanding of ligand interactions, it is important to focus on each subtype individually to investigate the binding modes of a variety of structurally diverse ligands.

Because of the high homology within the putative transmembrane helices, the binding site for α_1-AR subtypes is expected to be mainly in the same location as in β_2 ARs. However, contradictory site-directed mutagenesis studies have been published. In the following discussion the numbering of amino acid residues corresponds to their position in the sequence of the human receptor. Mutation of D125 (the conserved aspartate in TM3) to A by one group[10] suggested that this substitution totally impaired the ability of the α_{1B}-AR to bind both agonists and antagonists. The same mutation showed no significant difference in ligand binding for antagonists and agonist binding, however, decreased only about three-fold according to another study.[11] This latter finding has been interpreted as indicating that α_1-antagonists may bind at least partly in the extracellular loop regions and this has also been suggested by findings from the same group[12] indicating that three residues in the extracellular loop of TM5 are fully responsible for the higher affinity of selective antagonists for the α_{1A}-AR. In a further report,[13] however, it was noted that, on replacement of all extracellular loop residues of the β_2-AR with those of the α_{1A}-AR, the binding of a set of α_1- and β_2-antagonists remains the same as for wild type β_2-receptors. We started our work with the assumption that α_1-AR antagonist- and agonist-binding sites overlap substantially, and the results appear compatible with this assumption.

The results of mutation studies for the two serine residues in TM5 for the α_{1A} subtype also require some comment. One group found that S192 (but not S188) is important for binding of both agonists and antagonists except niguldipine and analogues.[14] The work of Perez et al.[15] has shown, however, that only the combined mutation of both serine residues decreased adrenaline binding, which indicates that both serines (S188 and S192) interact with the catechol ring of adrenaline. The α_{1B} and α_{1D} subtypes have one extra serine residue, which for the α_{1B} subtype (S208) was demonstrated as having no effect on agonist binding affinity and functional responsiveness.[16] The first serine residue (S207) was also studied for the α_{1B} receptor and was established as the one interacting with the catechol ring of adrenaline.[10]

The aromatic residues involved in a $\pi-\pi$ interaction with the catechol ring of adrenaline differ between the subtypes. For the α_{1A} subtype, F193 in TM5 was found to be important for binding due to a decrease in the adrenaline binding to the F193L mutant of this subtype.[14]

Visualization of this interaction using a model based on the structure of bacteriorhodopsin failed because F193 was pointing outside the binding pocket. The model was modified by rotating TM5 20° clockwise to bring the phenylalanine residue inside the binding pocket.[14] For the α_{1B} receptor it was shown that F310 in TM6 binds the aromatic ring.[17]

There are numerous other important amino acids in the α_1 ARs. For example the Y203A (TM5) and Y338A (TM7) mutants of the α_{1B} subtype showed that these residues play important roles in preserving the receptor structure rather than directly interacting with the agonists.[10]

Investigation of the role of the amino acids which are different between the α_{1A} and α_{1B} subtypes indicates that mutations of A204 and L314 of the α_{1B} subtype to the α_{1A} subtype counterparts (the A204V and L314M mutants of the α_{1B} subtype) changed the binding profile of agonists from the α_{1B} to the α_{1A} phenotype, and reversal of these residues in the α_{1A} to those in the α_{1B} (V185A and M293L) reversed the binding profile to that of the α_{1B} phenotype.[15] Docking studies by the same authors showed that agonists with vicinal substituents in the phenyl ring interact with these residues.

Niguldipine and its analogues, which were not affected by S188A, S192A and F193L mutations,[14] were found to interact with F86 in TM2 of the α_{1A} receptor, because they were adversely affected by a F86M mutation. In addition, the selectivity of these antagonists for the α_{1A} site may be explained with the same mutation because at this position only the α_{1A} subtype has the phenylalanine residue.[18]

There are a number of models of the α_1-ARs that have been built for various reasons, including visualization of the experimental results of site directed mutagenesis,[10,12-18] structure-based QSAR studies using docking techniques,[8,19] investigation of receptor dynamics to determine the active and inactive conformations of the receptor,[20-22] and determination of inter- and intra-helical interactions including the role of proline residues.[23]

21.3. 3D Model Building and Docking

The initial receptor models of the α_{1A}- and α_{1B}-ARs were obtained from Dr. Peter Riek, of the Victor Chang Cardiac Research Institute, Sydney.

In the building process, the size of the TM domains was determined by using an algorithm[24] based on the weighted pairwise comparisons of aligned residues of α_1 sequences. The type and sequence number of the residues included in our helices are listed in Table 21.1 together with the position in the helix.

Table 21.1. Amino acid residues included in the helices of the α_1-AR models in this study.

Position*	Residue type		Residue number#		Position*	Residue type		Residue number#	
	α_{1A}	α_{1B}	α_{1A}	α_{1B}		α_{1A}	α_{1B}	α_{1A}	α_{1B}
1(1)	I	I	27	46		T	T	78	97
2(1)	L	S	28	47		V	V	79	98
	L	V	29	48		L	L	80	99
	G	G	30	49		P	P	81	100
	V	L	31	50		F	F	82	101
	I	V	32	51		S	S	83	102
	L	L	33	52		A	A	84	103
	G	G	34	53		I	A	85	104
	G	A	35	54	1(3)	I	I	101	120
	L	F	36	55	2(3)	W	W	102	121
	I	I	37	56		A	A	103	122
	L	L	38	57		A	A	104	123
	F	F	39	58		V	V	105	124
	G	A	40	59		D	D	106	125
	V	I	41	60		V	V	107	126
	L	V	42	61		L	L	108	127
	G	G	43	62		C	C	109	128
	N	N	44	63		C	C	110	129
	I	I	45	64		T	T	111	130
	L	V	46	65		A	A	112	131
	V	L	47	66		S	S	113	132
	I	V	48	67		I	I	114	133
	L	I	49	68		M	L	115	134
	S	L	50	69		G	S	116	135
	V	S	51	70		L	L	117	136
	A	V	52	71		C	C	118	137
	C	A	53	72		I	A	119	138
1(2)	H	N	62	81		I	I	120	139
2(2)	Y	Y	63	82		S	S	121	140
	Y	F	64	83		I	I	122	141
	I	I	65	84		D	D	123	142
	V	V	66	85		R	R	124	143
	N	N	67	86		Y	Y	125	144
	L	L	68	87		I	I	126	145
	A	A	69	88		G	G	127	146
	V	M	70	89		V	V	128	147
	A	A	71	90	1(4)	Q	R	140	159
	D	D	72	91	2(4)	R	R	141	160
	L	L	73	92		R	L	142	161
	L	L	74	93		G	A	143	162
	L	L	75	94		L	I	144	163
	T	S	76	95		M	L	145	164
	S	F	77	96		A	A	146	165

Continued on next page

Position*	Residue type		Residue number#		Position*	Residue type		Residue number#	
	α_{1A}	α_{1B}	α_{1A}	α_{1B}		α_{1A}	α_{1B}	α_{1A}	α_{1B}
	L	L	147	166		I	I	276	298
	L	L	148	167		V	V	277	299
	C	S	149	168		V	V	278	300
	V	V	150	169		G	G	279	301
	W	W	151	170		C	M	280	302
	A	V	152	171		F	F	281	303
	L	L	153	172		V	I	282	304
	S	S	154	173		L	L	283	305
	L	T	155	174		C	C	284	306
	V	V	156	175		W	W	285	307
	I	I	157	176		L	L	286	308
	S	S	158	177		P	P	287	309
	I	I	159	178		F	F	288	310
	G	G	160	179		F	F	289	311
	P	P	161	180		L	I	290	312
	L	L	162	181		V	A	291	313
	F	L	163	182		M	L	292	314
	G	G	164	183		P	P	293	315
1(5)	G	F	183	202		I	L	294	316
2(5)	Y	Y	184	203		G	-	295	-
	V	A	185	204		S	-	296	-
	L	L	186	205		F	-	297	-
	F	F	187	206		F	-	298	-
	S	S	188	207	1(7)	V	V	311	329
	A	S	189	208	2(7)	F	F	312	330
	L	L	190	209		L	K	313	331
	G	G	191	210		V	V	314	332
	S	S	192	211		V	V	315	333
	F	F	193	212		F	F	316	334
	Y	Y	194	213		W	W	317	335
	I	I	195	214		L	L	318	336
	P	P	196	215		G	G	319	337
	L	L	197	216		Y	Y	320	338
	A	A	198	217		L	F	321	339
	I	V	199	218		N	N	322	340
	I	I	200	219		S	S	323	341
	L	L	201	220		C	C	324	342
	V	V	202	221		L	L	325	343
	M	M	203	222		N	N	326	344
	Y	Y	204	223		P	P	327	345
	C	C	205	224		I	I	328	346
	R	R	206	225		I	I	329	347
	V	V	207	226		Y	Y	330	348
	Y	Y	208	227		P	-	331	-
1(6)	T	T	273	295		C	-	332	-
2(6)	L	L	274	296		S	-	333	-
	G	G	275	297		S	-	334	-

* *Position in helix (helix number in brackets).*
# *Number in human receptor sequence.*

The TM regions were constructed as α-helices using Insight/Discover™ software (MSI) by the overlaying of putative α_1-AR transmembrane residues with the transmembrane coordinates of bacteriorhodopsin.[2]

The loop regions are omitted from the models. These helices were subsequently repacked with respect to the adjacent helices according to the α_{1B}-AR mutagenesis data where possible.[17,25,26] The projection of the helices proposed by Baldwin et al.[3] were used to determine the tilt of each helix. Finally, the overall structure was minimized as previously described.[27] The α_{1A} model was created specifically for the docking aspects of this project. The amino acid side chains were replaced on the α_{1B} model to create the α_{1A} model.

21.3.1. Revision of the Models

The models built as described above had the same problem with the rotational orientation of TM5 as previously described in the literature.[14] Additionally, we found that docking experiments did not give the expected ligand-receptor interactions. The helical packing of the receptors was therefore revised by superimposing the amino acids in the most conserved positions onto Baldwin's α-carbon template of rhodopsin.[6]

First, the initial model was positioned onto the template and the helices moved individually to match with the template. Homology data[6] was used to anchor each helix to the correct position on the template, matching a few conserved residues (see Table 21.2). For example, in the case of TM2, it was found that 97% of the GPCRs have a leucine residue in position 10 of this helix.[6] Using this data, TM2 was moved to align the leucine residues in the middle of the helix. The major problem with this approach hinges on the fact that the helices in the template are treated as ideal helices. In our model, however, helices were built individually according to biophysical considerations allowing them to kink at the point of the proline residues in helices 2, 4, 5, 6, and 7. Helices 6 and 7 are far from the ideal helix structure compared to the others because of the proline residues in these helices.

Table 21.2. The most conserved residues within the GPCR TM regions used to revise our models.

AAs	TM2			TM3			TM4	TM5	TM6	TM7
conserved*	N9	L10	A11	E/D24	R25	Y26	W11	Y22	P18	N17
residues	91%	97%	96%	99%	100%	74%	99%	91%	99%	93%
α_{1A}	N67	L68	A69	D123	R124	Y125	W151	Y204	P267	N326
α_{1B}	N86	L87	A88	D142	R143	Y144	W170	Y223	P309	N344

* *position in helix is given.*

After revision of the models, a minimization process was used which allowed the side chains to relax and the helices to move as a whole without unwinding. All the characteristic i, i+4 backbone hydrogen bonds were constrained, using a simple harmonic function (the force constant was set to the default value of 1) for both the upper and lower target distances between the backbone carbonyl oxygen atom and the backbone hydrogen atom connected to the nitrogen. The target distances were set to 2.1 Å for the lower and 2.5 Å for the higher limit and the maximum allowed force to be used was 1000 kcal/mol. An initial minimization of 100 steps of steepest descents was undertaken, followed by 2000 steps of conjugate gradients minimization, which was repeated until the maximum derivative was less than 0.001 kcal/mol. After minimization, only a very small number of amino acid pairs capable of forming the backbone hydrogen-bonding characteristic for α-helices (3 for α_{1A}, 5 for α_{1B}) were found not to meet the very stringent criteria for a hydrogen bond in the Insight software.

21.3.2. Docking of Adrenaline

As a test for the quality of the models, adrenaline-receptor complexes were generated and binding energies were compared with the experimental data to test the revised models. The adrenaline-AR complexes were obtained by manually docking the protonated agonist into the binding site of the minimized structure of the AR, keeping the positively charged nitrogen atom within 2 to 4 Å of the negatively charged aspartate side chain and minimizing steric conflicts. This can be monitored "on the fly" in the docking module of the Insight/Discover software (MSI) by observing how the interaction energy between the protein and the ligand changes upon movement of the ligand. The complexes were then energy minimized, employing the hydrogen-bond constraints discussed above to avoid distortion of the protein and unravelling of the helices. Minimizations were repeated several times, with different initial orientations of both the ligand and the receptor side chains to optimize the interactions known to be important by site-directed mutagenesis experiments. The interactions observed from the docking experiments were in agreement with the experimental data.[10,14-16,22] Apart from a salt bridge between the protonated nitrogen of adrenaline and the conserved aspartate in TM3 for both subtypes, we observed for the α_{1A} receptor the following interactions with adrenaline: a hydrogen bond between S192 in TM5 and the OH group in the 4-position in the aromatic ring of adrenaline, and an aromatic interaction between adrenaline and F193 (TM5). For the α_{1B} subtype, the S211 residue in TM5 (which is in the same position as S192 in α_{1A}) again interacts with the 4-OH group, but the aromatic interaction is now observed with F310 in TM6. One of the hydrogen atoms on the protonated adrenaline N interacts additionally with the backbone O of A313 (TM6), and the conserved aspartate (D125, TM3) also interacts with the α-OH group on adrenaline. This is a novel finding, and can help explain the higher affinity of the natural (R) enantiomer of adrenaline. The equivalent orientation of adrenaline interacts with the α_{1A} AR model with a slightly lower binding energy than the chosen orientation above, where the α-OH group on adrenaline does not hydrogen bond with the aspartate. We do not find any interactions involving either the 3-aromatic OH-group on adrenaline or the other serine residues in TM5. As was expected, adrenaline binds to the α_{1A} subtype slightly better than it does to the α_{1B} subtype (binding energy for α_{1A} is -141 kcal/mol versus -134 kcal/mol for α_{1B}). Interaction energies (IE) between the receptor and the ligand were calculated within the docking module of the Insight software (MSI) and distortion energies of the receptors (ER) and the ligands (EL) were also calculated in order to estimate the binding energies (BE; BE = IE + ER + EL).[8] Distortion energies were obtained as follows.

The ligand was taken out of the minimized receptor-ligand complex and for both the ligand and the receptor, the energy of this bound conformation was obtained by minimizing for one iteration only and noting the initial energy. For the receptor, the hydrogen-bond constraints as explained above were also employed to ensure minimization conditions were identical. This energy of the distorted receptor was compared to the minimum energy as obtained for the receptor before any docking was carried out (described above). For the ligand, the docked conformation was minimized to convergence to the closest local minimum and the energy of this was used to calculate the distortion energy. This initial attempt at quantifying the binding energy does not include the entropic contributions, and the possibility of multiple bound states has also not been considered.

From these docking results of the natural ligand, our receptor models were considered sufficiently sound to continue with the docking experiments of other ligands.

21.3.3. Docking of a Rigid Antagonist (IQC)

Because our design study focused on rigid compounds, we docked our isoquinolinocarbazole α_1 ligand IQC (1)[28] into our models, assuming that this antagonist binds at the same site as adrenaline (see above). Figure 21.1 shows a comparison of the structures of the two ligands.

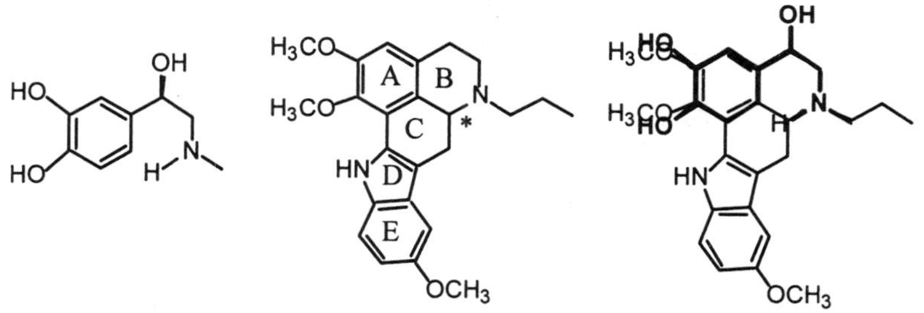

Adrenaline   1   Overlap of 1 and **Adrenaline**

Figure 21.1. Structures of Adrenaline and IQC (1).

IQC was placed into the binding pocket with the indole ring pointing towards the extracellular side, the protonated nitrogen atom close to the aspartate (D106 for the α_{1A} and D125 for the α_{1B} subtype), and the dimethoxy portion close to the serine residues in TM5. Other orientations were also tested, but they were found to lead to lower interaction energies. The R enantiomer of IQC was used in the docking, whereas the binding data were determined for the racemic mixture. Upon protonation, the N atom of IQC becomes a second stereogenic center, and the S enantiomer was studied. The routine minimization process was run to optimize the IQC-receptor complex structures and the interaction energies were calculated for both subtypes (Table 21.3). The binding data correlates with the binding energies very well. This also confirms our assumption that the binding pocket for IQC in the α_{1A} and α_{1B} AR subtypes is likely to be at the same site where adrenaline binds in each case. As will be discussed in more detail below, the interaction between the

α_{1B} receptor and IQC is actually more favorable than between the α_{1A}-receptor model and the ligand. This is more than offset, however, by the large distortion energy required for the α_{1B} receptor.

Table 21.3. Activity and energy data for IQC on the α_{1A}- and α_{1B}-AR subtypes.

	pK_i^{28}	**BE**	**IE**	**DL**	**DR**
		kcal/mol			
α_{1A}	8.4	-164	-175	8	3
α_{1B}	6.6	-134	-181	2	45

21.4. Construction of Docking-Derived Pharmacophores

Analysis of the ligand-receptor model complexes indicated that the main interaction between IQC and the receptor models is the salt bridge between the conserved aspartate and the basic nitrogen of the ligand. The propyl group of IQC was surrounded by amino acid side chains from TM3 and TM4 in both subtypes. This is in accordance with experimental binding studies where the highest activity for IQC derivatives was reported with the propyl chain rather than other substituents on the nitrogen (unpublished data). The affinity of the methyl derivative to α_1-AR containing tissues was observed to be about ten-fold lower than for the n-propyl derivative. The branched isopropyl chain lowered affinity about three-fold when compared to the methyl compound, and this is presumably related to steric factors.

Other important interactions are the same as in the adrenaline-receptor complexes. S192 for α_{1A} is hydrogen-bonded to the oxygen atom of the upper methoxy group on the isoquinoline-based system (ring A, Figure 21.1), while the phenylalanine groups (F193 and F310 for α_{1A} and α_{1B} respectively) interact with ring A of the isoquinoline system of IQC. In addition, another aromatic residue (W285) also interacts with the same aromatic system in the α_{1A} subtype. In the α_{1B} receptor, the serine in TM5 interacting with the lower methoxy group on ring A of the isoquinoline system is not S211, as for adrenaline, but S208. The main differences between the two subtypes are in the weak interaction of the indole system of IQC with the α_{1B} model, where there is a $\pi-\pi$ stacking interaction between F330 and ring E of IQC, and a hydrogen bond between the carbonyl oxygen atom of L314 (α_{1B}) and the NH group of the indole ring. There are no interactions between the indole system of IQC and the α_{1A} site.

Using the interactions between IQC and the receptor models from the above docking studies, we constructed what we have termed "docking-derived pharmacophores" using the Catalyst software. The procedure was essentially the same as the one described by Greenidge et al.[29] (see also previous chapter). Information about the regions sterically forbidden to the ligand by the receptor was also included as excluded volumes.

The IQC-receptor complexes were edited by creating a subset including residues within 9 Å from IQC. This subset was further analyzed to identify atoms of IQC involved in interactions with the receptor. The Cartesian coordinates of these atoms and pseudo-atoms for the aromatic ring centers were noted. Atoms of the receptor close to IQC were also identified to produce the coordinates for the excluded volumes. A large number of excluded volumes were used (80-100). All these coordinates were used to edit a template command file for the "hypoedit" utility to translate into Catalyst pharmacophores (hypotheses).[30,31] In the command file, all features (chemical groups) were described by giving Cartesian coordinates of the ideal location for the feature, size of the location constraint (a sphere centered on the ideal location), and feature name (hydrogen-bond acceptor or donor, hydrophobic group, positive ion, aromatic ring, and hydrophobic aromatic features). Default settings were used for the size of the location constraints (150 pm for the feature on the ligand, 200 pm for the corresponding interacting feature on the receptor, and 250 pm for the excluded volumes).

21.4.1. The α_{1A} Pharmacophore

The docking-derived α_{1A} pharmacophore without excluded volumes (for clarity) is shown in Plate 21.1. The red sphere represents the positive ion interacting with D106. The blue spheres are the hydrophobic groups for the propyl chain on the protonated nitrogen atom and the methyl moiety of the upper methoxy group. The phenyl ring of the isoquinoline system of IQC is involved in an aromatic interaction with F193 and this is represented by a brown sphere and a blue plane (the arrow points towards the interacting π system on the receptor; F193). The last feature is the H-bond acceptor group on the oxygen atom of the upper methoxy group interacting with S192 which is represented by green spheres (the smaller sphere describes the location of the group on the ligand, the larger sphere the interacting group on the receptor; S192). The pharmacophore with the excluded volumes is shown in Plate 21.2. The picture was taken from the extracellular opening of the binding site. The black spheres represent the excluded volumes.

21.4.2. The α_{1B} Pharmacophore

The docking-derived pharmacophore for the α_{1B} subtype is more complicated (Plate 21.3). The red sphere for the positive ion is again located on the protonated nitrogen atom interacting with D125. Hydrophobic groups on the propyl chain, and on two of the methoxy groups of ring A in IQC are darker blue. Aromatic rings are represented by lighter blue spheres on the rings A and E of the molecule. This representation was chosen over the more stringent aromatic ring feature in Catalyst, which also restricts the location of the plane of the aromatic system, as used above for the α_{1A} subtype. This was done because the $\pi-\pi$ interactions between the α_{1B} receptor and IQC were weaker, with the interacting groups further apart than for the α_{1A} receptor. There is one hydrogen-bond acceptor group located on the oxygen atom of the lower methoxy group (green spheres) and a hydrogen-bond donor group on the NH group of the indole ring (purple spheres). The excluded volumes were also included for this subtype (Plate 21.4).

21.4.3. Comparing the Docking-Derived Pharmacophores

The comparison between the pharmacophores can give an indication of the features important for selectivity between these subtypes. The docking-derived pharmacophores are very similar over the isoquinoline based ring system (rings A and B), including the positive ion feature, H-bond acceptor group, and the hydrophobic groups. However, the main difference between the subtypes is that there is no feature on the indole ring involved in the interaction with the α_{1A} subtype. On the other hand, interaction between the indole ring and the α_{1B} subtype is very strong. A hydrogen-bond donor group, an aromatic ring, and a hydrophobic group are involved in the interaction. This difference can be seen in Plate 21.5 which shows the two pharmacophores superimposed on each other (without excluded volumes). It could be argued that this information was already available from the receptor-IQC model complexes obtained via docking. This is true, but converting this information into pharmacophores will now allow access to database searching with the two pharmacophores with the aim of finding lead compounds which fit very well onto the α_{1B} docking-derived pharmacophore, but not very well onto the corresponding α_{1A} pharmacophore.

Another advantage of the docking-derived pharmacophores is that they simplify the analysis of the steric requirements of the binding sites in the two different receptor proteins. The major difference is that the binding pocket of the α_{1A} subtype is very tight, leading to a better affinity for the IQC ligand, whereas the α_{1B} subtype has a very large space above the bound IQC. The potential problem here is that the α_{1A} pocket seems to be more flexible (see below), as noted also by De Benedetti et al.[8] This is probably the reason why most known ligands, including adrenaline and IQC, have a higher affinity for the α_{1A} receptor, since the pocket can mold itself around the ligand.

21.4.4. Design of Potentially α_{1B}-Selective Ligands

The large space above IQC in the binding pocket could possibly be used to design an α_{1B}-selective ligand. Three series of target compounds, (2) to (4) (Figure 21.2), could serve for this purpose if the alkyl groups are added stereoselectively as shown. The target compounds were constructed within Catalyst and conformational models calculated.[32] However, prior to obtaining fit data on the docking-derived pharmacophores, further modification was necessary.

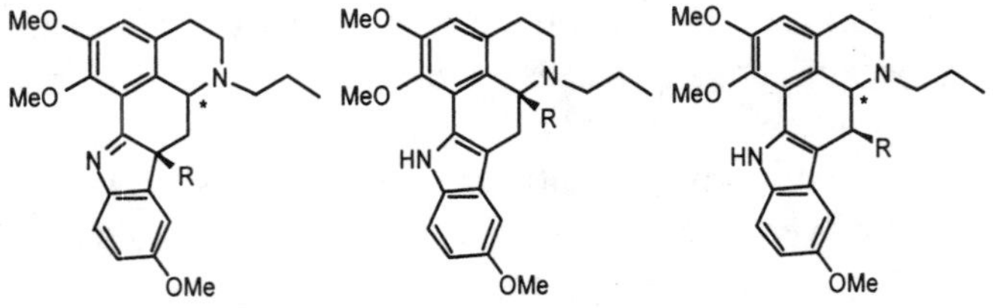

(2)   (3)   (4)

R = CH$_3$ (a)
    CH$_2$CH$_3$ (b)
    CH$_2$CH$_2$CH$_3$ (c)
    CH$_2$CH$_2$CH$_2$CH$_3$ (d)
    CH(CH$_3$)$_3$ (e)
    CH$_2$CH(CH$_3$)$_2$ (f)
    CH$_2$C$_6$H$_5$ (g)
    CH$_2$CH$_2$CH$_2$CH$_2$CH$_3$ (h)

Figure 21.2. Structures of the target compounds.

The docking-derived pharmacophores with excluded volumes represent the observed interactions between IQC and the receptor models within the Insight suite of software. Within Catalyst, however, they cannot be used as they are, since IQC (in the conformation from its receptor complexes) cannot be mapped completely onto all features of these pharmacophores. For both pharmacophores, one of the methoxy groups on the tetrahydroisoquinoline ring of IQC has two features mapped to it, a hydrogen-bond acceptor on the oxygen and a hydrophobic group on the methyl group. Catalyst does not map both these features together and the less discriminating feature, the hydrophobic group, was deleted in both pharmacophores. This problem arises because Catalyst only considers functions to be available if they are surface accessible. For the hydrogen-bond acceptor feature this criterion seems particularly stringent: The hydrogen-bond acceptor functionality observed in the docking studies for the α_{1A}-AR-IQC complex cannot be mapped onto the correct methoxy group for the α_{1A}-docking-derived IQC conformation and had to be replaced by a simple oxygen atom functionality. The hydrogen-bond donor functionality in the α_{1B} pharmacophore does not map to the indole nitrogen and had to be modified. This is because the default hydrogen-bond donor feature within Catalyst does not allow for an indole nitrogen; features can, however, be edited (using

"Exclude/OR QuickTool") to the specifications desired by the user. A hypothesis containing a user-defined feature such as this cannot, however, be constructed using "hypoedit." The α_{1B} pharmacophore used for fitting the target compounds was constructed within Catalyst by placing features onto the IQC template (using the "show function mapping" and "add function" tools). The features were merged into a hypothesis which was exported as a .chm file. This file needed to be edited in a Unix shell so that the coordinates matched the correct ones for the respective atoms in the receptor-ligand complex. Finally, the excluded volumes were pasted into the .chm file and this was imported back into Catalyst.

Table 21.4 shows the fit of IQC (**1**) and of the target molecules onto these two modified pharmacophores.

Table 21.4. The target ligands and their fit values[a] on the docking-derived pharmacophores with excluded volumes.[b]

Ligands	Fit values		Ligands	Fit values	
	α_{1A}	α_{1B}		α_{1A}	α_{1B}
(**1**)	0.80	0.92	(**3d**)	n.m.	n.m.
(**2a**)	0.40	0.53	(**3e**)	0.25	n.m.
(**2b**)	0.28	0.40	(**3f**)	0.12	n.m.
(**2c**)	0.15	0.64	(**3g**)	0.44[d]	0.52
(**2d**)	n.m.[c]	0.55	(**4a**)	0.52	0.51
(**2e**)	0.12	0.62	(**4b**)	0.60	0.39
(**2f**)	n.m.	0.47	(**4c**)	n.m.	0.42
(**2g**)	n.m.	0.63	(**4d**)	n.m.	0.59
(**2h**)	n.m.	0.38	(**4e**)	0.63	0.02
(**3c**)	0.31	0.49	(**4f**)	0.26	0.49

[a] *fit values are calculated by the software indicating how well the features in the pharmacophore overlap with the chemical features in the ligand and normalized for the number of features in the hypotheses;*
[b] *see text for explanation as to which pharmacophores were used;*
[c] *no mapping possible;*
[d] *wrong mapping.*

As can be seen for all three series of compounds, the α_{1B} receptor site can accommodate quite a large substituent attached in different positions in ring C. The fit of the series (**2**) compounds to the α_{1B} pharmacophore is even more remarkable since these molecules do not have a hydrogen-bond donor group in the indoline system. However, upon calculation of electrostatic potential maps (using the Wavefunction, Inc. Spartan™ software, after geometry optimization at the *ab initio* RHF/STO 3-21 G level, data not shown), it was apparent the indoline nitrogen in compounds (**2**) carries a very large negative potential. In a previous study[28] this was found to be deleterious for good binding for the thiadiazole compound (**5**) (Figure 21.3). This compound had high negative electrostatic potentials associated with the nitrogens in the thiadiazole ring, unlike IQC, where the indole nitrogen (ring D) displayed a positive potential. The binding affinity of (**5**) for all three α_1 AR subtypes was greatly reduced relative to IQC.[28]

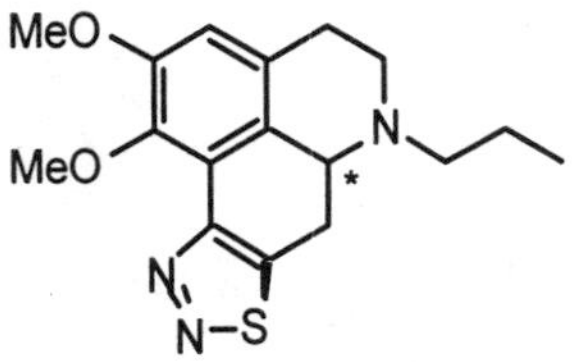

(**5**)

Figure 21.3. Structure of the thiadiazole derivative (**5**).

The series (**4**) compounds, in particular (**4c**) and (**4d**), appeared most promising as α_{1B} selective ligands. They fit quite well onto the α_{1B} pharmacophore, but not at all onto the α_{1A} pharmacophore. Furthermore, the indole system of IQC is undisturbed and the positively charged nitrogen of the tetrahydroisoquinoline system is still accessible.

It was therefore decided to manually dock (**4d**) into the two α_{1A} and α_{1B} models as described above for IQC.

Unfortunately, the high flexibility of the α_{1A} site still allows it to accommodate this ligand, resulting in a binding energy of -166 kcal/mol, which comes from a higher interaction energy. The distortion energy for the receptor went up only slightly (from 3 kcal/mol for IQC to 17 kcal/mol for (**4d**)). Our strategy has been supported, however, by the energy data upon docking of (**4d**) into the α_{1B} receptor site. The binding energy improved from -134 kcal/mol for IQC to -145 kcal/mol for (**4d**), with the interaction energy improving by 11 kcal/mol and the distortion energy of the receptor actually going down by 1 kcal/mol as compared to IQC binding. Careful analysis of the fit values in Table 21.4 suggests that the α_{1A} receptor site can still accommodate a certain degree of steric bulk, especially branching in the carbon atom directly attached to the IQC system (the e series of compounds, Figure 21.2), whereas long unbranched alkyl chains and branching further out seem to be detrimental. These options are currently under further investigation, but, more importantly, the results of the docking of (**4d**) indicate that the flexibility of the α_{1A} site will need to be considered as well. One potential way of doing this is to reduce the size and/or the number of the excluded volume spheres for the α_{1A} docking-derived pharmacophore, while leaving the α_{1B} mod-el as it is.

Refinement of the docking-derived pharmacophore methodology, which has the potential for generalization to other receptor model systems and associated selective ligand design studies, is being actively pursued.

Acknowledgements

The award of a scholarship from Zonguldak Karaelmas University in Turkey to Burak Coban, and research support from the ARC and NHMRC are gratefully acknowledged. We also thank Professor R. M. Graham and colleagues at the Victor Chang Cardiac Research Institute, Sydney, Australia, for the initial receptor models and for helpful discussions.

References

1. Beck-Sickinger A: **Structural characterization and binding sites of GPCRs.** *Drug Discovery Today* 1996, **1**:502-513.

2. Pebay-Peyroula E, Rummel G, Ceska TA, Rosenbush JP, Landau EM: **X-ray structure of bacteriorhodopsin at 2.5 angstroms from microcrystals grown in lipidic cubic phases.** *Science* 1997, **277**:1676-1681.

3. Unger VM, Hargrave PA, Baldwin JM, Schertler GFX: **Arrangement of rhodopsin transmembrane α-helices.** *Nature* 1997, **389**:203-206.

4. Krebs A, Villa C, Edwards PC, Schertler GFX: **Characterization of an improved two-dimensional p22$_1$2$_1$ crystal from bovine rhodopsin.** *J Mol Biol* 1998, **282**:991-1003.

5. Savarese TM, Fraser CM: *In vitro* mutagenesis and research for structure function relationships among GPCRs. *Biochem J* 1992, **283**:1-19.

6. Baldwin JM, Schertler GFX, Unger VM: An alpha-carbon template for the transmembrane helices in the rhodopsin family of G-protein-coupled receptors. *J Mol Biol* 1997, **272**:144-164.

7. (a) Hieble JP, Bondinell WE, Ruffolo Jr RR: α- and β-adrenoceptors: From the gene to the clinic. 1. Molecular biology and adrenoceptor subclassification. *J Med Chem* 1995, **38**:3415-3444; (b) Ruffolo Jr RR, Bondinell W, Hieble JP: α- and β-adrenoceptors: From the gene to the clinic. 2. Structure-activity relationships and therapeutic applications. *J Med Chem* 1995, **38**:3681-3716.

8. DeBenedetti PG, Fanelli F, Menziani MC, Cocchi M, Testa R, Leonardi A: α_1-adrenoceptor subtype selectivity: molecular modeling and theoretical quantitative structure-activity relationships. *Bioorg Med Chem* 1997, **5**:809-816.

9. Strader CD, Sigal IS, Dixon RAF: Structural bases of the β-adrenergic receptor function. *FASEB J* 1989, **3**:1825-1832.

10. Cavalli A, Fanelli F, Taddei C, DeBenedetti PG, Cotecchia S: Amino acids of the α_{1B}-adrenergic receptor involved in agonist binding: Differences in docking catecholamines to receptor subtypes. *FEBS Lett* 1996, **399**:9-13.

11. Porter JE, Hwa J, Perez DM: Activation of the α_{1B}-adrenergic receptor is initiated by disruption of an helical saltbridge constraint. *J Biol Chem* 1996, **271**:28318-28323.

12. Zhao MM, Hwa J, Perez DM: Identification of critical extracellular loop residues involved in α_1-adrenergic receptor subtype-selective antagonist binding. *Mol Pharmacol* 1996, **50**:1118-1126.

13. Zhao MM, Gaivin RJ, Perez DM: The third extracellular loop of the beta(2)-adrenergic receptor can modulate receptor G protein affinity. *Mol Pharmacol* 1998, **63**:524-529.

14. Wetzel JM, Salon SA, Tamm JA, Forray C, Craig D, Nakanishi H, Cui W, Vaysse PJJ, Chiu G, Weinshank RL, Hartig PR, Branchek TA, Gluchowski C: Modeling and mutagenesis of the human α_{1A}-adrenoceptor: Orientation and function of transmembrane helix V side chains. *Receptors and Channels* 1996, **4**:165-177.

15. Hwa J, Perez DM: The unique nature of the serine interactions for α_1-adrenergic receptor subtype agonist binding and activation. *J Biol Chem* 1996, **271**:6322-6327.

16. Hwa J, Graham RM, Perez DM: **Identification of critical determinants of** α_1**-adrenergic receptor subtype-selective agonist binding.** *J Biol Chem* 1995, **270**:23189-23195.

17. Chen S, Xu M, Lin F, Riek P, Graham RM: **Identification of Phe310 in TM6 of the alpha1B-adrenergic receptor as a key switch residue involved in catecholamine ring aromatic bonding.** *23rd Lorne Conference on Protein Structure and Function*, Lorne, Vic, Australia, 8-12 Feb. 1998:B-55.

18. Hamaguchi N, True TA, Saussy DL, Jeffs PW: **Phenylalanine in the second membrane-spanning domain of** α_{1A}**-adrenergic receptor determines subtype selectivity of dihydropyridine antagonists.** *Biochemistry* 1996, **35**:14313-14317.

19. Fanelli F, Menziani MC, Scheer A, Cotecchia S, DeBenedetti PG: *Ab initio* **modeling and molecular dynamics simulation of the** α_{1B}**-adrenergic receptor activation.** *Methods: A Companion to Methods in Enzymology* 1998, **14**:302-317.

20. Scheer A, Fanelli F, Costa T, DeBenedetti PG, Cotecchia S: **Constitutively active mutants of the** α_{1B}**-adrenergic receptor: Role of highly conserved polar amino acids in receptor activation.** *EMBO J* 1996, **15**:3566-3578.

21. Fanelli F, Menziani MC, DeBenedetti PG: **Computer simulations of signal transduction mechanism in** α_{1B}**-adrenergic and m3-muscarinic receptors.** *Prot Eng* 1995, **8**:557-564.

22. Scheer A, Fanelli F, Costa T, DeBenedetti PG, Cotecchia S: **The activation process of the** α_{1B}**-adrenergic receptor: Potential role of protonation and hydrophobicity of a highly conserved aspartate.** *Proc Natl Acad Sci USA* 1997, **94**:808-813.

23. Riek P: **Hydrogen bonding around transmembrane helical segments containing proline.** *(MM98) Fourth Australian Molecular Modeling Workshop*, Sydney, Australia, July 1998 Talk (T4).

24. Riek RP, Handschumacher MD, Sung SS, Tan M, Glynias MJ, Schuluchter MD, Novotny J, Graham RM: **Evolutionary conservation of both the hydrophilic and hydrophobic nature of transmembrane residues.** *J Theor Biol* 1995, **172**:245-258.

25. Graham RM, Perez DM, Hwa J, Piascik MT: α_1**-adrenergic receptor subtypes: Molecular structure, function, and signaling.** *Circ Res* 1996, **78**:737-749.

26. Hwa J, Graham RM, Perez DM: **Chimeras of** α_1**-adrenergic receptor subtypes identify critical residues that modulate active state isomerization.** *J Biol Chem* 1996, **271**:7956-7964.

27. Sung SS, Riek P, Handshumacher M, Novotny J, Graham RM: **A model for the three-dimensional structure of the** α_{1B}**-adrenergic receptor.** *FASEB J* 1991, **5**:A804.

28. Bremner JB, Griffith R, Coban B, Groenewoud KM, Yates BF: Ligand design for α_1-adrenoceptor subtype selective antagonists. *Bioorg Med Chem*, in press.

29. Greenidge PA, Carlsson B, Bladh LG, Gillner M: **Pharmacophores incorporating numerous excluded volumes defined by X-ray crystallographic structure in 3D database searching: Application to the thyroid hormone receptor.** *J Med Chem* 1998, **41**:2503-2512.

30. Greene J, Kahn S, Savoy H, Sprague P, Teig S: **Chemical function queries for 3D database search.** *J Chem Inf Comput Sci* 1994, **34**:1297-1308.

31. Barnum D, Greene J, Smellie A, Sprague P: **Identification of common functional configurations among molecules.** *J Chem Inf Comput Sci* 1996, **36**:563-571.

32. Smellie A, Teig SL, Towbin P: **Poling—Promoting conformational variation.** *J Comput Chem* 1995, **16**:171-187.

33. Bremner JB, Coban B, Griffith R: **Docking derived pharmacophores provide a novel approach to adrenoceptor ligand design.** In: *Solutions Life Sciences*, Issue 2, Belevance L, ed. 1999:6.

22

Technique for Developing a Pharmacophore Model that Accommodates Inherent Protein Flexibility: An Application to HIV-1 Integrase

**Kevin M. Masukawa, Heather A. Carlson,
and J. Andrew McCammon**

Abstract

We present a new method for the development of pharmacophore models that accounts for the inherent flexibility of a target active site. The flexibility of the enzymatic system is described by collecting many conformations of the uncomplexed protein from a molecular dynamics (MD) simulation. The binding sites for functional groups that complement the active site are determined through a series of multi-unit search for interacting conformers (MUSIC) simulations. MUSIC simulations are conducted for each saved conformation of the protein, providing a large collection of potential complementary sites. The active sites from each protein conformation are overlaid, and the pharmacophore model is described by the conserved binding regions for the probe molecules. The "dynamic" pharmacophore model presented in this study is the first reported receptor-based pharmacophore model for HIV-1 integrase. Using standard protocol for multiple-copy simulations, "static" pharmacophore models were developed with the crystal structure that was used to initialize the MD studies and two additional crystal structures that became available after the completion of the MD study. The pharmacophore models were compared to known inhibitors of the integrase. The dynamic model compares much more favorably with the set of known inhibitors than do the static models, implying that new compounds determined with the dynamic model have a greater potential for inhibition than those identified with the static models.

22

Technique for Developing a Pharmacophore Model that Accommodates Inherent Protein Flexibility: An Application to HIV-1 Integrase

Kevin M. Masukawa, Heather A. Carlson,
and J. Andrew McCammon

University of California at San Diego, La Jolla, California

22.1. Introduction

The aim of a pharmacophore model is to describe the most important characteristics of ligands that tightly bind to a given receptor. In receptor-based pharmacophores, the model reflects the complementary interactions that exist between the ligand and protein; these hand-in-glove interactions are typically the driving force for ligand binding. However, many models neglect the penalties incurred by the ligand and receptor upon binding. More sophisticated models attempt to account for solvent effects through the scoring functions used to identify molecules that fit the model. This can be quite difficult because the role of solvent is very different for hydrophobic versus hydrophilic environments. Desolvation is the driving force for hydrophobic ligand-receptor binding, but it is a penalty for the association of hydrophilic ligands and receptors. Other penalties are the entropic costs of reduced flexibility and possible changes in conformation for both the ligand and the active site.[1,2] While rigid versions of the ligands can be synthesized to reduce such penalties, this is the first method introduced to reduce similar entropic penalties incurred by the receptor.

The goal of developing a dynamic pharmacophore model is to identify compounds that complement the protein while causing minimal disruption of the conformation and flexibility of the active site, potentially reducing the entropic penalties incurred by the protein. Multiple configurations of a protein receptor can be obtained from a molecular dynamics (MD) simulation; they could also be provided from multiple crystal structures or NMR structures.[2] The multiple configurations from any of these methods describe the inherent flexibility of the uncomplexed receptor under the influence of explicit solvent molecules. Binding sites for various functional groups within the receptor can be determined with calculations employing multiple-copy methods. In this study, the multi-unit search for interacting conformers (MUSIC) method has been used to determine the binding sites within the active site of multiple protein configurations of HIV-1 integrase, provided from an MD simulation. The MUSIC procedure is a Monte Carlo (MC) simulation that simultaneously calculates multiple, gas-phase minimizations for hundreds of probe molecules within the active site. For example, this study uses methanol molecules as probes to define binding positions and orientations for hydroxyl groups. The many configurations of the protein are then overlaid to reveal conserved binding sites that are highly occupied over the course of the MD simulation despite the motion of the active site. These conserved binding sites define a pharmacophore model for inhibitors that should in theory bind to the active site and still allow for almost the same flexibility.

HIV-1 integrase is a good test case for the dynamic method since it has an active site that is shallow, solvent exposed, and minimally restricted in conformational sampling. While a complete structure of the integrase is unavailable, the structures of the N- and C-terminal domains have been described by NMR[3-5] and several crystal structures are now available for the catalytic core.[6-9] Inhibitors for the integrase are being pursued for anti-HIV therapies because integration of viral DNA is an early step in the viral lifecycle and there is no native homologous process in the host cell. The integrase inserts viral DNA into the host chromosome, catalyzing both the 3'-preprocessing of the viral DNA and its insertion into the host DNA.[10]

The first MD studies of the catalytic core domain of HIV-1 integrase have recently appeared.[9] Using configurations of the protein from those MD simulations, we have developed the first receptor-based pharmacophore model for the active site of the integrase.[11] We also compare the performance of the dynamic model to three "static" models derived from MUSIC simulations using three available crystal structures of the catalytic core of HIV-1 integrase. The use of a single conformation from a crystal structure is a standard practice for pharmacophore development with multiple-copy methods.[1,2,12-18] When fitting known inhibitors of HIV-1 integrase to the models, the dynamic model fits many more inhibitors than any of the static models. It appears that flexibility in the active site is necessary for proper prediction of active inhibitors of HIV-1 integrase.

22.2. Computational Details

22.2.1. The MD Simulation and Preparation of the Available Crystal Structures

500 ps of sampling were available for this study, but later the MD simulation was extended to 1 ns.[9] For brevity, the protocol for the MD simulations are not repeated here, but it should be noted that they were derived from well-established protocol, the NWchem v3.2 program,[19] the AMBER force field,[20] and the SPC/E water model.[21] The complete MD study presented two 1 ns simulations for the catalytic core of the integrase, both with and without the catalytic magnesium ion present in the active site.[9,11] The simulation with the magnesium ion present were used for the development of the dynamic pharmacophore model. The dynamics of that system were consistent over the 1 ns, and the behavior of the first 500 ps is representative of the entire simulation.

Eleven configurations from the MD calculation were obtained for the development of the pharmacophore by saving the equilibrated structure and additional configurations of the system at 50 ps intervals. Only the protein structure in each snapshot was used; the magnesium ion and all water molecules were removed for the MUSIC studies. For the MUSIC simulations, H66 was protonated to match its ionization state without divalent ions present[22] and the N- and C-termini were changed from charged termini to neutral methyl amides. The later change was made to avoid any false minima associated with the terminal charges at residues 57 and 210 since they are not present in the full integrase enzyme.

For the initial crystal structure from the MD studies, the complete structure of the protein, including positions for the hydrogen atoms, was available from the setup of the MD calculations.[9] The pepz utility[23] available with BOSS[24] and MCPRO[25] programs was used to add hydrogens to the two new crystal structures of the catalytic core from Maignan et al.[6] (monomer C of 1BI4 in the protein data bank) and Goldgur et al.[7] (monomer B in 1BIS). Ionization states for each side chain were kept consistent with the MD study with the exception of H66 and the termini as mentioned above. These two crystal structures are the first to resolve a flexible loop adjacent to the active site. In the MD study, this unresolved loop was modeled after the homologous loop in the crystal structures of the integrase from Avian Sarcoma Virus.[26]

22.2.2. MUSIC

Multiple-copy methods were introduced in 1991 by Miranker and Karplus[12] based on ideas presented with the development of the GRID method.[27] The method was quickly embraced and is now a standard practice in computational drug design.[1,2,13,28-31] Multiple-copy methods like MUSIC are based on a simulation technique where the active site of a protein is flooded with many copies of non-interacting probe molecules. MD, MC, steepest-decent, or other sampling methods can be used to simultaneously minimize all probe molecules into local minima within the active site. In addition to the position and orientation of the probes clustered within a local minimum, information about the relative favorability of the binding sites can be evaluated by interaction energy with the protein or occupancy of the site.

MUSIC is a procedure available in the Monte Carlo program BOSS.[24] Current releases of BOSS are capable of simulating user-defined solvent. Also, the solvent-solvent and solute-solute energetics can be set to zero with a flag in the BOSS input files. Probe molecules (designated as solvent in a MUSIC simulation) can be small, organic molecules such as methanol to represent hydroxyl groups, benzene for aromatic groups, or ions like guanidinium ions. For this study, we used methanol and methyl ammonium ions to describe binding sites that complement the catalytic residues D64 and D116. The probe molecules and the protein were described with the all-atom OPLS force field.[32,33] Large cutoff radii were used so that no non-bonded interactions were neglected.

The protein side chains can be fully flexible in a MUSIC simulation, and this may be necessary for certain systems. In this application, the protein configurations were held rigid because the flexibility was represented through the use of many snapshots from the MD simulations. Studies have demonstrated the need for protein flexibility in ligand docking and multiple-copy simulations in order to achieve proper results;[34,35] however, the large majority of publications continue to report the use of only one static structure for multiple-copy simulations.[1,2,13-18]

The protein structures were not rotated or translated during the MUSIC studies, and probe molecules were held internally rigid. Sampling moves for the probes were limited to displacements of 0.15 Å or less and rotations of 15° or less. The system was initiated with a 17.0 Å sphere of densely packed probe molecules centered at the active site (εO of Q62), resulting in 358-423 copies of methanol or 329-399 methylammonium ions depending on the protein configuration. A half-harmonic potential was applied at the boundary of the 17.0 Å sphere (force constant of 5 kcal/mol·Å^2) to keep the probes from possibly dissociating from the protein. In the case of charged probe molecules, the interaction energy with the protein was rather large, and the half harmonic potential was unnecessary though still used. The simulated annealing protocol was 10^6 iterations of sampling at 300°C, 10^6 iterations at 200°C, 10^6 iterations at 100°C, 10^6 iterations at 0°C, and finally 2×10^6 iterations at -100°C.

22.2.3. The Dynamic Pharmacophore Model for HIV-1 Integrase

The MUSIC procedure was used to generate binding sites for methanol probes within the active sites of 11 conformations of the integrase core.

The hundreds of probes clustered into many local minima within the receptor. Each cluster of probes was represented by its parent molecule, the probe in the cluster with the most favorable interaction energy with the protein. The MidasPlus[36,37] program was used to overlay the MUSIC results for all 11 configurations and to identify the conserved binding regions. Each protein structure was overlaid with the 250 ps structure by an RMS fit of γC of D64, γC of D116, δC of Q62, and the Mg^{+2} position from the MD simulation. Four points are required for the RMS fit in MidasPlus and the four atoms above are central to the active site. Though E152 is an essential catalytic residue within the active site of HIV-1 integrase, its position was widely sampled and was not appropriate for incorporation into the RMS fitting or the final pharmacophore model.

Plate 22.1, a and b, shows the overlay process and displays the six conserved binding regions for the methanol probes that were used in the dynamic pharmacophore model. Conserved binding regions were required to contain three or more parent molecules. Furthermore, the parents had to be identified with protein structures from early and late in the MD simulation. A site was not considered conserved if it was only observed for structures from the beginning or end of the MD simulation.

Based on the Cartesian coordinates from the overlays, the average position for γC of D64, γC of D116, and δC of Q62 were used as the centers for three excluded volumes with radii of 1.5 Å in the pharmacophore model. The excluded volumes were used to eliminate compounds likely to have steric conflicts with the protein. Though the conserved binding regions are specifically for hydroxyl groups, the criteria were extended for the pharmacophore model to include any oxygen, nitrogen, or sulfur that could donate a hydrogen bond (bound to one, two, or three hydrogens). The center of each hydrogen-bond donor site in the pharmacophore model was equal to the average position of the methanol oxygens from the parent molecules in each conserved binding region. The radii of the hydrogen-bond donor sites were set to double the RMS deviation of the parent oxygens. This resulted in a pharmacophore model with nine sites, three excluded volumes, and six hydrogen-bond donor sites. The dynamic pharmacophore model is the first model presented in Table 22.1.

Table 22.1. Characteristics of the dynamic pharmacophore model based on the MD simulations and the static pharmacophore models based on three crystal structures. Atoms with gray spheres are hydrogen-bond donors; the black spheres are excluded volumes based on active site residues.

	Radius	X	Y	Z (Å)
Dynamic Model				
HBdonor1	1.316	7.249	4.783	2.405
HBdonor2	1.088	9.543	4.462	1.849
HBdonor3	0.388	11.037	3.382	1.497
HBdonor4	1.106	10.877	1.845	-2.410
HBdonor5	1.088	8.232	7.622	-1.851
HBdonor6	1.494	9.072	8.404	-4.178
Q62	1.5	5.842	4.291	-3.330
D64	1.5	7.819	2.218	0.311
D116	1.5	10.461	5.219	-2.795
Static Model 1 from crystal structure in the MD study				
HBdonor1	0.364	5.127	-1.955	-2.406
HBdonor2	0.748	7.612	-2.655	-2.819
HBdonor3	0.534	9.487	-2.311	-3.876
HBdonor4	0.250	11.464	-0.353	1.304
HBdonor5	0.692	12.149	-0.340	-0.079
Q62	1.5	6.573	0.345	2.229
D64	1.5	4.765	1.167	-1.907
D116	1.5	9.278	0.472	-1.425
Static Model 2 from crystal structure of Maignan et al.[a]				
HBdonor1	0.464	6.346	-4.762	10.626
HBdonor2	0.590	9.455	-4.219	14.306
HBdonor3	1.510	11.052	-2.038	9.695
HBdonor4	0.804	11.056	1.222	9.286
O of L63[b]	1.5	7.763	0.359	16.393
D64	1.5	7.409	-2.046	12.892
D116	1.5	12.001	0.425	12.406
Static Model 3 from crystal structure of Goldgur et a				
HBdonor1	0.920	-7.970	2.051	-3.353
HBdonor2	0.470	-9.712	-0.847	-4.840
HBdonor3	0.740	-9.794	-2.587	0.591
HBdonor4	1.008	-10.858	-6.280	-5.223
Q62	1.5	-8.909	-0.797	4.047
D64	1.5	-8.019	-1.392	-1.845
D116	1.5	-11.446	-5.914	-1.851

[a] *Reference[6];*

[b] *The side chain of Q62 is in an orientation away from D64 and D116 in the structure by Maignan et al. For this structure, the carbonyl oxygen of L63 was chosen to represent the bottom of the active site;*

[c] *Reference[7].*

MUSIC studies were also conducted with methylammonium ions for probe molecules. A single conserved site close to the position of the magnesium ion was located from the overlays (radius = 0.598 and Cartesian coordinates of x = 8.155, y = 5.249, and z = -0.428, relative to the dynamic model in Table 22.1). Originally, we had incorporated this tenth site into the pharmacophore model; however, technical issues made the use of this site unsuccessful later in the project when database searching was initiated. The Catalyst program[38] was used to identifying readily purchased compounds from the Available Chemicals Directory (ACD) Database that fit the pharmacophore model. Most of the compounds appear in the ACD in their neutral form (free base amines, protonated acids, etc.) and simply do not fit the criteria of a pharmacophore containing the conserved binding site for methylammonium ions.

22.2.4. Static Pharmacophore Models

The second model (Static Model 1) in Table 22.1 is the static pharmacophore model based on the crystal structure used to initiate the MD studies.[9] The third and fourth models in Table 22.1 are from the crystal structures of Maignan et al.[6] and Goldgur et al.,[7] referred as Static Model 2 and Static Model 3, respectively. Again, MUSIC calculations with methanol molecules were used to identify hydrogen-bond donor sites. The protocol was the same in the determination of the dynamic and static models. Seeking to develop the static models in a similar fashion as the dynamic model, the centers and radii of the hydrogen-bond donor sites were calculated from the coordinates of the oxygen atoms of all the probes in an individual cluster rather than just the parent molecule.

22.2.5. Using the Catalyst Program

For the test set of known inhibitors of HIV-1 integrase, 59 compounds from the literature[39-44] were built into a user-defined database through the 3D viewer interface in the Catalyst program.[38] Structures of all the compounds were given as Supplemental Information in a previous publication,[11] and readers are referred to that source and the cited sources in Table 22.2 for additional information about the compounds used in the test set. Conformations of the inhibitors were created with the "fast" conformational generator employing the default limits and the built-in force field used in Catalyst. They were fit to the pharmacophore models using both the "fast" and "best" routines (F and B in the following discussions). The F routine is the more stringent routine, which simply evaluates the geometry of the conformers of the compounds to test for fit. The B routine is more generous and allows for an additional cycle of fitting to refine the inherent conformations of the compound to better fit the pharmacophore model. Results for fitting the inhibitors to the pharmacophore models with both F and B fitting routines are given in Table 22.2.

Table 22.2. Performance of the pharmacophore models tested against compounds from the literature that have been tested for inhibitory activity. Compounds ordered by inhibitory activity.

Compound	IC50s 3'/ST	Dynamic		Static 1 doubled radii				Static 2 Maignan et al.[a]		Static 3 Goldgur et al.[b]	
		fast	best	fast	best	fast	best	fast	best	fast	best
Chichoric Acid[c]	0.15/0.13	✓	✗								
107[c]	0.23/0.11	✓	✗								
4,5-DCQA[c]	0.25/0.46	✓	✗								
81[c]	0.4/0.2	✓	✗			✓	✗		✗		
67[c]	0.5										
71[c]	0.5		✗								
85[c]	0.5/0.2	✓	✗	✗		✓	✗	✓	✗		
3,5-DCQA[c]	0.64/0.66	✓	✗								
3,4-DCQA[c]	0.79/0.54	✓	✗								
1,5-DCQA[c]	0.68/1.08		✗								
NSC 118695[d]	0.9/0.3	✓	✗						✗		
Quercategetin[e]	1.3/0.6		✗								
105[c]	0.98/0.81	✓	✗								
NSC 64205[d]	1.1/0.5	✓	✗						✗		
NSC 158393[f]	1.5/0.8							✓	✗		
NSC 607319[d]	1.4/1.0	✓	✗				✗	✓	✗		
NSC 309121[d]	1.7/1.0	✓	✗			✓	✗		✗		✗
68[c]	1.7	✓	✗								
Myricetin[e]	2/0.6		✗								
Doxorubicin[c]	0.9/2.4	✓	✗		*Very Active Compounds*				✗		
Purpurogallin[g]	2.1				*Active Compounds*						
111[c]	2.3/1.1										
NSC 310217[f]	2/1.5										
NSC 64452[d]	1.2/3.6	✓	✗								
Quinalizarin[e]	4/1										
83[c]	3.3/1.9	✓	✗								
NSC 261045[d]	2.3/4.1		✗						✗		
90[c]	1.38/4.71	✓	✗								
NSC 642710[f]	5.3/5.0	✓	✗					✓	✗		
NSC 115290[h]	5		✗								
Ellagic Acid[g]	5.1										
115[c]	6.7/5.2										
Mitoxantrone[c]	3.8/8.0	✓	✗			✓	✗	✓	✗		✗
89[c]	9/4	✓	✗								
Tyrophostin A51[e]	10/3										
110[c]	9.1/5.8										
92[c]	9.5/7.8	✓	✗								
141[c]	11.6/7.9		✗								
Hypericin[g]	10										
UCSD1[g]	17/5										
NSC 318213[d]	23.9/14.0										
66[c]	21.4/5.4	✓	✗								
NSC 233026[d]	20.6/19.7										
NSC 371056[f]	29.9/16.5	✓	✗					✓	✗		✗
NSC 48240[f]	26/20.6	✓	✗								
97[c]	33/33	✓	✗		*Active Compounds*				✗		✗

Continued on next page

Compound	IC50s 3'/ST	Dynamic		Static 1 doubled radii				Static 2 Maignan et al.[a]		Static 3 Goldgur et al.[b]	
		fast	best	fast	best	fast	best	fast	best	fast	best
Chlorogenic Acid[e]	87.8/45.8		✗	*Ineffective Compounds*							
13[h]	120/96										
NSC 641547[f]	224/134	✗				✗					
NSC 674503[d]		✗									
NSC 635971[f]		✓	✗								
NSC 642651[d]		✓	✗					✓	✗		
112[c]		✓	✗						✗		
9[h]		✓	✗								
52[h]		✓	✗	✓	✗			✓	✗	✓	✗
NSC 281311[d]		✓	✗				✗		✗		
103[c]		✓	✗					✓	✗		✗
5[f]											
NDGA[g]		✓	✗								

[a] *Ref.[6]*; [b] *Ref.[7]*; [c] *Ref.[42]*; [d] *Ref.[41]*; [e] *Ref.[43]*; [f] *Ref.[40]*; [g] *Ref.[44]*; [h] *Ref.[39]*

The numbers listed for some of the compounds are the labels given in the referenced papers.

22.3. Results and Discussion

To test the selectivity of the pharmacophore models, non-inhibitory compounds with structures similar to known inhibitors were included in the test set. Twenty compounds in the test set had IC$_{50}$s under 1 µM for 3'-preprocessing or strand transfer (referred to as very active compounds in Table 22.2 and the following discussions). Twenty-six additional compounds had IC$_{50}$s between 1-35 µM for both catalyzed processes (active compounds). Three ineffective inhibitors (IC$_{50}$s of 46-224 µM) and ten non-inhibitors were also included. All compounds chosen to test the pharmacophore models contained at least four hydrogen-bond donors. The inhibitors that are most likely to bind to the side chains of D64 and D116 must contain many hydrogen-bond donors to complement the carboxylate groups.

The most dramatic result of testing the models against the set of known inhibitors is the extraordinary performance of the dynamic pharmacophore model; the excellent fit rate for the very active compounds is particularly encouraging (see Table 22.2). The Dynamic Model fits 70% with the stringent F method and 90% with the B method. The active compounds are fit with less success, with 42% identified with F and 54% with B. Somewhat discouraging is the number of ineffective compounds that fit the Dynamic Model (8 of 13 with F and 11 of 13 with B), but it is emphasized that the ineffective compounds chosen for the study closely resembled the very active compounds. They were specifically chosen to be a difficult counter-test of the models. Given the excellent performance of the Dynamic Model in fitting the very active compounds, it will most likely be very useful in identifying highly effective inhibitors in our current searches of the ACD. Most of the compounds in the test set were identified by searching the non-proprietary half of a small molecule database maintained by the National Cancer Institute (NCI). If the Dynamic Model were used to search the NCI database, it too would have identified these same successful compounds.

We were surprised at the very poor performance of Static Model 1. Since the crystal structure used to generate the first static model was the starting point for the MD simulations, we expected similar performance. Though, many compounds fit the Dynamic Model, *no inhibitors fit Static Model 1 with the F method and only one compound fit with the B method.* From the crystal structure and snapshots of the protein available from the MD studies, it appears that the inclusion of flexibility is required to accurately describe binding to the active site of HIV-1 integrase.

Because the static models are based on single conformations of the active site, the radii of the hydrogen-bond donor sites are somewhat smaller, which may account for the poorer performance of Static Model 1 (smallest radii of all the models). Doubling the radii in the static model provided a set of hydrogen-bond donor sites with radii ranging from 0.500-1.496 Å, as compared to the radii of the dynamic model that range 0.388-1.494 Å. Even with doubled radii, Static Model 1 only fits five of the 59 test compounds (including one non-inhibitor) when using the F routine and eight compounds (three non-inhibitors) with the B routine.

Similarly poor performance is seen for Static Model 3. When using the F routine, only one non-inhibitor fits the model. With the B routine, only six compounds fit the model, most of which have IC_{50}s well over 10 μM. The structure solved by Goldgur et al.[7] was used to develop Static Model 3. It is very different from the MD structures and the crystal structure by Maignan et al.[11] In the structure by Goldgur et al., the flexible loop adjacent to the active site is oriented away from the catalytic residues. Those same co-workers reported the first crystal structure of HIV-1 integrase and proposed that the active site of the integrase resembled DNA polymerase,[8] but this newest structure would have to place the flexible loop over the active site to have a similar structure.

The homologous loop in the integrase of Avian Sarcoma Virus is known to adopt various conformations under different crystallization conditions; similar behavior is expected for the flexible loop in HIV-1 integrase. Though the flexible loops are very different, the relative positions of D64 and D116 are almost the same in the Goldgur et al. and the Maignan et al. structure; it is the orientation of other nearby residues that disagree and lead to different pharmacophore models. While the structure solved by Goldgur et al. does not appear to be appropriate for this particular set of inhibitory compounds, it might well be appropriate for other classes of inhibitors. Many inhibitors of HIV-1 integrase contain mostly hydrogen-bond acceptor functionalities and would be expected to dock in sites other than the active site or perhaps force the active site into a different conformation.

Static Model 2 employing the B routine has the best performance of the static models. The F routine fits nine compounds, three in each category in Table 22.2. The B routine identifies 18 compounds; eight of which are very active compounds. The structure solved by Maignan et al.,[6] that was used to develop Static Model 2, is very similar to the MD structures.[11] It is reasonable that this static model has the most similar performance to the Dynamic Model. Table 22.3 presents a comparison of the performance of the Dynamic Model and Static Model 2.

Table 22.3. Comparison of the performance of the Dynamic Model versus Static Model 2 in fitting the compounds in the test set given in Table 22.2. The performance is evaluated for the fit of the very active compounds and the fit of all active compounds.

% Yield = (Active Compounds Fit to Model/All Compounds Fit to Model)				
% Actives = (Active Compounds Fit/All Active Compounds in Test Set)				
Enrichment = (Active Fits/Total Fits)/(All Active Compounds in Test Set/All in Test Set)[a]				
	Dynamic Fast	Dynamic Best	Static 2 Fast	Static 2 Best
Active Compounds = 20 Very Active Compounds				
% Yield	42%	42%	33%	44%
% Actives	70%	90%	15%	40%
Enrichment	1.25	1.23	0.98	1.31
Active Compounds = All 46 Active Compounds				
% Yield	76%	74%	67%	72%
% Actives	54%	70%	13%	28%
Enrichment	0.97	0.95	0.86	0.93

[a] *Enrichment of 1.0 indicates that the model is fitting compounds with the same ratio of active compounds as exist in the original test set. Enrichment values over 1 reveal that the model is identifying a higher percentage of active compounds (model is preferentially identifying active compounds). Enrichment less than 1 implies that model is preferentially fitting non-inhibitors.*

When using the B routine Static Model 2 is comparable to the Dynamic Model in percent yield and enrichment. The excellent enrichment values for both models fitting the very active compounds are particularly notable. However, the Dynamic Model is clearly superior in the number of active compounds that it identifies (% Actives in Table 22.3).

22.4. Conclusion

The dynamic pharmacophore model compares very well with a set of known inhibitors of HIV-1 integrase, particularly those with very low IC_{50} values. Given the excellent performance of the Dynamic Model at fitting almost all of the most inhibitory compounds, we are confident that the compounds it identifies in searches of the ACD will have a much higher success rate than compounds identified with any of the static models. The performance of the Dynamic Model is approximately the same when using "fast" or "best" fitting, with the "best" fitting giving a higher number of compounds and thus a higher percentage of the active compounds. Either method appears to be valid in searching databases for appropriate compounds.

Static Model 2 using the "best" fitting routine gave the only acceptable performance for the static models. The number of fits was much lower for this model, giving a low rate for fitting active compounds and making the dynamic pharmacophore model the more favorable choice. Static Model 2 was developed with the crystal structure solved by Maignan et al.,[6] which closely resembles the MD structures used for the dynamic model.[11]

In closing, it is interesting to note that the Dynamic Model was developed from an incomplete crystal structure. Unresolved regions in crystal structures make computer-assisted drug design particularly difficult. The method of developing dynamic pharmacophore models with MD simulations and homology modeled missing loops appears to be an effective tool—particularly for systems like HIV-1 integrase where incomplete crystal structures were available for several years before complete structures were solved.

Acknowledgements

We would like to thank MSI for their generous donation of the Catalyst software and the ACD database. Furthermore, we are grateful for the structures from the MD simulations provided by Prof. James M. Briggs and his student Roberto D. Lins, who both appear as authors in the original paper presenting the dynamic pharmacophore model.[11] We are also indebted to Prof. William L. Jorgensen for providing the BOSS program with the MUSIC routine, the pepz utility, and the ChemEdit program. HAC is grateful to the American Cancer Society for a postdoctoral fellowship (#PF-4427). She is also thankful for participation in the La Jolla Interfaces in Science Training Program, funded through the generosity of the Burroughs-Wellcome Fund. KMM would like to thank the UCSD Student Affiliate of the American Chemical Society for a summer undergraduate research award. This work is supported by NIH grants GM56553 and GM31749, NSF grant MCB-9722173, and through generous grants of supercomputer time from the National Partnership for Advanced Computational Infrastructure.

References

1. Böhm H-J, Klebe G: **What can we learn from molecular recognition in protein-ligand complexes for the design of new drugs?** *Angew Chem Int Ed Engl* 1996, **35**:2588-2614.

2. Walters WP, Stahl MT, Murcko MA: **Virtual screening—An overview.** *DDT* 1998, **3**:160-178.

3. Eijkelenboom APAM, Puras Lutzhe RA, Boelens R, Plasterk RHA, Kaptein R, Hård K: The **DNA-binding domain of HIV-1 integrase has an SH3-like fold.** *Nature Struct Biol* 1995, **2**:807-810.

4. Cai M, Zheng R, Caffrey M, Craigie R, Clore GM, Gronenborn AM: **Solution structure of the N-terminal zinc binding domain of HIV-1 integrase.** *Nature Struct Biol* 1997, **4**:567-577.

5. Eijkelenboom APAM, van den Ent FMI, Vos A, Doreleijers JF, Hård K, Tullius TD, Plasterk RHA, Kaptein R, Boelens R: **The solution structure**

of the amino-terminal HHCC domain of HIV-2 integrase: A three-helix bundle stabilized by zinc. *Curr Biol* 1997, **7**:739-746.

6. Maignan S, Guilloteau J-P, Zhou-liu Q, Clément-Mella C, Mikol V: **Crystal structures of the catalytic domain of HIV-1 integrase free and complexed with its metal cofactor: High level of similarity of the active site with other viral integrases.** *J Mol Biol* 1998, **282**:359-368.

7. Goldgur Y, Dyda F, Hickman AB, Jenkins TM, Craigie R, Davies DR: **Three new structures of the core domain of HIV-1 integrase: An active site that binds magnesium.** *Proc Natl Acad Sci USA* 1998, **95**:9150-9154.

8. Dyda F, Hickman AB, Jenkins TM, Engelman A, Craigie R, Davies DR: **Crystal structure of the catalytic domain of HIV-1 integrase: Similarity to other polynucleotidyl transferases.** *Science* 1994, **266**:1981-1986.

9. Lins RD, Briggs JM, Straatsma TP, Carlson HA, Greenwald J, Choe S, McCammon JA: **Molecular dynamics studies on the HIV-1 integrase catalytic domain.** *Biophys J* 1999, **76**:2999-3011.

10. Asante-Appiah E, Skalka AM: **Molecular mechanisms in retrovirus DNA integration.** *Antiviral Res* 1997, **36**:139-156.

11. Carlson HA, Masukawa KM, Rubins K, Bushman RD, Jorgensen WL, Lins RD, Briggs JM, McCammon JA: **Developing a Dynamic Pharmacophore Model for HIV-1 Integrase.** *J Med Chem*, in press.

12. Miranker A, Karplus M: **Functionality maps of binding sites: A multiple copy simultaneous search method.** *Proteins* 1991, **11**:29-34.

13. Zheng Q, Kyle DJ: **Computational screening of combinatorial libraries *via* multicopy sampling.** *DDT* 1997, **6**:229-234.

14. Miranker A, Karplus M: **An automated method for dynamic ligand design.** *Proteins* 1995, **23**:472-490.

15. Joseph-McCarthy D, Fedorov AA, Almo SC: **Comparison of experimental and computational functional group mapping of an RNase A structure: Implications for computer-aided drug design.** *Protein Eng* 1996, **9**:773-780.

16. Joseph-McCarthy D, Hogle JM, Karplus M: **Use of the multiple copy simultaneous search (MCSS) method to design a new class of picornavirus capsid binding drugs.** *Proteins* 1997, **29**:32-58.

17. Leclerc F, Karplus M: **MCSS-based predictions of RNA binding sites.** *Theor Chem Acc* 1999, **101**:131-137.

18. Castro A, Richards WG, Lyne PD: **The design of novel acetylcholinesterase inhibitors using the multiple copy simultaneous search method.** *Med Chem Res* 1999, **9**:98-107.

19 Anchell J, Apra E, Bernholdt D, Borowski P, Clark T, Clerc D, Dachsel H, Deegan M, Dupuis M, Dyall KH, Fruchtl GF, Gutowski M, Harrison R, Hess A, Jaffe J, Kendall R, Kobayashi R, Kutteh R, Lin Z, Littlefield R, Long X, Meng B, Nichols J, Nieplocha J, Rendall A, Stave M, Straatsma TP, Taylor H, Thomas G, Wolinski K, Wong A: *NWChem, A computational chemistry package for parallel computers, Version 3.2.* Richland, Washington: High performance Computational Chemistry Group, Pacific Northwest Laboratory, 1998.

20. Cornell WD, Cieplak P, Bayly CI, Gould IR, Merz Jr. KM, Ferguson DM, Spellmeyer DC, Fox T, Caldwell JW, Kollman PA: **A second generation force field for the simulation of proteins, nucleic acids, and organic molecules.** *J Am Chem Soc* 1995, **117**:5179-5197.

21. Berendsen HJC, Grigerra JR, Straatsma TP: **The missing term in effective pair potentials.** *J Phys Chem* 1987, **91**:6269-6271.

22. Briggs JM: Unpublished data.

23. Tirado-Rives J, Jorgensen WL: *pepz.* New Haven, Connecticut: Yale University, 1998.

24. Jorgensen WL: *BOSS, Version 3.8.* New Haven, Connecticut: Yale University, 1996.

25. Jorgensen WL: *MCPRO, Version 1.5.* New Haven, Connecticut: Yale University, 1997.

26. Bujacz G, Jaskólski M, Alexandratos J, Wlodawer A, Merkel G, Katz RA, Skalka AM: **High-resolution structure of the catalytic domain of avian sarcoma virus integrase.** *J Mol Biol* 1995, **253**:333-346.

27. Goodford PJ: **A computational procedure for determining energetically favorable binding sites on biologically important macromolecules.** *J Med Chem* 1985, **28**:849-857.

28. Kuntz ID: **Structure-based strategies for drug design and discovery.** *Science* 1992, **257**:1078-1082.

29. Colman PM: **Structure-based drug design.** *Curr Opin Struct Biol* 1994, **4**:868-874.

30. Blundell TL: **Structure-based drug design.** *Nature* 1996, **Suppl 384**:23-26.

31. Marrone TJ, Briggs JM, McCammon JA: **Structure-based drug design: Computational advances.** *Ann Rev Pharmacol Toxicol* 1997, **37**:71-90.

32. Kaminski G, Duffy EM, Matsui T, Jorgensen WL: **Free energies of hydration and pure liquid properties of hydrocarbons from the OPLS all-atom model.** *J Phys Chem* 1994, **98**:13077-13082.

33. Jorgensen WL, Maxwell DS, Tirado-Rives J: **Development and testing of the OPLS all-atom force field on conformational energetics and properties of organic liquids.** *J Am Chem Soc* 1996, **118**:11225-11236.

34. Zheng Q, Kyle DJ: **Multiple copy sampling: Rigid versus flexible protein.** *Proteins* 1994, **19**:324-329.

35. Totrov M, Abagyan R: **Flexible protein-ligand docking by global energy optimization in internal coordinates.** *Proteins* 1997, **Suppl 1**:215-220.

36. *MidasPlus.* Computer Graphics Lab, University of California, San Francisco.

37. Ferrin TE, Huang CC, Jarvis LE, Langridge R: **The MIDAS display system.** *J Mol Graphics* 1988, **6**:13-27.

38. *Catalyst.* San Diego, California: Molecular Simulations Inc., 1996.

39. Nicklaus MC, Neamati N, Hong H, Mazumder A, Sunder S, Chen J, Milne GWA, Pommier Y: **HIV-1 integrase pharmacophore: Discovery of inhibitors through three-dimensional database searching.** *J Med Chem* 1997, **40**:920-929.

40. Hong H, Neamati N, Wang S, Nicklaus MC, Mazumder A, Zhao H, Burke Jr. TR, Pommier Y, Milne GWA: **Discovery of HIV-1 integrase inhibitors by pharmacophore searching.** *J Med Chem* 1997, **40**:930-936.

41. Neamati N, Hong H, Sunder S, Milne GWA, Pommier Y: **Potent inhibitors of human immunodeficiency virus type 1 integrase: Identification of a novel four-point pharmacophore and tetracyclines as novel inhibitors.** *Mol Pharmacol* 1997, **52**:1041-1055.

42. Neamati N, Sunder S, Pommier Y: **Design and discovery of HIV-1 integrase inhibitors.** *DDT* 1997, **2**:487-498.

43. Farnet CM, Wang B, Lipford JR, Bushman FD: **Differential inhibition of HIV-1 preintegration complexes and purified integrase protein by small molecules.** *Proc Natl Acad Sci USA* 1996, **93**:9742-9747.

44. Farnet CM, Wang B, Hansen M, Lipford JR, Zalkow L, Robinson Jr. WE, Siegel J, Bushman FD: **Human immunodeficiency virus type 1 cDNA integration: New aromatic hydroxylated inhibitors and studies of the inhibition mechanism.** *Antimicrob Agents Chemother* 1998, **42**:2245-2253.

PART IV

New Algorithms in Pharmacophore Development

- **Pharmacophores Derived from the 3D Substructure Perception**

- **The Electron-Conformational Method of Identification of Pharmacophore and Anti-Pharmacophore Shielding**

- **Developnent and Optimization of Property-Based Pharmacophores**

- **Effects of Variable Weights and Tolerances on Predictive Model Generation**

23

Pharmacophores Derived from the 3D Substructure Perception

Sandra Handschuh and Johann Gasteiger

Abstract

Identifying structural similarity is an important task in drug design and pharmaceutical research. Similarity indices are obtained from superimposing images of the three- dimensional structure of a set of molecules. This superimposition and the identification of the maximum common substructure (MCSS) in a set of compounds having the same biological activity is an important step in the identification of their pharmacophore pattern. The method developed for multiple superimposition of flexible three-dimensional structures is based on the combination of a numerical optimization method and a genetic algorithm. A major goal of this hybrid procedure is to adequately address the conformational flexibility of ligand molecules. Thus, only one conformation per structure is necessary, and the program can work even when only one conformation of a compound is stored in a database. The genetic algorithm optimizes in a non-deterministic process the size and the geometric fit of the overlay. The geometric fit of the conformations is further improved by changing torsion angles, combining the genetic algorithm and the directed tweak method.

23

Pharmacophores Derived from the 3D Substructure Perception

Sandra Handschuh and Johann Gasteiger

Universität Erlangen-Nürnberg, Erlangen, Germany

23.1. Introduction

The investigation of a series of ligands binding to the same receptor is usually performed by defining the similarities between the ligands through a pharmacophore pattern. The pharmacophore pattern of a set of ligands can be derived from the largest 3D substructure that these compounds have in common. Initially, the methods developed for searching for the three-dimensional maximum common substructure (MCSS) worked with a single, rigid conformation, not taking into account conformational flexibility of the ligands.[1-3] The first detailed study of distance-based methods for 3D similarity searching was published by Pepperrell and Willett.[4] More recently Sheridan et al.[5] reported on distance-based methods using several conformations per structure. Angle-based and fragment-based methods[6,7] like those of Fisanick et al.[8] were also used to calculate 3D similarities. Wagener et al. developed an approach for MCSS search that is based on atom mappings. The approach was initially developed to be applied to the constitution of a molecule as given by a connection table.[9] However, it was shown that this method can be extended to the 3D structure of a molecule including conformational flexibility of the ligands.[9,10] The 3D substructure search starts with one conformation for each structure and investigates the conformational flexibility during the optimization process. A "query-directed" conformational search technique was implemented[10] by combining evolutionary theories with a numerical optimizer.[11] This hybrid technique of a genetic algorithm and a directed tweak method based on numerical optimization is a flexible search system that accounts for conformational flexibility by rotation around single bonds during the optimization process.

In this approach, the superposition of 3D structures is monitored by matching atoms, and an optimum assignment of the atoms is determined by the algorithm. The 3D structures are obtained by the 3D structure generator CORINA.[12,13] The superimposition algorithm not only optimizes the mutual assignment of the atoms but also automatically identifies rotatable bonds. The conformations of the superimposed molecules are then adapted to each other during the flexible overlay. The assignment of the atoms and the geometric fit of the overlay is first optimized by the genetic algorithm, and then the geometric fit of each obtained solution is improved by the directed tweak method.

This hybrid method has been extended to a method for the superimposition of a set of conformationally flexible molecules, called GAMMA (genetic algorithm for multiple molecule alignment). An approach was chosen that is able to include specific knowledge on the problem. Thus, special features to explore the pharmacophore have been implemented. Physicochemical atom properties, like electronegativity or atomic charges, can be chosen as matching criterion. The default matching criterion is the atomic number. It is possible to preselect atoms that must or should be part of the substructure. Rotatable bonds are automatically recognized or alternatively can be selected by the user, and last but not least entire molecules can be chosen as rigid or flexible.

23.2. General Principles of the Genetic Algorithm

Genetic algorithms (GAs) represent robust optimization methods that are based on the mechanisms of natural selection and genetics.[14-17] They can efficiently solve problems involving large search spaces and thus can even be applied to problems beyond the reach of classical exhaustive search methods.[16,17] A GA imitates nature's methods for adapting to a changing environment. Optimization does not start from a single point, but from a population of starting points that is randomly generated. These starting points correspond to the chromosomes or individuals of a population representing potential solutions to the search problem. The individuals are usually represented by a special coding of the parameters of the function to be optimized, i.e., in the form of a bit string. The genetic operators *selection, mutation,* and *crossover* are iteratively applied to the population. In the method presented here, two additional operators that are tailored to the specific problem are implemented, called *creep* and *crunch* (see section 23.3.3). The course of the program (Figure 23.1) starts with a selection based on the so-called Pareto fitness (see section 23.4). The Pareto fitness is not based on one fitness function but on several parameters that are treated independently of each other. After selection, the genetic operators are applied to the chromosomes and a new population forms the offspring generation. Consequently, one complete GA run begins with initialization of the individuals and ends in obtaining one set of optimized solutions after running through all generations (Figure 23.1).

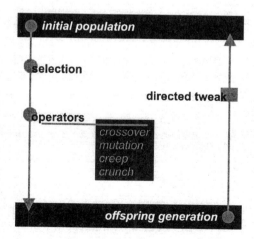

Procedure of one genetic algorithm run

Figure 23.1. The procedure of a complete GA run. The directed tweak mechanism improves on the geometric fit of the individuals.

Genetic operators are not based on a deterministic procedure. Therefore, optimization by a GA does not necessarily arrive at the optimum solution. In order to alleviate this problem, an additional method, the *directed-tweak*[11] procedure, was implemented to match the conformations of the molecules to be overlaid. The geometric fitness of the offspring population is assessed by minimizing differences in the conformations during the *directed-tweak* procedure (Figure 23.1). Usually more than one GA run is performed to arrive at an optimum solution.

23.2.1. Encoding of the Individuals

A major task in adapting a genetic algorithm to a specific problem is the encoding of the individuals of the population, i.e., the representation of the genetic information.[14] We have chosen an approach that represents an individual by a data structure consisting of two independent parts or chromosomes. The first chromosome of the individual consists of an atom mapping which is coded by integers and is represented as a fixed-length linked list of matching atoms (Figure 23.2). The match list defines the number, n, of molecules to be superimposed and the size of the substructure N (number of complete match tupels, Figure 23.2: $N=3$).

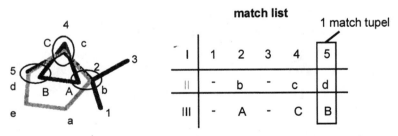

Figure 23.2. The first part of the individual of a multiple superimposition problem: the match list. The number of molecules, n, is 3 and the size of the substructure, N, is 3.

The match lists are fixed-length linked lists comprising all individuals. Each atom may appear only once. The first step is the calculation of all permutation of atom mappings. The maximum number of possibilities is $N_x N_y N_z$, where N_x is the number of atoms in molecule x.

In building these match tupels, matching criteria such as atom types, or an interval for a given physicochemical property (e.g., partial atomic charge) are taken into account (see also later in section 23.4).

The individuals are built by randomly selecting match tupels from the initialized complete set of match tupels. The number of individuals is defined by the size, i, of the population. If an atom is doubly referenced, i.e. an atom appears twice in the match list, after random combination of match tupels, this atom is changed into an atom not yet part of the list or, alternatively, into a zero mapping. Zero mappings are marked by a dash in Figure 23.2.

The second chromosome of the data structure is a list of bit strings representing possible torsional angles of the flexible molecules (Figure 23.3). Each bond that is at both ends connected to at least one multi-atom substituent, but is not a ring bond (e.g., a methyl group), is defined as rotatable. Each possible change of a torsional angle is binary coded in 8-bit. All torsional angles are concatenated to one bit strings. Thus, each bit string of torsional angles has the length of $8n_{tor}$, with n_{tor} being the number of torsional angles in all molecules (in Figure 23.3, $n_{tor} = 1$).

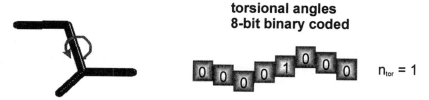

torsional angles
8-bit binary coded

$n_{tor} = 1$

Figure 23.3. Second part of an individual: the torsion angles.

Both chromosomes, the match list, and the bit string of angles represent together one individual. Several individuals build the population of one generation.

23.2.2. Optimization Criteria

The search for the MCSS of a set of molecules takes into account two optimization criteria: The size of the substructure, as given by the number, N, of match tupels (Figure 23.2), and the geometric fit of the matching atoms. The geometric fit is represented by a distance parameter, D (Figure 23.4). The distance parameter, D, consists of the sum of the squared differences of corresponding atom distances in the molecules.

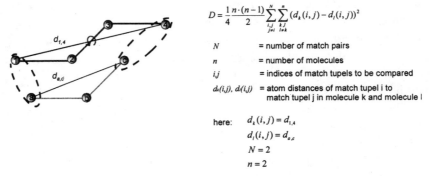

$$D = \frac{1}{4} \frac{n \cdot (n-1)}{2} \sum_{\substack{i,j \\ j \neq i}}^{N} \sum_{\substack{k,j \\ l \neq k}}^{n} (d_k(i,j) - d_l(i,j))^2$$

N	= number of match pairs
n	= number of molecules
i,j	= indices of match tupels to be compared
$d_k(i,j), d_l(i,j)$	= atom distances of match tupel i to match tupel j in molecule k and molecule l

here: $d_k(i,j) = d_{1,4}$
$d_l(i,j) = d_{a,c}$
$N = 2$
$n = 2$

Figure 23.4. The two optimization criteria: size N of the substructure and the distance parameter D.

D is related to the **root mean square** (*rms*) error of the distances of corresponding atoms in an optimized superimposition.

The *rms* value, however, is subject to large changes even if the mapping changes only slightly. Therefore, the distance value, D, is better adapted to the specific use during a GA optimization than the *rms* value. The *rms* value of the obtained superimposition is calculated only once at the end of each GA run in order to show the results.

23.2.3. The Genetic and Nongenetic Operators—A Short Description

23.2.3.1. Mutation

The genetic operators change the two chromosomes of the individuals, the match list and the coding of the changes of the torsional angles, in a different manner.

The mutation operator on the match lists randomly changes atom tupels (Figure 23.5). To mutate the match list of a superimposition of n molecules, n-1 mutation points are selected at random (Figure 23.5). The atoms of all molecules except those of the first (largest) molecule in the match list can be mutated. The corresponding atom of a match tupel (for the first mutation, an atom of the second molecule; for the second mutation an atom of the third molecule. . .) is mutated by obeying the following boundary condition: None of the atoms is allowed to appear more than once and the matching criterion has to be taken into account. Hence, the considered atom has to be changed into one that is not yet in the match list. If all atoms of a molecule are already referenced, the atom is changed into a zero mapping (section 23.2.1). Zero mappings can also be introduced randomly (see 1. mutation in Figure 23.5: The match tupel 1,a,-is mutated to 1,-,-).

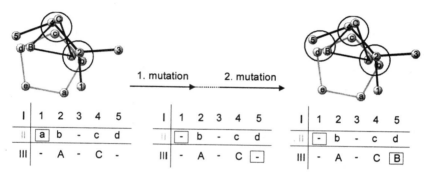

Figure 23.5. The mechanism of the multiple mutation operator for the match lists. If a superimposition contains n (=3) molecules, n-1 (=2) mutations are performed. For each mutation, an atom of a match tupel is selected and changed (marked here by a rectangle).

Mutation in the chromosome representing the torsion angles inverts one bit of a binary coded torsion angle string (1 into 0 and *vice versa*). As mentioned in section 23.2.1, each chromosome of the torsional angles is a bit string of length $8n_{tor}$ (n_{tor} = number of rotatable bonds in all molecules). One mutation is performed for every angle. The first mutation point is selected randomly and each additional point has an 8-bit distance to the first one. Thus, an equal distribution of the mutations on the torsional angles is guaranteed.

23.2.3.2. Crossover

The crossover operator exchanges random parts of two individuals, i.e., partial substructures, and combines partial solutions of the MCSS search problem in a new, and potentially better, way. Two points are randomly chosen in the match lists of the two parental individuals (Figure 23.6).[18] The information string that is to be crossed is contained in between these two points. Each partial list has to be of equal length and is copied to the tail of the other parental individual. In this first step, double references may be introduced that later have to be deleted: If an atom of molecule I appears twice in the match list, the corresponding original match pair has to be replaced by the new one that was copied to the tail (e.g., in Figure 23.6 match tupel 4,e,- replaces 4,-,- and 3,c,A replaces 3,a,C). Any double references remaining after this process in molecules II and III are replaced by randomly chosen ones conforming to the constraints (the matching criteria). If there are no more atoms that obey these restrictions, a zero mapping has to be introduced. This procedure ensures that the match lists always have the same length and that each atom is referenced only once.

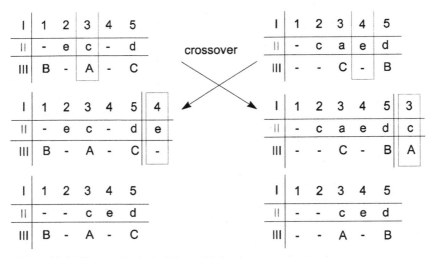

Figure 23.6. The mechanism of the multiple crossover operator.

The crossover operator working on the representation of the torsion angles is a one-point crossover. One point has to be chosen randomly at the same position in both parental strings. Crossover exchanges two parts of the two chosen parental strings of torsion angles. This leads to new conformations for which the geometric fit has to be assessed.

23.2.3.3. Two Non-Genetic Operators: Creep and Crunch

Two additional operators were developed to improve the efficiency of the GA: The *creep* and the *crunch* operator. These operators do not act stochastically like the genetic operators crossover and mutation but make use of knowledge specific to the problem to be solved.[19] Hence, they are called "knowledge-augmented operators".[14]

The *creep* operator increases the size of the substructure by adding a matching tupel of atoms to the match list while obeying restrictions imposed by the spatial arrangement of the atoms (Figure 23.7). The new matching atom tupel must not cause a large increase in the *rms* value of the original match. In this way, the creep operator leads to a "hill climbing" mechanism in the GA.

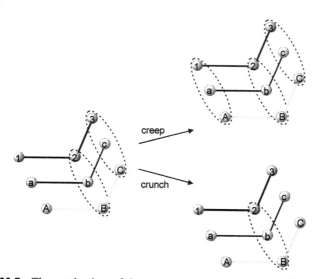

Figure 23.7. The mechanism of the creep and crunch operators. The creep operator leads to a larger substructure, whereas the crunch operators produces in a smaller substructure.

The *crunch* operator (Figure 23.7) acts as an antagonist to the creep operator in reducing the size of the substructure. The goal of the crunch operator is to eliminate match pairs which are responsible for bad geometric distance parameters. This operation should help the search to avoid becoming trapped in local minima during the optimization process.

23.2.4. The Pareto Fitness of Individuals

The MCSS search is a multicriteria optimization problem, where the notion of optimality is difficult to define. Two main parameters contribute to the fitness of a superimposition and have to be optimized: the size of the substructure and its geometric fit. These criteria are contradictory: The substructure size has to be as large as possible whereas the deviation in the positions of the superimposed atoms should be as low as possible. An optimum must be found which takes into account both criteria. Vilfredo Pareto developed a concept for solving multicriteria optimization.[14,15] Pareto optimization means that an optimized state is reached if none of the parameters can be improved further without making another one worse.

Pareto optimality applied to the MCSS search problem in a three-dimensional space results in simultaneously maximizing the size of the substructure and optimizing the geometric fit. This does not result in obtaining only one probably perfect substructure; instead, an optimal geometric fit is produced for each possible size of the common substructure.

The application of Pareto optimization to the superimposition of vinylcyclobutane and propylcyclobutane is shown in Figure 23.8. The atoms marked in grey are those of the common substructure. The result of a Pareto optimization is a set of common substructures for which the geometric deviation cannot be further minimized. Four different superimpositions are shown in Figure 23.8, three of them corresponding to Pareto optimality. Superimposition I dominates superimposition IV (Figure 23.8). In this sense, superimposition I represents a Pareto optimal solution because no other substructure can be found which has a better geometric correspondence. Superimpositions II and III are also members of the Pareto set and no other superimpositions having the same sizes and better geometric fits can be found. Taken together, superimpositions I, II, and III represent the set of equivalent Pareto solutions and none dominates the other.

For each specific superimposition a Pareto diagram can be calculated. It presents the development of the *rms* error with the size, N, of the substructure during the GA optimization runs. Figure 23.9 shows the Pareto diagram for the superimposition of two angiotensin antagonists[20] (Figure 23.10). Fourty GA optimization runs were performed. The superimposition with a substructure size of 18 and an *rms* error of 0.15 Å appears to be the best one. The corresponding point in the Pareto diagram is indicated by a circle.

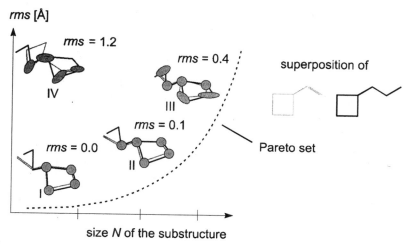

Figure 23.8. The Pareto set of a superimposition of vinylcyclobutane and *n*-propylcyclobutane.

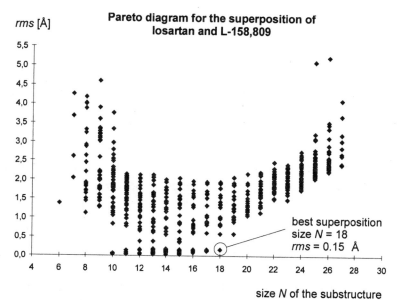

Figure 23.9. The Pareto diagram of the superimposition of losartan and L-158,809 (see Figure 23.10) in 40 GA runs. Each run results in one Pareto set: one best solution for each substructure size.

The best superimposition of losartan and L-158,809 extracted from the Pareto diagram is presented in Figure 23.10.

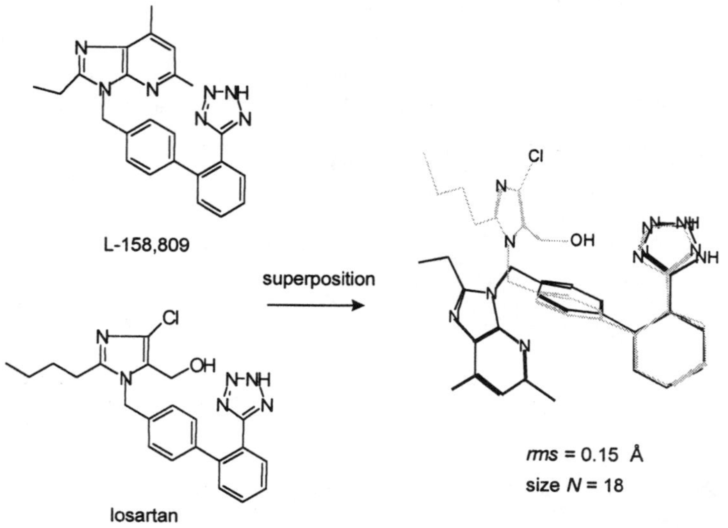

Figure 23.10. The best superimposition of losartan and L-158,809 extracted from 40 GA runs.

As an example for multiple superimposition, the alignment of three cytochrome P450c17 inhibitors[21] is chosen (Plate 23.1).

The *rms* value in the Pareto diagram increases with the substructure size of the alignment of three cytochrome P450c17 inhibitors. A substructure size of 10 with an *rms* value of 0.46 Å was extracted as the best superimposition. Substructure sizes higher than 10 atoms show strongly increasing *rms* values. The MCSS of a set of molecules which bind to the same receptor points out pharmacophore features that are predominantly responsible for the corresponding receptor affinity.

23.3. Matching the Conformations—Directed Tweak

The directed tweak method reported by T. Hurst[11] was implemented in our procedure based on a Davidon-Fletcher-Powell[22] optimizer. The objective was to combine non-deterministic genetic mechanisms with a numerical optimizer in order to improve potential solutions. After each generation, the fitness of each individual is determined in order to evaluate the winner of the restricted tournament selection for the next generation. Before determination of the fitness, the geometric fit of each individual or superimposition is improved by mapping torsional angles by the directed tweak method. The selection of the new individual is then based on these new values. However, the next generation consists of the original individuals before applying the directed tweak to avoid loss of genetic information or premature convergence.

The technique makes use of the Davidon-Fletcher-Powell optimizer to minimize differences in the conformations (Figure 23.11). The squared differences of the distances of corresponding atom pairs (i.e., 1,4 and a, c in Figure 23.11) are used to minimize the differences in the geometry of the superimposed structures by changing torsion angles. The obtained superimpositions are not limited to low-energy conformations. This allows one to find conformations of ligands that correspond to those found in the binding of a ligand to a receptor but do not correspond to low-energy conformations in the free state. However, an energy penalty value is added to the distance parameter, D, if a close contact of nonbinding atoms is be found in a conformation (see section 23.4).

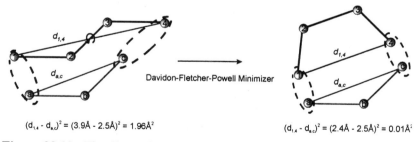

$$(d_{1,4} - d_{a,c})^2 = (3.9\text{Å} - 2.5\text{Å})^2 = 1.96\text{Å}^2 \qquad (d_{1,4} - d_{a,c})^2 = (2.4\text{Å} - 2.5\text{Å})^2 = 0.01\text{Å}^2$$

Figure 23.11. The directed tweak method is used to minimize differences in the conformations of the two structures to be superimposed.

The superimposition of methylcyclohexane and *n*-butylcyclopropane (Figure 23.12) shows the adaptation of the conformations of two molecules during the optimization process. The dihedral angle c-d-e-f of n-butylcyclopropane fits onto the rigid cyclohexane conformation after rotation around the bond d-e.

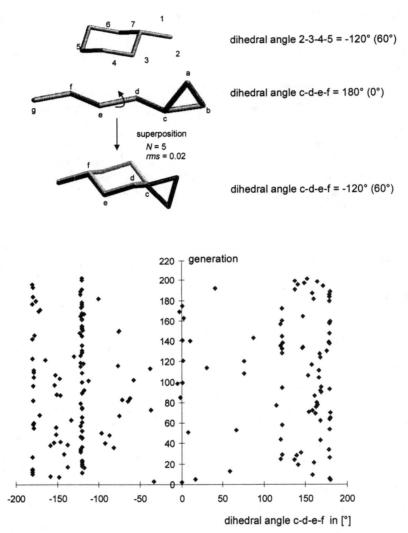

Figure 23.12. Adaptation of the conformations of methylcyclohexane and *n*-butyl-cyclopropane.

The optimization process covers the entire conformational space of bond d-e during the generations. Figure 23.11 shows the distribution of the dihedral angle c-d-e-f of n-butylcyclopropane during one run of the genetic algorithm. The optimization culminates most often in the angle of -120° (or 180°-120° = 60°) which corresponds to the conformation of cyclohexane (dihedral angle 2-3-4-5).

23.4. Special Features of the Program

23.4.1. Close Contact Check of van der Waals Radii

The algorithm treats atoms as or points: They have no spatial expansion. To prevent conformations from having an overlap of van der Waals radii, the distances of non-bonded atoms are calculated and compared with the sum of the corresponding van der Waals radii (Figure 23.13).

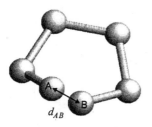

$$min_{AB} = 0.75 \cdot (vdW(A) + vdW(B))$$

$$fac = \frac{d_{AB}}{min_{AB}}$$

if

fac < 0.5 : close contact

fac > 0.5 : no close contact

Figure 23.13. Close contact check of the van der Waals radii.

The van der Waals radii close contact check was implemented as a penalty factor to the geometric fitness parameter D. If a close contact is found, the distance parameter D is multiplied by a corresponding penalty factor. Consequently, the individual representing an unfavorable conformation obtains a high D parameter (bad geometric fitness) and will never dominate in a Pareto tournament.

23.4.2. Matching Criteria

Many surface properties, e.g., hydrogen-bonding potential, electrostatic potential, or hydrophobicity, are responsible for high receptor binding affinities. These binding properties are mainly based on dipole-dipole interactions and are related to various electronic effects. Thus criteria other than the atomic number, such as physicochemical properties of atoms, ranges of partial atomic charges (sigma, q_σ, pi, q_π, or total q_{tot}), electronegativity, χ, or polarizability, α, can be chosen as restrictions for superimposition. Other atom properties, such as distinguishing between aromatic and non-aromatic ring atoms, or ring and non-ring atoms, can also be selected as mapping conditions. These physicochemical parameters are calculated by the program package PETRA.[23,24] The atoms to be overlaid must conform to the given matching criterion or interval of the physicochemical property. For example, if the matching criterion interval is chosen to be $q_{tot} = \pm 0.05e$ and q_{tot} of an atom of the first molecule is -0.2e, only atoms in the interval of q_{tot} = [-0.25, -0.15] are allowed to build match tupels with the first atom.

As an example, the superimposition of iproniazid (a monoaminooxidase inhibitor) and disulfiram (aldehyde dehydrogenase inhibitor)[25] has been investigated. Figure 23.14 shows the different superimposition results that are obtained by choosing different matching criteria. In the upper part, the two chemical structures are shown with the calculated q_{tot} values of all nonhydrogen atoms.[24] In the first case, the atoms are required to have the same atomic numbers (first superimposition in Figure 23.14). In the second case, the partial charges of the atoms are required to differ only by 0.25 electron units; that is, $q_{tot}(i) = q_{tot}(j) \pm 0.25$ (second superimposition in Figure 23.14).

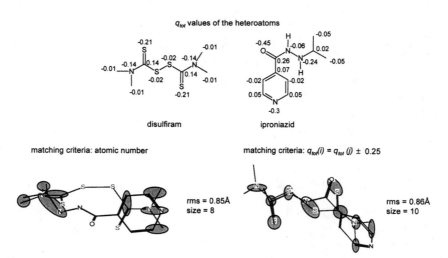

Figure 23.14. Different substructures with different matching criteria.

The MCSS of both superimpositions are marked by grey circles. In the first alignment, the aliphatic C-S-S-C substructure of disulfiram is not part of the MCSS, because there is no equivalent matching partner (sulfur atom) in the iproniazid structure. However, both sulfur atoms (q_{tot} = -0.02) have physicochemical properties that are similar to those of the nitrogen atoms (q_{tot} = -0.06 and -0.24) of iproniazid and are part of the MCSS in the second superimposition. In addition, the carbonyl group (q_{tot}: C: 0.26, O: -0.45) and the thiocarbonyl group (q_{tot}: C: 0.14, S: -0.21) are only matched in the second superimposition.

23.4.3. Superimposition Restrictions

Problems may occur when matching molecules of quite different sizes. As an example, the superimposition of angiotensin II and the angiotensin II antagonist losartan[20] is shown in Figure 23.15. The upper superimposition is performed without any alignment restrictions. It is the best superimposition extracted from the Pareto diagram. The *rms* value increases rapidly for substructure sizes larger than 16 atoms. The structure of losartan is matched into the middle part of the peptide angiotensin II. However, the C-terminus is mainly responsible for affinity to the angiotensin II receptor.[20] Thus, in a second superimposition (lower part of Figure 23.15) the C-terminus was selected for mapping onto the antagonist's structure. Again, the superimposition has been extracted from the Pareto set as best one. Thus, GAMMA can be used to explore different pharmacophore hypotheses.

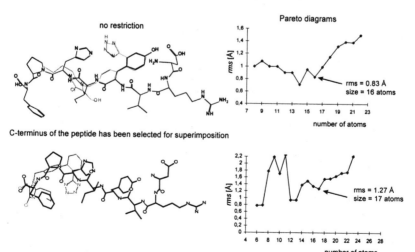

Figure 23.15. Two superimpostions of angiotensin II and losartan. The first superimposition was obtained without any superimposition restrictions, the second one by selecting the C-terminus of the peptide structure to be part of the match list. (Angiotensin was considered as rigid; losartan was considered as flexible.)

In another example, the superimpositions of two P450c17 (human) inhibitors (Plate 23.2) were investigated. In the first superimposition without any constraints, the A,B,C-rings of both structures and the hydroxyl group at the A-ring fit well onto each other, but the distances of the nitrogens are rather high. Inside the receptor binding pocket the nitrogen of the ligand is connected to the iron center of the P450 protein. The nitrogen, therefore, is a key element in substructure searching. In addition, the hydroxyl group at the A-ring is also responsible for receptor binding by generating a hydrogen bond to the receptor pocket.[21,26] Consequently, in a second superimposition it was required that the hydroxyl group and the nitrogen atoms have to be part of the match list and the mapping of the remaining structural parts is to be investigated (Plate 23.2, right-hand superposition.)

23.5. Summary

The program GAMMA (genetic algorithm for multiple molecule alignment) described here overlays and aligns several structures independent of the initially chosen conformation. An unlimited number of structures can be treated. Only one conformation per structure is necessary and thus the program can work even when only one conformation of a compound is stored in a database. The automatic finding of structural similarities has its particular efficiency in a hybrid method, the combination of a genetic algorithm and a numerical optimization method—the directed-tweak method. The genetic algorithm process leads to an optimization of atom assignment in the form of match lists. An optimization of the geometric fit by adapting the conformations of molecules to each other is obtained by the combination of the genetic algorithm with the directed-tweak technique. The genetic algorithm is further improved by two additional operators which are tailored to the superposition problem: the creep and crunch operators. The problems studied here have to optimize several conflicting criteria. Therefore, a set of so-called Pareto solutions is always obtained at the end of each GA run. During optimization of the superposition, the conformations of the structures are adapted to each other.

The program allows one to choose a template structure as rigid and then adapts the conformation of the other molecules onto this template. Rotatable bonds are found automatically or can be selected by the user itself. Special features like selecting an atom list that should be part of the match list or defining different matching criteria allow the user to include specific knowledge to the pharmacophore search problem. The calculated MCSS of a set of three-dimensional structures having the same biological activity can indicate certain pharmacophore points.

Acknowledgements

We thank the BMBF and the Merck KGaA for financial support of our research and the "Fonds der Chemischen Industrie" for a scholarship to Sandra Handschuh. We acknowledge the contributions of Dr. Markus Wagener in the development of this approach.

References

1. Sheridan RP, Nilakantan R, Rusinko III A, Baumann N, Haraki KS, Venkataraghavan R: **3DSEARCH: A System for three-dimensional substructure searching.** *J Chem Inf Comput Sci* 1989, **29**:255-260.

2. Greene J, Kahn SD, Savoi H, Sprague P, Teig S: **Chemical function queries for 3D-database search.** *J Chem Inf Comput Sci* 1994, **34**:1297-1308.

3. (a) Martin YC, Danaher EB, May CS, Weininger D: **MENTHOR, a database system for the storage and retrieval of three-dimensional molecular structures and associated data searchable by substructural, biological, physical, or geometric properties.** *J Comput-Aided Mol Des* 1988, 2:15-29; (b) Van Drie JH, Weininger D, Martin YC: **ALADDIN: An integrated tool for computer-assisted molecular design and pharmacophoric pattern recognition from geometric, steric and substructure searching of three-dimensional molecular structures.** *J Comput-Aided Mol Des* 1989, **3**:225-251.

4. Pepperrell CA, Willett P: **Techniques for the calculation of three-dimensional structural similarity using inter-atomic distances.** *J Comput-Aided Mol Des* 1991, **5**:455-474.

5. Sheridan RP, Miller MD, Underwood DJ, Kearsley SK: **Chemical Similarity Using Geometric Atom Pair Descriptors.** *J Chem Inf Comput Sci* 1996, **36**:128-136.

6. Bath PA, Poirrette AR, Willett P, Allen FH: **Similarity searching in files of three-dimensional chemical structures: Comparison of fragment-based measures of shape similarity.** *J Chem.Inf Comput Sci* 1994, **34**:141-147.

7. Lauri G, Bartlett PA: **CAVEAT: A program to facilitate the design of organic molecules.** *J Comput-Aided Mol Des* 1994, **8**:51-66.

8. Fisanick W, Cross KP, Rusinko III A: **Similarity searching on CAS registry substances. 1. Global molecular property and generic atom triangle geometric searching.** *Chem Inf Comput Sci* 1992, **32**:664-674.

9. Wagener M, Gasteiger J: **The determination of maximum common substructures by a genetic algorithm: Application in synthesis design and for the structural analysis of biological activity.** *Angew Chem* 1994, **106**:1245-1248; *Angew Chem Int Ed Engl* 1994, **33**:1189-1192.

10. Handschuh S, Wagener M, Gasteiger J: **Superposition of three-dimensional chemical structures allowing for conformational flexibility by a hybrid method.** *J Chem Inf Comput Sci* 1998, **38**:220-232.

11. Hurst T: **Flexible 3D searching: The directed tweak technique.** *J Chem Inf Comput Sci* 1994, **34**:190-196.

12. (a) Sadowski J, Gasteiger J: **From atoms and bonds to three-dimensional atomic coordinates: automatic model builders.** *Chem Reviews* 1993, **93**:2567-2581; (b) Sadowski J, Gasteiger J, Klebe G: **Comparison of automatic three-dimensional model builders using 639 X-ray structures.** *J Chem Inf Comput Sci* 1994, **34**:1000-1008.

13. *CORINA* can be accessed via the internet: http://www.2.ccc.uni-erlangen.de/software/corina/index.html or ordered from Molecular Network GmbH (info@mol-net.de.

14. Goldberg DE: *Genetic Algorithms in Search Optimization and Machine Learning.* New York: Addison-Wesley Publishing Company, 1989.

15. Fonseca CM, Fleming PJ: **Genetic algorithm for multiobjective optimization: Formulation, discussion and generalization.** In: *Proceedings of the 5th International Conference on Genetic Algorithms.* Forrest S, ed. San Mateo, CA: Morgan Kaufmann Publishers, Inc., 1993:416-423.

16. Jones G: **Genetic and evolutionary algorithms.** In: *Encyclopedia of Computational Chemistry.* Schleyer P.v.R, Allinger NL, Clark T, Gasteiger J, Kollman PA, Schaefer III HF, Schreiner PR, eds. Chichester, UK: John Wiley & Sons, Inc., 1998:1127-1136.

17. Venkatasubramanian V, Sundaram A: **Genetic algorithms: Introduction and applications.** In: *Encyclopedia of Computational Chemistry.* Schleyer P.v.R, Allinger NL, Clark T, Gasteiger J, Kollman PA, Schaefer III HF, Schreiner PR, eds. Chichester, UK: John Wiley & Sons, 1998:1115-1127.

18. Oliver IM, Smith DJ, Holland JRC: **A study of permutation crossover operators on the travelling salesman problem. Genetic algorithms and their applications.** In: *Proceedings of the 2nd International Conference on Genetic Algorithms.* Grefenstette JJ, ed. Hillsdale, NJ: Lawrence Erlbaum Associates, 1987:224-230.

19. Davis L: **Adapting operator probabilities in genetic algorithms.** In: *Proceedings of the 3rd International Conference on Genetic Algorithms.* Schaffer D, ed. San Mateo, CA: Morgan Kaufmann Publishers,1989:61-69.

20. Wexler RR, Greenlee WJ, Irvin JD, Goldberg MR, Prendergast K, Smith RD, Timmermans PBMWM: **Nonpeptide angiotensin II receptor antagonists: The next generation in antihypertensive therapy.** *J Med Chem* 1996, **39**:625-656.

21. Wachall B, Hartmann RW. University of the Saarland, 1998, personal communication.

22. Press HW, Teukolsky SA, Vetterling WT, Flannery BP: *Numerical Recipes in C.* Cambridge: Cambridge University Press, 1997.

23. Gasteiger J: **Emprical methods for the calculation of physicochemical data of organic compounds.** In: *Physical Property Prediction in Organic Chemistry.* Jochum C, Hicks MG, Sunkel J, eds. Heidelberg: Springer Verlag, 1988:119-138.

24. http://www.2.ccc.uni-erlangen.de/software/petra/index.html.

25. Böhm HJ, Klebe G, Kubinyi H: *Wirkstoffdesign.* Heidelberg: Spektrum Akademischer Verlag, 1996.

26. Van den Bosche H: **Inhibitors of P450 dependent steroid biosyntheses: From research to medical treatment.** *J Steroid Biochem Molec Biol* 1992, **43**:1003-1021.

24

The Electron-Conformational Method of Identification of Pharmacophore and Anti-Pharmacophore Shielding

Isaac B. Bersuker, Süleyman Bahçeci, and James E. Boggs

Abstract

We present here the main features of an improved version of our electron-conformational (EC) method of pharmacophore identification and bioactivity prediction. For a set of molecules with known activity (the training set), the heavily populated conformations are identified. For each of them, the electronic structure is calculated and the electronic and geometry parameters are arranged in a special matrix. By processing these matrices in comparison with activities, a smaller number of matrix elements are revealed that are present in all the active molecules (conformations), but not present in the same combination in the inactive compounds. This submatrix of activity represents the pharmacophore. A major improvement of this approach was achieved by introducing the anti-pharmacophore shielding (APS) and other auxiliary groups (AG) which, being outside the pharmacophore, significantly influence the magnitude of activity by either hindering the proper docking of pharmacophore with the bioreceptor or enhancing the hydrophobicity. A formula has been derived which estimates the activity as a function of the APS and AG parameters, and a package of programs has been worked out that realizes this approach. The method is illustrated by its application to two problems: angiotensin-converting enzyme (ACE) inhibitors and rice blast activity. The qualitative (yes or no) prediction of the activity is very high, about 100% (within experimental error), while quantitatively the prediction is by orders of magnitude only.

24

The Electron-Conformational Method of Identification of Pharmacophore and Anti-Pharmacophore Shielding

Isaac B. Bersuker, Süleyman Bahçeci, and James E. Boggs

The University of Texas at Austin, Austin, Texas

24.1. Introduction: Improved Definition of Pharmacophore

The concept of a pharmacophore has proved to be very useful in drug design and toxicology, as well as in other structure-property relationships (see, for example, references[1-7] and references therein). Assuming that for the bioactivity under consideration there is only one (unique) pharmacophore, it can be defined as a group of specific atoms in a given geometric arrangement which represent the bioactivity under consideration in a series of compounds. To identify the pharmacophore means to be able to predict the presence or absence of the bioactivity. In this form the pharmacophore is a tool for qualitative (yes or no) prediction of the activity without any quantitative indication of the activity.

However, a purely qualitative measure of activity may be insufficient for practical use. For instance, if the pharmacophore is present but the activity is small, the compound will be classified experimentally as inactive. The heuristic value of the pharmacophore concept would increase significantly if complemented with a *quantitative* measure of predicting the activity, at least by orders of magnitude.

In the electron-conformational (EC) method of pharmacophore identification[8-14] the molecular system is described by means of a matrix in which the matrix elements are parameters of its electronic structure and geometry; the pharmacophore is identified by a small number of these matrix elements that are approximately the same for all the active compounds of the chosen training set, but are not present in the same combination in the inactive compounds (see below). The absolute values of the matrix elements that represent the pharmacophore may vary from one compound to another within some limits (tolerances), and these variations may be assumed to contribute to the changing values of activity.

Based on the experience accumulated with the EC method, we are able to extend and improve the idea of pharmacophore by introducing the following three important specifications:

(1) The pharmacophore should be defined not just by atoms from the periodic table, but by appropriate atom-in-molecule electronic characteristics which may be the same for different atoms but different for the same atoms in different compounds;

(2) Both the electronic characteristics and geometry parameters vary from one active compound to another within certain limits (tolerances), and the activity may be a function of these variations;

(3) The pharmacophore is a necessary but not sufficient condition of activity. In the presence of pharmacophore the activity of the molecule may be reduced (down to zero) by anti-pharmacophore shielding (APS) groups that hinder its proper docking with the bioreceptor, or enhanced by other auxiliary groups (AG) that provide for other properties (e.g., hydrophobicity).

The influence of APS and AG can be parameterized to approximately take into account their role in the activity. Similar to pharmacophore, this parameterization is based on describing AG and APS groups by the same (in principle) electronic and geometry parameters known from the ECMC. Then by processing these parameters for the training set in comparison with the activities and performing a least-square minimization procedure, described below, we get the constants that represent the weight of each of these parameters in the activity. Adding also the Boltzmann population of each conformation as a function of its energy and temperature, we obtain a formula of quantitative prediction of the bioactivity.

Thus the EC method, by complementing the pharmacophore with parameterized APS and AG, elevates the concept of pharmacophore to a higher level from a qualitative to a quantitative tool of bioactivity prediction. In this chapter we describe briefly this EC method of pharmacophore identification and quantitative (more precisely, semiquantitative) bioactivity prediction and demonstrate how it works in solving the problems for angiotensin converting enzyme (ACE) inhibitors and rice blast activity (RBA).

24.2. Description by EC Matrices and Pharmacophore Identification

Assume that we have a training set of molecular systems that have been tested for the activity under consideration and we know their activity quantitatively (the training set should include inactive compounds). By performing a molecular mechanics (MM) conformational analysis on each of these systems, we determine their heavily populated (at room temperature) conformations and their energies (in principle, these data can be retrieved from a database). Heavily populated means those with energies ≤ 1-1.5 kcal/mol above the ground state conformation. Then we calculate the electronic structure of each of these conformations and arrange the corresponding electronic and geometry parameters in a matrix $s \times s$ (s is the number of atoms), called the EC matrix of congruity (ECMC) (Figure 24.1). The ECMC is symmetric, so only its upper part with $s(s + 1)/2$ matrix elements is employed.

The diagonal elements of the ECMC a_{ii} are electronic characteristics of the atoms. In the earlier and some recent versions of this method, the a_{ii} values are taken as atomic charges. The results obtained in this way show that, in general, this is not a bad choice. In many ways atomic charges are similar to electrostatic fields. However, neither charges nor electrostatic fields take into account the orbital-controlled part of the interaction of the drug with the bioreceptor which may be most important in donor-acceptor interactions and hydrogen bond formation.

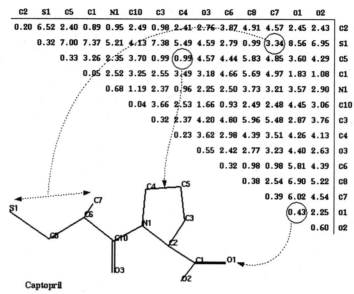

Figure 24.1. The general appearance of the electron-conformational matrix of congruity (ECMC) illustrated, by way of example, for the compound M21 (Captopril) in the ACE inhibitors problem. Reprinted with permission from[14]. © 1999 American Chemical Society.

We now introduce an atomic index of charge-and-orbital-controlled interaction (ICOCI) with the target atom, or more simply, Interaction Index (II)[15] instead of charges. The II of a given atom in a given molecular environment is defined as the *maximum* energy of interaction with a target atom that can be exerted by this atom in the molecule. With this definition the well-known Klopman-Fukui perturbation theory formulas for intermolecular (interatomic) interactions[16] can be simplified and then conveniently normalized. The final formula of II for atom A is:[15]

$$II(A) = g^A \exp(-2\sqrt{2E_A}) \qquad (24.1)$$

where g^A is the occupation number of the outermost atomic orbital in the HOMO of the molecule and E_A is the energy of ionization of the valence state of this atomic orbital, which is a function of the charge and configuration of the atom in the molecule. In fact, the right-hand side of Equation 24.1 represents the slightly modified exponential of the outermost decreasing part of the wavefunction (density) of the atom A in the molecule. Both the g^A and E_A values are available from the electronic structure data.

The off-diagonal elements a_{ij} are of two kinds. For direct chemically bonded pairs i and j, $a_{ij}{}^*$ is one of the parameters of the bond: bond order, Wiberg index, polarizability, etc. So far only bond orders and Wiberg indices have been employed. For all other pairs of directly non-bonded atoms, $a_{ij}=R_{ij}$ is their interatomic distance. In this way ECMC contains a rather full presentation of both the geometry (interatomic distances) and electronic properties (*II* and bond orders).

The next step is to process the ECMC by means of a special program of matrix comparisons in order to reveal the EC submatrix of activity (ECSA), namely those matrix elements (geometry and electronic parameters) that, within a chosen tolerance, are the same for all the active compounds and that are not present in the same combination in the inactive compounds. The ECSA (its geometry and electronic characteristics) represents the pharmacophore.

This procedure for pharmacophore identification is delicate and not straightforward. Practically, we first choose the structurally simplest compounds of the training set that have the smallest number of conformations for pharmacophore identification. Since the Pharmacophore should be the same in all compounds, the one obtained from the simplest structures may serve as a first approximation to the exact pharmacophore. If some of the compounds involved in this procedure have more than one conformation (with sufficiently low energy), the comparisons of the ECMC should be carried out for each combination that includes one conformation from each molecular systems. With multiple comparisons, inactive conformations can be abandoned.

However, the pharmacophore obtained from a limited (small) number of the simplest structures may contain extra atoms that are not needed in the pharmacophore of the activity under consideration and hence are not necessarily present in other active compounds. Moreover, there is no way to get sufficiently accurate tolerances for the pharmacophore parameters without comparison with the other compounds of the training set, especially with the inactive compounds. The procedure is to check for the presence of the ECSA, obtained from the simplest compounds, in the ECMC of each of the remaining compounds of the training set (in each of its heavily populated conformations) and to reveal a new common ECSA that includes all the active compounds (conformations). The number of matrix elements in the improved ECSA may be smaller than that obtained in the first approximation, and the comparison with the inactive compounds will further limit the tolerances.

One of the important features of the pharmacophore revealed in this way is that, as mentioned above, not just atoms of the periodic table represent the pharmacophore, but a specific arrangement of atomic *II* (or charges in the simpler versions) which *may be the same for different atoms and different for the same atoms.* There are many accumulated examples showing that the activities indeed are represented by electronic properties, not atoms, and different atoms in different molecular environment may produce the same activity.[8-14]

Another important feature of the EC method is that *it incorporates chirality influence on the activity*: Although the values of single matrix elements (*II*, bond orders and distances) are the same in two enantiomers, their arrangement in the ECMC is different provided the chosen order of atom numeration (e.g., "clockwise" or "counterclockwise" with respect to the pharmacophore plane) is kept the same in all compounds (see below).

24.3. Anti-Pharmacophore Shielding and Other Auxiliary Groups. Formula of Activity

As mentioned in the introduction, the knowledge of just the pharmacophore, even though it is a very important indication of activity, may not be sufficient for practical prediction of activity. In particular, the concept of pharmacophore, as defined above, does not explain why different compounds with the same pharmacophore have quite different activities. The situation clarifies significantly with the introduction of anti-pharmacophore shielding (APS) and other auxiliary groups (AG).

The APS and AG are defined as atoms and/or atomic groups that are positioned outside the pharmacophore and hinder its proper docking with the bioreceptor (APS) or provide for some other requisite general property (AG) (e.g., hydrophobicity). Somewhat similar to that of the pharmacophore, the influence of such groups is very specific and depends on their position and reactivity. But distinguished from the pharmacophore atoms (more precisely, pharmacophore geometry and electronic parameters) the APS and AG parameters may vary radically from one compound to another (in general they look arbitrary), and there is no way to include them in the pharmacophore. However, a more attentive consideration allows us to introduce appropriate APS and AG parameters that approximately link these groups to the activities. We introduce the function S to take into account AG and APS as follows:

$$S_{ni} = \sum_{j=1}^{N} \kappa_j a_{ni}^{(j)} \qquad (24.2)$$

where $a_{ni}^{(j)}$ is the jth parameter of the ith conformation of the nth compound, and κ_j are adjustable constants, N being their number. Taking also into account the statistical (Boltzmann) population of each conformation as a function of its energy E_{ni} (for the ground state $E_{n0}=0$) and temperature, we get the following general formula for the activity A_n of the nth compound:

$$A_n = A_0 \frac{\sum_{i=1}^{m_n} \delta_{ni}[Pha] e^{-S_{ni}} e^{-E_{ni}/kT}}{\sum_{i=1}^{m_n} e^{-E_{ni}/kT}} \qquad (24.3)$$

where Pha is a pharmacophore, δ is a kind of Dirac δ-function:

$$\delta_{ni}[Pha] = \begin{cases} 1, \text{ when Pha is present} \\ 0, \text{ when Pha is absent} \end{cases} , \qquad (24.4)$$

and m_n is the number of conformations that are kept as significantly populated (note that the contribution of conformations with $E_{ni}/kT > 1$ kcal/mol is less than 15%).

The constant A_0 may be obtained by choosing one of the compounds, say $n=l$, as a reference system. Then after Equation 24.3 (m_l is the number of conformations of compound l):

$$A_l = A_0 \frac{\sum_{i=1}^{m_l} \delta_{li}[Pha] e^{-S_{li}} e^{-E_{li}/kT}}{\sum_{i=1}^{m_l} e^{-E_{li}/kT}} \qquad (24.5)$$

and by substituting A_0 from this expression into Equation 24.3 we get:

$$A_n = A_l \frac{\sum\limits_{i=1}^{m_l} e^{-E_{li}/kT} \sum\limits_{i=1}^{m_n} \delta_{ni}[Pha]\, e^{-S_{ni}}\, e^{-E_{ni}/kT}}{\sum\limits_{i=1}^{m_n} e^{-E_{ni}/kT} \sum\limits_{i=1}^{m_l} \delta_{li}[Pha]\, e^{-S_{li}}\, e^{-E_{li}/kT}} \qquad (24.6)$$

In equations 24.3-24.6 the dependence of activity on S is chosen as exponential which seems to be more appropriate to the intermolecular interactions that underlie the activity, while the δ-function excludes all the conformations that have no Pharmacophore. With properly chosen APS and AG parameters $a_{ni}^{(j)}$, the adjustable constants κ_j can be determined from a regression analysis, say, by a least-square minimization of the expression $|A_n - A_n^{exp}|^2$ as a function of κ_j, where A_n^{exp} are the experimental data of the activities of the compounds in the training set.

The computational scheme of this method is illustrated in Figure 24.2. The main computational algorithms and programs needed for its realization are based on existing commercial packages for electronic structure calculations and molecular mechanics simulations (e.g., Spartan[17]). The additional programs have been written in the Matlab[18] environment and C/C++. The electronic structure calculations may be performed by either semiempirical or some low-level *ab initio*. The latter is preferable when there are difficulties in fine-tuning of the tolerances of the ECSA parameters. In the examples below 3-21G(*) *ab initio* single-point calculations were performed.

After calculating the κ_j constants from the training set data, one can estimate the expected activity of any compound outside the training set using Equation 24.6. Thus it remains to show how to choose the $a_{ni}^{(j)}$ parameters.

24.4. Parameterization and Results

The choice of the parameters $a_{ni}^{(j)}$ in Equation. 24.2 makes strongest demand on chemical intuition and skills. There are no *a priori* (rigid) rules how to do that, but the experience from solving previous problems may be very useful. The approach is that the role of AG and APS should,

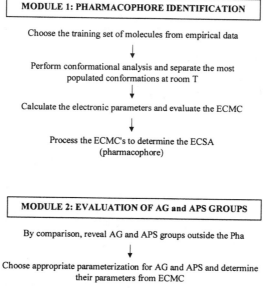

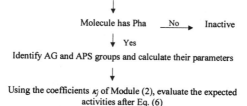

Figure 24.2. Algorithms and computer implementation of the EC method.

in principle, be determined in a manner similar to what is done for the pharmacophore identification: comparison of structural and electronic characteristics in relation to activities. Therefore, with the known pharmacophore, different active compounds (conformations) of the training set should be superimposed to see explicitly the positions of outside atoms and atomic groups, while the corresponding numerical values of distances and electronic parameters are known from their ECMC (or directly from structural data).

Since the positions of the atoms in these APS and AG, as compared to those in the pharmacophore, are much less specific and change significantly from one active compound to another, there is no need to specify each of these atoms; it is sufficient to take them into account with one or two parameters for a whole group, as they presumably take part in the interaction with the bioreceptor (e.g., as a shielding group or a hydrophobicity group). However, the shielding groups may require more geometric restrictions than other AG. The following two examples demonstrate these differences in more detail.

24.4.1. Angiotensin Converting Enzyme (ACE) Inhibitors[14]

This problem has been intensively discussed in the literature[19-24] and references therein. In our treatment[14] the chosen training set contains 68 compounds, including 215 heavily populated conformations. The pharmacophore revealed, as described above, is shown in Figure 24.3.

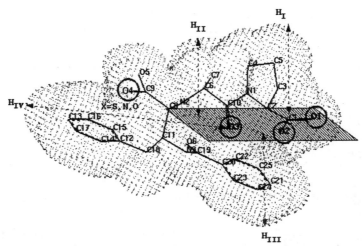

Figure 24.3. The active fragment (pharmacophore) responsible for ACE inhibitors activity contains three oxygen atoms, O1, O2, O3, and one atom X (X=S,N,O), more precisely, four reactivity points with limited values of Π situated at distances shown in the submatrix of activity (ECSA). The four types of hydrophobic groups H_p, p=I, II, III, IV as well as some other AG and APS groups are also shown.

It contains three oxygen atoms, O1, O2, and O3, with limited II values (given in the ECSA) which form a relatively rigid triangle (the pharmacophore plane), plus an additional atom X (X=S, N, O) located at an approximately constant distance from O3, but with a changeable (from one compound to another) angle a between the line X-O3 and the pharmacophore plane. The angle flexibility is seen from the large tolerances in the corresponding distances in the ECSA. This semi-flexibility of the position of one of the atoms of the pharmacophore is an interesting feature which, to our knowledge, has not been discussed in literature as yet.

Now, by superposition and inspection of the conformations one can see that several AG groups can be distinguished outside the pharmacophore, some of them apparently serving as hydrophobic groups, the others being more likely APS groups. After several trial comparisons, we chose the following twelve parameters illustrated by an example shown in Figure 24.3:

$$a_{ni}^{(1)} = R_{ni}(O1 - O3)$$
$$a_{ni}^{(2)} = R_{ni}(O2 - O3)$$
$$a_{ni}^{(3)} = R_{ni}(X - O3)$$
$$a_{ni}^{(4)} = R_{ni}(O6 - O3)$$
$$a_{ni}^{(5)} = R_{ni}(O5 - O4)$$
$$a_{ni}^{(6)} = \angle(XO3 - [O1O2O3])$$
$$a_{ni}^{(7)} = II(X), \ X = S, N, O \tag{26.7}$$
$$a_{ni}^{(8)} = II(O2)$$
$$a_{ni}^{(9)} = \log R_{ni}(H_I - [O1O2O3])$$
$$a_{ni}^{(10)} = \log R_{ni}(H_{II} - [O1O2O3])$$
$$a_{ni}^{(11)} = \log R_{ni}(H_{III} - [O1O2O3])$$
$$a_{ni}^{(12)} = \log R_{ni}(H_{IV} - O3)$$

The first three parameters are just some interatomic distances employed to take into account the influence of their limited variation on the activity; $a^{(4)}$ is the distance to the additional oxygen atom, where available; $a^{(5)}$ stands for the APS of a second oxygen (O5) when the X atom is O4 from a carboxyl group; $a^{(6)}$ is the angle a between the X-O3 line and pharmacophore plane; $a^{(7)}$ and $a^{(8)}$ are the II of the X and O2 atoms, respectively; the last four parameters take into account four types of hydrophobic groups (defined as H_p, p=I, II, III, IV) that may strongly influence the activity. The group H_I and H_{II} are those above the O1O2O3 plan (the numeration O1→O2→O3 is clockwise when looking from these groups), the group H_{III} is below the plane, and H_{IV} is the distance to the O3 atom (not specified with respect to the pharmacophore plane). Since the positions of these hydrophobic groups are less specific (in the sense that they vary significantly from one active compound to another), we characterize them by $\log R$ instead of R, where for H_I, H_{II}, and H_{III} R is the distance from the pharmacophore plane [O1O2O3] to the farthest carbon atom of the hydrophobic group plus 1.5 Å to take into account the C-H distance and the van der Waals radius of hydrogen. For the fourth group H_{IV}, the most remote one, the distance to the O3 atom proved to be more appropriate to represent its influence.

Substituting the $a_{ni}^{(j)}$ values from 24.7 into Equation 24.2, and then into Equation. 24.6 and performing the least-square minimization analysis on the twelve κ_j constants, we obtain their optimized values together with calculated vs. experimental values of $\log A_n$. The κ_j values are: κ_1=2.12, κ_2=1.20, κ_3=1.09, κ_4=0.48, κ_5=0.76, κ_6=3.25, κ_7=-28.75, κ_8=-20.99, κ_9=-0.13, κ_{10}=7.29, κ_{11}=-0.14, κ_{12}=9.82. The resulting r^2 = 0.78.

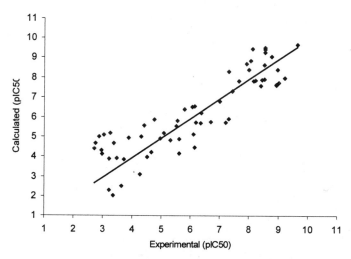

Figure 24.4. Calculated (optimized) vs. experimental pIC_{50} values in the training set of ACE inhibitors. The values of the constants ki are shown in the table; r^2 = 0.78. Reprinted with permission from reference[14]. © 1999 American Chemical Society.

Since all the constants κ_j are generally different and also different for the groups H_p above and below the pharmacophore plane, there is no mirror symmetry with respect to this plane, and this property is important to distinguish chirality influence. Plate 24.1 illustrates the differences in parameter values of the compounds M27 and its enantiomer (M66)[14] which differ in activity. It is seen that while compound M27 has the group H_I and a positive angle α, its enantiomer has a negative α value and the H_{III} group, but not H_I.

With known values of κ_j, any new compound can be tested for this activity by following module 3 of the computational scheme of the EC method (Figure 24.2): revealing its conformations, calculating the ECMC, checking whether it has the pharmacophore, and if it does, estimating the $a_{ni}^{(j)}$ values and calculating the activity from Equation 24.6. The results for 18 compounds, 64 conformations, chosen for validation of the method are shown in Figure 24.5. Note that, although the values of activity are not very accurate quantitatively ($r^2 = 0.52$), qualitatively the prediction of activity (yes or not) based on the presence or absence of pharmacophore is almost 100% (within the experimental error), and the quantitative estimate gives the order of magnitude that allows also us to exclude the ambiguity for compounds with weak activity, mentioned in the introduction.

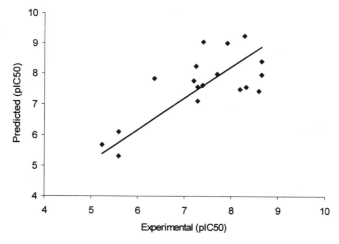

Figure 24.5. Validation of the EC method with a set of new ACE inhibitors (18 compounds, 64 conformations); $r^2 = 0.52$. Reprinted with permission from[14]. © 1999 American Chemical Society..

24.4.2. Rice Blast Activity (RBA)[12,13]

Distinguished from the ACE inhibitors, the RBA compounds are less flexible in the sense that there are fewer variable groups that change positions from one active compound to another.[25] The training set contains 85 compounds presented in 96 conformations. The ESCA and pharmacophore revealed are shown in Plate 24.2.[12,13] It is seen that the four atoms of pharmacophore stand for a polar group with ±0.46 charges, and a hydrophobicity group realized by the hydrogens at the distal carbon atoms. As compared with ACE inhibitors this pharmacophore is rather rigid.

The comparison of conformations reveals a variety of AG, most of them seem to be APS groups. For a better account of their role in the RBA activity, we used a more elaborate approach to their parameterization (Figure 24.6).

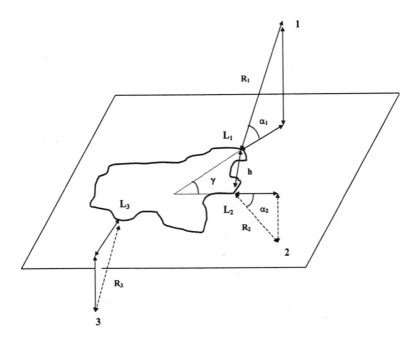

Figure 24.6. The scheme for estimation of the anti-pharmacophore shielding. The molecular group outlined on the plane is the basic skeleton, while the sterical restricting groups that may include also competing charges are indicated as 1, 2, and 3. Reprinted with permission from reference[12]. © 1999 Kluwer Academic Publishers.

First, we realized that outside the pharmacophore there may be atoms that do not influence the activity (apparently, because they just fill in some neutral cavities in the bioreceptor). We call the pharmacophore together with these atoms the *basic skeleton*. Then we found that the greatest contribution to the shielding comes from the extension of the groups outside the basic skeleton *along the pharmacophore plane*. This means that it is appropriate to take the outstanding projection (on the pharmacophore plane) of the distance to these groups as the APS parameters. If the projections of two groups overlap (within a given tolerance),[12,13] only the larger one should be taken into account.

Second, we noticed that the influence of out-of-plane positioned groups are not significant if they are unilateral, i.e., if there is only one such group which is not backed with another APS group in the other side of the pharmacophore plane. Apparently, this is due to the fact that one-sided groups do not hinder the possible docking of the molecule to the bioreceptor with its other side. This assumption is not true when chirality influences the activity (as is seen from the above example of the ACE problem where the two sides of the pharmacophore plane have different influences on the activity). Probably chirality is not important in RBA.

The presence of highly charged atoms close to the dipolar group of the pharmacophore may also be important because these additional charges may compete with the pharmacophore in the interaction with the bioreceptor, thus hindering their proper docking.

To accommodate these specifics of the APS influence, the $a_{ni}^{(j)}$ parameters in equation 24.2 are taken as follows (Figure 24.6):

$$a_{ni}^{(1)} = R_1 \cos \alpha_1$$
$$a_{ni}^{(2)} = R_2 \cos \alpha_2$$
$$a_{ni}^{(3)} = R_3 \cos \alpha_3$$
$$a_{ni}^{(4)} = R_4 \cos \alpha_4$$
$$a_{ni}^{(5)} = R_5 \cos \alpha_5$$
$$a_{ni}^{(6)} = R_6 \cos \alpha_6 \qquad\qquad (26.8)$$
$$a_{ni}^{(7)} = \sum_{i \neq j} R_i \sin \alpha_i R_j \sin(-\alpha_j) \quad \text{with} \sin \alpha = 0 \text{ for } \alpha < 0$$
$$a_{ni}^{(8)} = q(X1)$$
$$a_{ni}^{(9)} = q(X2)$$
$$a_{ni}^{(10)} = q(X3)$$

The first six parameters are the above-mentioned outstanding projections of the distances from six possible different kinds of APS groups to their nearest atoms L_i of the basic skeleton (Figure 24.6) (usually only 1-3 groups are present); $a^{(7)}$ takes into account the APS of only two-sided groups excluding one-sided ones (the angles are read off from the pharmacophore plane and it is imposed that $\sin\alpha = 0$ for $\alpha < 0$); $a^{(8)}$, $a^{(9)}$, and $a^{(10)}$ are distinguished charges in the APS groups which may compete with the polar group in the interaction with the bioreceptor.

With this choice of parameters, we performed a least-square minimization that yielded the following values of ten adjustable constants in Equation 24.6[12,13]: $\kappa_1 = 0.55$, $\kappa_2 = 1.11$, $\kappa_3 = 0.32$, $\kappa_4 = 0.65$, $\kappa_5 = 0.71$, $\kappa_6 = 0.57$, $\kappa_7 = 0.37$, $\kappa_8 = 1.45$, $\kappa_9 = 1.72$, $\kappa_{10} = 0.54$, with $r^2 = 0.88$. Reasonable validation was achieved by calculating the expected activities of 39 compounds in comparison with their experimental activities, although in this case $r^2 = 0.66$ is lower.[12,13]

24.5. Conclusions

The EC method briefly outlined in this chapter is based on a rather full description of the molecular system to represent its interaction with the bioreceptor. Distinct from some other methods, it allows for quantitative or semiquantitative prediction of the activity of any kind (without limitation), provided there are experimental data to form a sufficiently representative training set.

This method has two parts: pharmacophore identification and parameterization of the influence of AG and APS. While the methodology for the former—which allows for almost 100% (within experimental error) prediction of the bioactivity qualitatively (yes or no)—is more perfected, the rules of AG and APS parameterization that complement the concept of pharmacophore to give quantitative estimates of the activity are less definitive. Fortunately, variation of the parameter choice within physically grounded limits does not change the results significantly; an acceptable accuracy can be achieved with any reasonable parameterization.

In this way a quantitative or semiquantitative (by orders of magnitude) prediction of the activity can be achieved. In general, quantitative predictions of bioactivity by structure-based methods cannot be of very high accuracy by definition. Indeed, there are a variety of factors that are not included in the structural presentation: In addition to several macro parameters (e.g., solubility, transport properties, etc.), the activity may also depend on conformational changes produced by drug-receptor interaction that may be different from that implicitly incorporated (statistically) in the properties of the molecular systems of the training set.

Within these limits of accuracy the EC method of pharmacophore identification complemented by AG and APS parameterization seems to take into account the basics of the phenomenon that allow one to approximately predict the bioactivity quantitatively or semiquantitatively (by orders of magnitude). The variety of problems solved by earlier version of this method[8-11] and by its improved modification[12-14] confirm this statement.

Acknowledgement

This work is based in part upon work supported by Texas Advanced Research Program under Grant No. 003658-345 and it has been supported in part by a grant from the Robert A. Welch Foundation.

References

1. Marshall GR: **Molecular modeling in drug design.** In: *Burger's Medicinal Chemistry and Drug Discovery.* Wolff ME, ed. New York: John Wiley, 1995:573-659.

2. Ghose AK, Wendoloski JJ: **Pharmacophore modeling: Methods, experimental verification, and applications.** In: *3D QSAR in Drug Design: Ligand-Protein Interactions and Molecular Similarity,* Vol. 2. Kubinyi H, Folkers G, Martin YC, eds. Boston: Kluwer/Escom, 1998:253-271.

3. *3D QSAR in Drug Design: Theory, Methods and Applications.* Kubinyi H, ed. Leiden, The Netherlands: ESCOM, 1993.

4. Holtje HD, Folkers G: **Molecular modeling: Basic principles and applications.** In: *Methods and Principles in Medicinal Chemistry.* Mannhold R, Kubinyi H, Timmerman H, eds. New York: VCH publishers, 1997:9-63.

5. *Guidebook on Molecular Modeling in Drug Design.* Cohen NC, ed. New York: Academic Press, 1996.

6. Oprea TI, Waller CL: **Theoretical and practical aspects of three-dimensional quantitative structure-activity relationships.** In: *Reviews in Computational Chemistry,* Vol. 11. Lipkowitz KB, Boyd DB, eds. New York: Wiley-VCH, 1997:127-182.

7. Martin YC: **Pharmacophore mapping.** In: *Designing Bioactive Molecules: Three-Dimensional Techniques and Applications.* Martin YC, Willett P, eds. Washington, D.C.: ACS, 1998:121-148.

8. Bersuker IB, Dimoglo AS: **The electron-topological approach to the QSAR problem.** In: *Reviews in Computational Chemistry,* Vol. 2. Lipkowitz KB, Boyd DB, eds. New York: VCH, 1991:423-460.

9. Bersuker I.B, Dimoglo AS, Gorbachov MYu, Vlad PF, Pesaro M: **Origin of musk fragrance activity: The electron-topological approach.** *New J Chem* 1991, **15**:307-320.

10. (a) Bersuker IB, Dimoglo AS, Gorbachov MYu, Greni AI, Vysotskaya LE, Mikhailova TV: **Study of the electronic and structural properties of the chemical compounds in garlic aroma.** *Die Nahrung-Food* 1989, **33**:405-411. (b) Dimoglo AS, Gorbachov MYu, Bersuker IB, Greni AI, Vysotskaya LE, Stepanova OV, Lukash EYu: **Structural and electronic origin of meat odour of organic hetero-atomic compounds.** *Die Nahrung-Food* 1988, **32**:461-473. (c) Bersuker IB, Dimoglo AS, Gorbachov MYu: **The electron-topologic approach to the QSAR problem illustrated by inhibitor activity for thymidine phosphorylase and a-chymo-trypsin.** In: *QSAR in Drug Design and Toxicology,* Vol. 10. Hadzi D, Jerman-Blazic B, eds. Amsterdam: Elsevier, 1987:43-48. (d) Bersuker IB, Dimoglo AS, Gorbachov MYu, Vlad PF, Koltsa MN: **Structural and electronic origin of odour properties of organic compounds as revealed by the electron-topologic approach to the QSAR problem.** In: *QSAR in Drug Design and Toxicology,* Vol. 10. Hadzi D, Jerman-Blazic B, eds. Amsterdam: Elsevier, 1987:340-342. (e) Bersuker IB, Dimoglo AS, Gorbachov MYu: **The electron-topologic approach to structure-activity relationships. Inhibition of thymidine phosphorylase by uracil derivatives.** *Bioorgan Khim* 1987, **13**:38-44. (f) Bersuker IB, Dimoglo AS: **Electron Topology of Garlic's Biologically Active Thioallyl Compounds.** In: *First World Congress on the Health Significance of Garlic and Garlic Constituents.* Washington, D.C., 1990. (g) Dimoglo AS,

Bersuker IB, Popa DP, Kuchkova KI: **Electron-topological study of plant growth-regulator activity in a series of analogs of abscisic acid.** *Theor i Eksp Khim* 1989, **5**:590-596.

11. (a) Guzel Y, Saripinar E, Yildirim I: **Electron-topological (ET) investigation of structure-antagonist activity of a series of dibenzo[a,d]cycloalkenimines.** *J Mol Struc (Theochem)* 1997, **418**:83-91. (b) Guzel Y: **Investigation of the relationship between the inhibitory activity of glycolic acid oxidase and its chemical structure: electron-topological approach.** *J Mol Struc (Theochem)* 1996, **366**:131-137.

12. Bersuker IB, Bahceci S, Boggs E.J, Pearlman RS: **An electron-conformational method of identification of pharmacophore and anti-pharmacophore shielding: Application to rice blast activity.** *J Comput-Aided Mol Des* 1999, **13**:419-434.

13. Bersuker IB, Bahceci S, Boggs EJ, Pearlman RS: **A novel electron-conformational approach to molecular modeling for QSAR by identification of pharmacophore and anti-pharmacophore shielding.** *SAR and QSAR in Env Res* 1999, **10**:157-173.

14. Bersuker IB, Bahceci S, Boggs EJ: **Pharmacophore and bioactivity of angiotensin-converting enzyme inhibitors: The electron-conformational approach.** *J Med Chem*, in press.

15. Bersuker IB: private communication.

16. (a) Fukui K: *Theory of Orientation and Stereoselection.* Berlin: Springer-Verlag, 1975:134. (b) Klopman G: *Chemical Reactivity and Reaction Paths.* New York: Wiley, 1974.

17. *SPARTAN, Ver. 5.1.2.* Wavefunction, Inc., 1998.

18. *MATLAB, Ver. 5.3.* Mathworks, Inc., 1999.

19. (a) DePriest SA, Mayer D, Naylor CB, Marshall GR: **3D-QSAR of Angiotensin-converting enzyme and thermolysin inhibitors: A comparison of CoMFA models based on deduced and experimentally determined active site geometries.** *J Am Chem Soc* 1993, **115**:5372-5384. (b) Waller CL, Marshall GR: **Three-dimensional quantitative structure-activity relationship of angiotensin-converting enzyme and thermolysin inhibitors. II. A comparison of CoMFA models incorporating molecular orbital fields and desolvation free energies based on active-analog and complementary-receptor-field alignment rules.** *J Med Chem* 1993, **36**:2390-2403.

20. Hangauer DG: **Computer-aided design and evaluation of angiotensin-converting enzyme inhibitors.** In: *Computer-Aided Drug Design: Methods and Applications.* Perun TJ, Propst CL, eds. New York: Marcel Dekker, 1989:253-295.

21. Petrillo EW, Trippodo NC, DeForrest JM: Antihypertensive agents. In: *Annual Reports in Medicinal Chemistry,* Vol. 25. Robertson DW, ed. New York: Academic Press, 1989:51-60.

22. Wyvratt MJ, Patchett AA: **Recent development in the design of angiotensin-converting enzyme inhibitors.** *Med Res Rev* 1985, 5:483-531.

23. (a) Bohacek R, De Lombaert S, Priestle J. Grutter M: **Three dimensional models of ACE and NEP inhibitors and their use in the design of potent dual ACE/NEP inhibitors.** *J Am Chem Soc* 1996, 118:8231-8249. (b) Vincent M, Schiavi P: **modeling, synthesis, and pharmacological study of perindopril (S 9490), an angiotensin i converting enzyme inhibitor.** In: Molecular Recognition Mechanism. Delaage M: ed. New York: VCH, 1991:81-112. (c) Saunders MR, Tute MS, Webb GA: **A theoretical study of angiotensin converting enzyme inhibitors.** *J Comput-Aided Mol Des* 1987, 1:133-142.

24. (a) Stanton JL, Sperbeck DM, Trapani AJ, Cote D, Sakane Y, Berry CJ, Ghai RD: **Heterocyclic lactam derivatives as dual angiotensin converting enzyme and neutral endopeptidase 24.11 inhibitors.** *J Med Chem* 1993, 36:3829-3833. (b) Pascard C, Guilhem J, Vincent M, Remond G, Portevin B, Laubie M: **Configuration and preferential solid-state conformations of perintoprilat (S-9780). Comparison with the crystal structures of other ACE inhibitors and conclusions related to structure-activity relationships.** *J Med Chem* 1991, 34:663-669. (c) Hausian RJ, Codding PW: **Crystallographic studies of angiotensin-converting enzyme inhibitors and analysis of preferred zinc coordination geometry.** *J Med Chem* 1990, 33:1940-1947.

25. Dreikorn BA, Durst GL: **Retrospective quantitative structure-activity relationship (QSAR) analysis of tetrazolo- and triazoloquinolines, a series of Rica blast control agents.** In: *Synthesis and Chemistry of Agrochemicals IV.* Baker DR, Fenyes JG, Basarab GS, eds. Washington, D.C.: ACS Symposium Series 584, American Chemical Society, 1995:354-374.

25

Development and Optimization of Property-Based Pharmacophores

Ali G. Özkabak, Mitchell A. Miller,
Douglas R. Henry, and Osman F. Güner

Abstract

We present a simplified method for the development and optimization of 3D pharmacophores. The method involves four steps: 1) flexible superposition of known drug molecules, 2) identification of possible pharmacophore points, 3) clustering of the pharmacophore points to define an initial pharmacophore, and 4) optimization of the pharmacophore constraints by repeated 3D searching. The variations, advantages, and limitations of the techniques we have selected are discussed.

25

Development and Optimization of Property-Based Pharmacophores

**Ali G. Özkabak,[†] Mitchell A. Miller,[‡] Douglas R. Henry,[†]
and Osman F. Güner[∇]**

[†]*MDL Information Systems, Inc., San Leandro,
California*
[‡]*NetGenics, Inc., Cleveland, Ohio*
[∇]*Molecular Simulations Inc., San Diego,
California*

25.1. Introduction

Since its introduction, the pharmacophore concept has experienced a variety of fates.[1] For most of the 20th century, chemists devised and used two-dimensional pharmacophores with almost no knowledge of the true topography of the receptor site. For example, the classical acetyl-cholinesterase pharmacophore (Figure 25.1, a), although it contains some of the essential features of the known G-protein receptor,[2] is far from complete. Nevertheless, such simple pharmacophores were and still are extremely useful tools for the chemist designing new therapeutic agents. Their simplicity is an advantage, allowing the chemist to focus on the important parts of the inhibitor molecule.

Today, with conformationally flexible 3D substructure searching of large drug databases, and much greater knowledge of therapeutically relevant receptor sites and drug-receptor interactions, pharmacophores have assumed new definitions and applications. For instance, pharmacophores may be classified as two- or three-dimensional, or some 2 ½-dimensional hybrid (Figure 25.1, b). They may further be classified as *ligand-based* (derived from known inhibitors without reference to the corresponding receptor), *receptor-based* (derived from a given receptor, without reference to particular inhibitors) or some combination of the two (Figure 25.1, c).[3,4] Also, pharmacophores may be classified according to whether they contain specific functional groups (*topological* pharmacophores), or contain features which are more general (*property-based* pharmacophores) (Figure 25.1, d).[5,6] Flexible pharmacophore queries have been described,[7] and finally, shape and surface-based pharmacophores are being used increasingly.[8,9,10]

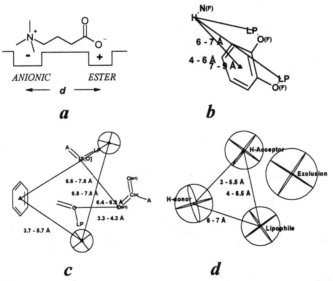

Figure 25.1. A variety of pharmacophore types: (a) conceptual pharmacophore, (b) mixed 2D/3D pharmacophore, (c) receptor-based pharmacophore, (d) physicochemical property-based pharmacophore.

The variety of pharmacophores that can be expressed is almost matched by the variety of modern applications. Originally, pharmacophores were used to express the notion of a particular drug-receptor interaction, a conceptual blueprint for a given class of drug. As 3D databases became available, along with fast 2D-to-3D converters, pharmacophores became useful as search queries. Today, in the climate of high-through-put chemistry, pharmacophores increasingly assume the role of filters for real and virtual libraries of structures. It is likely they will increasingly be used as filters for alternative drug actions, side effects, and pharmacokinetic and metabolic property predictions.

Methods for pharmacophore development have evolved over time as well. Originally, pharmacophores were designed by visual comparison of rigid analogs with known potency and selectivity. Topological and pseudostructure methods were next used.[11] When modeling and display techniques became available, pharmacophores could be developed using conformational analysis and superposition of flexible analogs. Marshall's active analog approach was a key development.[12] With the introduction of flexible 3D searching and large structural databases, pharmacophore development becomes, in modern terminology, a problem in structural data mining. Several automated methods for pharmacophore development have appeared.[13-16] The interest in optimization techniques such as the sequential simplex[17] and genetic algorithms[18,19] prompted us to develop a pharmacophore optimization approach that we have termed Optiquery.[20]

This chapter describes an interactive approach to the development and optimization of property-based pharmacophores, which does not require specialized software. The approach is similar to published methods, with simple but effective modifications. The main aspects of this approach are:

1. Flexible superposition of active structures onto a rigid or docked analog using the program Sculpt.[21]

2. Identification of relevant functional and physicochemical property groups using the chemical perception and manipulation language Cheshire.[22]

3. Hierarchical clustering of the identified groups to visually guide the selection of an initial pharmacophore.[23]

4. Optimization of the pharmacophore using the program Optiquery.[20]

The emphasis of this discussion will be on methodology and application, rather than results.

25.2. Flexible Substructure- or Field-Based Superposition of Structures

Although there are currently over 10,000 crystal structures stored in the Protein Data Bank,[24] only a relative handful have therapeutically relevant ligands docked. Consequently, the most convenient way to define an initial three-dimensional pharmacophore is by superposition and comparison of analogs of known potency. Two general approaches to this are: 1) atom- and bond-matching methods, often using a maximal common substructure approach (MCSS), and 2) field overlap methods (steric, electronic, or lipophilic fields, or some mix of these). For drug-sized molecules and for a few structures at a time, MCSS methods can be run interactively. They yield their best results with structures that have a common framework. Approaches to solving MCSS problems include backtracking techniques,[25] and detecting and comparing *cliques*, which are fully connected subgraphs.[26]

Field methods permit the comparison of analogs which are more heterogeneous or bioisosteric in nature. Since they rely on optimization, they are non-deterministic, yielding different results depending on the starting point. A well known example is Smith and Kearsly's SEAL method, which allows mixing of steric and electrostatic fields when rigidly overlapping a mobile structure onto a fixed template structure.[27,28] The SEAL force field is designed to simulate the binding of two small structures to the active site of a protein, without knowing the details of the receptor site. It incorporates terms for steric and electrostatic interactions, and ignores solvent effects. In the force field definition, the signs of the various terms are reversed, to create attractive rather than repulsive interactions. Some assumptions of the SEAL method include: 1) the putative active site is assumed to be the same for all inhibitor molecules, 2) the active site is constant and undistorted by the binding of structures, 3) a constant dielectric of 1.0 Debye is assumed, 4) polar group interactions are assumed to exclude water molecules, rather than involve them, and 5) structures are presumed to be rigid (various implementations of SEAL remove this limitation by allowing molecules to relax). A key feature of the SEAL method is the complementary scaling of the steric and electrostatic energies to give a total energy:

$$E_{tot} = P \times E_{(electrostatic)} + (1.0 - P) \times E_{(steric)}.$$

Sculpt is an interactive visualization and modeling program which implements both the MCSS method and the SEAL method, combined with a simplified force-field relaxation of the molecules.[21] Sculpt can automatically superimpose a flexible mobile structure onto a flexible or rigid template structure using either the MCSS method or the SEAL approach. The MCSS method finds the largest substructure common to both structures using a backtracking graph-matching technique.[25] The resulting atoms which are matched are linked by "tethers," which are virtual bonds between atoms. The tethers can be minimized as the mobile structure is allowed to relax and to superimpose onto the template structure (see Plate 25.1). The SEAL approach is implemented without tethers. In both approaches, structure relaxation proceeds via a local constrained energy minimization. When overlapping structures, intermolecular forces are ignored, except for the tethers and the SEAL forcefield. The force field for intramolecular minimization includes terms for covalent bond lengths, bond angles, and single-value dihedral angles. Additional potential energy terms account for explicit hydrogen bonds, variable dihedral angles, van der Waals interactions, electrostatic interactions, and user-applied tethers.

The van der Waals interactions in Sculpt are modeled with a modified Lennard-Jones function between atoms within 6 Å of each other. Coulombic interactions are modeled using a distance-dependent dielectric between atoms within 10 Å of each atom. Constrained energy minimization is carried out by evaluating the sum of the constraint and energy functions and their derivatives, then solving a system of nonlinear equations. This is performed rapidly enough to give real-time updates to the atom coordinates.

For the purpose of pharmacophore development, the selection of the template structure is important. The ideal candidate is the crystal structure of a bound ligand, which is usually a luxury to obtain. Lacking this, the least flexible analog with a given potency is often considered the candidate of choice, assuming that it undergoes little deformation when binding, and it more correctly presents the pharmacophore to the receptor. The flexibility of a ligand is usually measured by counting the number of rotatable single bonds in the structure (i.e., the "torsional degrees of freedom"). Rotatable single bonds usually exclude amide linkages, bonds between sp^2-hybridized centers, and bonds in small or unsaturated rings. Other considerations in choosing a template are the size of the template structure and the possibility of alternate binding modes. Choosing a smaller template structure will reduce the number of calculations needed for the MCSS and the SEAL alignment procedures. However, a very small template may adopt a unique binding mode, which cannot be adopted by a larger ligand due to steric interaction with the receptor, or it may only partially occupy the receptor site. Nothing in our approach depends on the selection of the template structure. We have not systematically investigated the effect of template size or flexibility on the quality of the pharmacophore that is generated. A prudent approach would be to use several structures in turn, as templates, and adopt the resulting pharmacophore that gives the best search selectivity.

25.3. Identification of Relevant Functional and Physicochemical Property Groups

Once a selection of active structures has been superimposed, the next step is to identify atoms and groups that could potentially interact with complementary atoms and groups in the receptor site. When doing this, it is important to consider the distinction between simple atom-based pharmacophores and more complex property-based ones. This has been discussed in the literature.[5] Computationally, all pharmacophores used for 3D searching are topological—i.e., structures are not stored and searched as properties, but as connection tables. To the chemist, however, it usually makes more sense to describe a functional group in a pharmacophore as a "hydrogen-bond donor," rather than specify that it can be the topologically equivalent "[N-H, O-H, or S-H]." In the case of more complex properties, the representation in chemical structure form or in some linear notation can become confusing.

For this reason, some 3D searching software allows definition of property-based pharmacophores using a limited number of common physicochemical properties.[16,29] This is usually augmented with custom properties expressed as molecule query files or in some linear notation such as SMARTS[30] or SLN.[31] For our purposes, we have applied the Cheshire chemical perception and manipulation language[22] to the identification of pharmacophore groups in superimposed structures. Cheshire is an object-oriented successor to the molecule editing language MEDIT, long used in MACCS-II. Cheshire features a JAVA-like command and control syntax, associative arrays, and transparent access to all atom, bond, fragment, ring, and collection information associated with a molecule. Using Cheshire, it is possible to integrate dynamic input/output, perception, and modification of structures into any ISIS server or client application.[32] The Cheshire language is primarily a scripting language, which can be compiled and cached for fast, repeated execution.

A simple example of a Cheshire script is seen in Figure 25.2. The first function, FindGroups(), identifies all 6-member aromatic ring centroids, and all H-bond donors. The script first defines the aromatic ring and H-donor substructures using MACCS query language. Then, for each structure it is applied to, it maps each query onto the structure, computes the average of the x, y, and z coordinates of the atoms in the substructure, and prints this average as a vector of numbers, along with an identifier for the feature. For large numbers of queries, arrays of molecules can be used. The second function Tdf(), counts the number of rotatable bonds in a structure. This function can be used to identify rigid analogs for superposition. Similar Cheshire functions were devised to identify hydrogen-bond acceptors, charged atoms and other familiar pharmacophore groups. The Tdf() function was run on all structures in the database which were reported to have ACE inhibitor activity, to identify the most rigid analogs. The pharmacophore point identification scripts were run on structures that had been superimposed using Sculpt as described in step 1. The result is simply a table listing the (x,y,z) location and type of each possible pharmacophore point in the ensemble of superimposed structures.

One advantage of using Cheshire is that perception can be combined with calculation of properties. Thus, in addition to computing the centroid of each aromatic ring, we could, with a bit more programming, compute an approximate surface area of the ring, the average Gasteiger charge, or perhaps some set of molecular connectivity indices, and print this information into the table as well. The result is a combined set of possible pharmacophore points and properties, to be used as the basis for designing an initial pharmacophore query. Perception of lipophilicity is always problematic, but approaches based on multiple substructures have been described.[33]

```
//****************************** map.cct ******************************************
// This Program contains unpublished confidential, proprietary, and
// trade secret material belonging to MDL Information Systems, Inc.
// (c) Copyright 1999 MDL Information Systems, Inc. All rights reserved.
//********************************************************************************
qA1 = CreateMol('A%A%A%A%A%A%@1');   // 6-member aromatic
qHBD = CreateMol("[N,O,S]H");        // H-donor
qCON = CreateMol("C(=O)-N");         // amide for tdf()

function FindGroups() {
// Find centers of various functional groups
  var itot = 0;
  var mi = MapIterator(qA1,FILTER_SYMMETRY);    // Aromatic centroid
  while((ic = mi.Next()).Count() > 0) {
    str = "";
    itot = itot + 1;
    str = String(ic.Avg(A_XCOORD)) + "," +
          String(ic.Avg(A_YCOORD)) + "," +
          String(ic.Avg(A_ZCOORD)) + " 1 0 0"; // Indicator vars
    Print(str);
  }
  mi = MapIterator(qHBD,FILTER_SYMMETRY);       // H-bond donor
  while((ic = mi.Next()).Count() > 0) {
    str = " ";
    itot = itot + 1;
    str = String(ic.List(A_XCOORD)) + "," +
          String(ic.List(A_YCOORD)) + "," +
String(ic.List(A_ZCOORD)) + " 0 1 0"; // Indicator vars
    Print(str);
  }
  return(itot);
}


function Tdf() {
// find rotatable single bonds
  var bi;
  var icount = 0;
  var c,cAlpha;
  // loop over single bonds (only chain)
  bi = Find(B_PTOPOLOGY,B_PTOPOLOGY_CHAIN).Find(B_TYPE,
            B_TYPE_SINGLE).BondIterator();
  while((c = bi.Next()).Count() > 0) {
    cAlpha = c.Alpha();
  // eliminate terminal single bonds (original bond + 2 atoms + one bond)
    if(cAlpha.Count() > 4) {                                    // two double bonds
      if(cAlpha.Find(B_TYPE,B_TYPE_DOUBLE).Count() < 2) { // two triple bonds
        if(cAlpha.Find(B_TYPE,B_TYPE_TRIPLE).Count() < 2) { // eliminate "C(=O)-N"
          if(cAlpha.Map(qCON).Count() == 0) {
            icount = icount + 1;
          }
        }
      }
    }
  }
  return(icount);
}
```

Figure 25.2. Example Cheshire code to identify aromatic ring centroids, H-bond donors, and to count the number of rotatable bonds in a structure.

25.4. Generating an Initial Pharmacophore

Automated methods of pharmacophore definition have been developed and are available commercially.[13,14,16,34] Chemists often prefer to let intuition and experience guide the pharmacophore development process. Both approaches basically involve a clustering or pattern recognition process—grouping similar patterns that are close to each other in 3D space. A simple extension of the process is to hierarchically cluster the pharmacophore points developed in step **2**, and allow the chemist to visually trim the dendrogram to include as many and whichever points appear to be meaningful for the pharmacophore. Presumably, this process could also be automated, based on input from the chemist about how many features to include, or using some cluster validity criterion to pick an optimal clustering of the points. We have not tried this.

Cluster analysis groups objects based on their proximity in some n-dimensional space. To the extent that the various dimensions represent the objects, this also represents a clustering by similarity, and this accounts for the popularity of cluster analysis in measuring diversity for combinatorial library development. Here, we are mainly concerned with the location (represented by x, y, z coordinates) and the nature (represented by some type, or by some vector of descriptors such as charge or surface area) of the various pharmacophore points identified in step **2**. The location of the points is represented by the Cartesian coordinates identified or calculated by the Cheshire script that perceived the pharmacophore points. The nature of the points could be represented by a single number, a set of indicator variables, or a vector of real or integer descriptor values. Clustering usually proceeds from a distance calculation (Tanimoto similarity coefficients are an alternative when only binary variables are used as descriptors). Accordingly, a single-valued measure of the type of a pharmacophore point is not acceptable; it implies some ordering to the types, which is not intended. For our purposes, we simply encode p pharmacophore point types with $(p-1)$ indicator or "dummy" variables. This makes it possible to include property calculations in the data to be clustered.

The resulting data matrix, containing one row for each putative pharmacophore point identified in step **2**, contains columns for x, y, z, and

(p-1) indicator variables. Depending on whether the indicator variables (0 or 1) are of a magnitude similar to the coordinates (typically within ±10 Å), we may standardize or autoscale the data. If property data two or more orders of magnitude greater or smaller than the coordinate data are included, it would be desirable to autoscale the columns to a mean of 0 and standard deviation of 1.0. Whether to autoscale also depends on the relative importance of the coordinate data, compared to the type or property data. If one wishes to force points of different pharmacophore types into different clusters, weighting of the type or property columns would be desirable. In general, scaling and weighting should be avoided in cluster analyses.

The clustering results depend on the input data and on the clustering method. For our purposes, a simple hierarchical clustering using either single-linkage or Ward's linkage is used.[23] The result of the cluster analysis is represented as a dendrogram (Figure 25.3). This tree diagram can be trimmed: 1) at whatever level yields the number of pharmacophore points desired, 2) based on some minimum distance criterion between pharmacophore points, or 3) based on a number of points per cluster or a majority membership by some particular pharmacophore point type. This is, of course, an empirical and subjective approach. Sometimes, the dendrogram shows clearly identifiable homogeneous clusters; at other times, there is considerable overlap. The process has not yet been automated.

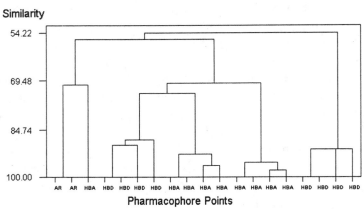

Figure 25.3. Hierarchical clustering of putative pharmacophore points for a set of superimposed ACE inhibitors. Points are aromatic ring centroids (AR), H-bond donors (HBD), and H-bond acceptors (HBA).

Figure 25.3 shows five well-separated clusters. The first, which contains two aromatic ring centroids and an acceptor, is not representative of all the compounds, and it can be ignored. When the distances among the centroids of the remaining clusters are sorted and examined (1-2: 1.03 Å, 2-3: 1.69 Å, 1-3: 2.96 Å, 3-4: 4.04 Å, 2-4: 6.09 Å, and 1-4: 6.94 Å), only four of the six possible distances are reasonable (say, greater than 2 Å). The first two distances are too short, due to overlap in the perception of donor/acceptor points. The two longest distances in this particular case (1-4 and 2-4) reflect distances to the carbonyl and ester oxygen atoms of the carboxylic acid group. Both distances could be retained for optimization, or just one of them could be selected and the carboxylate group would then be redefined as donor-or-acceptor.

Some other aspects of this approach need mentioning. The first is the use of inactive structures to help define sterically excluded regions of the pharmacophore. It is possible to either 1) separately cluster inactive structures which have been superimposed on the template structure, or 2) include active and inactive structures together, with one or more indicator variables of sufficient magnitude to keep the resulting clusters separate from those generated for active structures. The cluster results for the inactive structures, when compared to those for active structures, may show pharmacophore groups in regions different from or adjacent to, the pharmacophore groups generated for the active structures. If we assume that these groups are preventing binding of the inactive structures due to steric interaction with the receptor, most 3D searching systems allow the groups to be expressed as exclusion spheres.[29,31,32,35]

A second aspect of this approach concerns the fuzziness of the assignment of atoms to different pharmacophore point types, and converting the resulting clusters into the initial pharmacophore points. A given atom, say -NH-, can often be considered either a hydrogen-bond donor or an acceptor, depending on its chemical environment. Including both definitions into a given cluster analysis is no problem from a computational point of view. Depending on how it is expressed, the resulting pharmacophore may or may not perform well in database searching. One approach is to explicitly include a pharmacophore point type of "donor/acceptor" or even just "Other".[36] Alternatives include Markush or "R-group" query representation,[37] and most simply, to not type the pharmacophore point and simply allow "N" or some list of bioisosteric atoms "[N,O,S]." An alternative to fuzziness in the pharmacophore points is to use fuzzy cluster analysis.[38]

Finally, the pharmacophore points should be as general to the structure set as possible. Selecting too few points will result in an inefficient pharmacophore, which, although it may hit all the actives in a database, will also hit large numbers of inactive structures. Selecting too many points will exclude active compounds. The dendrogram is a useful tool for visualizing the relationship of pharmacophore points to each other. Another useful strategy is to develop the pharmacophore in a stepwise fashion: Begin with the two largest, most homogeneous clusters of points, run a scaled-down pharmacophore optimization, then add the next cluster. This is in lieu of testing every possible combination of clusters.

25.5. Optimizing the Pharmacophore

The initial pharmacophore generated in step **3** must be refined before it can be used for routine database searching. This refinement can be accomplished using molecular modeling or X-ray crystallography, if the time and resources are available. A simpler approach is to mine the information in 3D structural databases, to produce a more selective pharmacophore with higher search yields. This is the approach we have taken with the program Optiquery.[20] This program is an ISIS/Host application that takes as input the following parameters:

- A 3D structural database identification file ("hview file").
- An initial pharmacophore query molecule file ("query molfile").
- An optional list of structures in the database on which to search ("list file").
- A set of search parameters if the search is a conformationally flexible substructure search ("CFS parameters").
- An output pharmacophore query molecule file-containing the optimal pharmacophore ("query output file").
- A logfile name ("log file").
- The fieldname in the database which contains the activity of interest ("activity field").
- The value in the activity field which specifies the activity of interest ("activity value").
- The optimization technique to use ("simplex" or "powell").

The program operates by performing repeated searches over the 3D database, and modifying the constraint parameters in the pharmacophore, to produce higher-yielding and/or more selective search results. The program uses either the sequential simplex or the Powell minimization algorithm.[39] Presently, the program is capable of only modifying the constraints for a fixed set of pharmacophore points. Using a genetic algorithm as an optimizer would presumably allow varying the number of points in the pharmacophore as well, although we have not yet implemented this.

Table 25.1 shows the training and prediction results for optimizing an ACE inhibitor pharmacophore against a set of 200 known inhibitors in the MDDR database.[40] For training, each inhibitor structure was paired with a non-inhibitor from MDDR which showed the highest Tanimoto similarity to the given inhibitor (400 structures total). The Tanimoto similarity was calculated on the basis of the ISIS 960 substructure search keys, which encode atom, bond, and substructural information. The prediction results were obtained against the entire MDDR database including the original 200 inhibitors. The simplex method was used, and two objective functions were examined:

Function 1: $\quad F = \dfrac{Actives\ in\ database + (Actives\ in\ hit\ list - Hit\ list\ size)}{Actives\ in\ hit\ list}$ $\quad$ (Ref.[20])

Function 2: $\quad F = \dfrac{Actives\ in\ hit\ list \times (Actives\ in\ database + Hit\ list\ size)}{2 \times Hit\ list\ size \times Actives\ in\ database}$ $\quad$ (Ref.[41*])

Iterations terminated when the change between the best achieved function value and the current best fell below 0.0005. A 4-point pharmacophore derived from the superposition of the mostly rigid ACE inhibitors was used as the starting point for the optimization (Plate 25.1), and standard simplex expansion and contraction parameters were used.[39]

Examination of Table 25.1 reveals several points which are tentative and based only on this simple example. First, the initial pharmacophore, derived solely from the overlayed structures, was already fairly useful for detecting ACE inhibitors (404/471 possible ACE inhibitors). This was partly a function of the example, plus the fact that several semi-rigid analogs were avalable to initialize the pharmacophore. By comparison, a published ACE inhibitor pharmacophore selected 356 ACE

---

* See Chapter 11.

inhibitors.[42] Next, we found that the yield of the pharmacophore could be improved significantly by optimization (from 404 to 425 hits). Each iteration of the 3D search over the small test set database took 1-2 CPU seconds on an SGI Challenge, which meant an optimization run was only a matter of minutes. The resulting optimized pharmacophores showed tightening of some ranges and some shifts of the mean values. A comparison of the optimization functions shows the second ("Goodness of Hit List") function converged more rapidly and yielded a pharmacophore with slightly better prediction performance. This function has been shown to be superior in extreme searching cases, as well.[41]

Table 25.1. Optimization Results for an ACE inhibitor Pharmacophore.

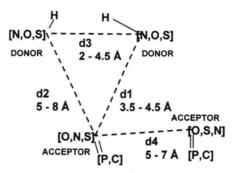

Parameter	Initial Value (mean)	Optimized Value (mean)
Optimizing function 1		
D1 (Å)	3.5-4.5 (4.04)	1.8-4.8 (3.30)
D2 (Å)	5.0-8.0 (6.94)	5.9-7.9 (6.90)
D3 (Å)	2.0-4.5 (2.96)	2.6-5.9 (4.25)
D4 (Å)	5.0-7.0 (6.09)	3.5-7.6 (5.55)
Function value	0.57	0.63
Iterations	53	
Yield (active, MDDR)	404	422
Optimizing function 2		
D1 (Å)	3.5-4.5 (4.04)	2.0-4.2 (3.10)
D2 (Å)	5.0-8.0 (6.94)	5.1-9.0 (7.05)
D3 (Å)	2.0-4.5 (2.96)	3.1-6.4 (4.75)
D4 (Å)	5.0-7.0 (6.09)	2.7-6.1 (4.40)
Function value	0.68	0.79
Iterations	36	
Yield (active, MDDR)	404	425

Finally, we have been primarily concerned here with yield (i.e., how many active structures can we hit), rather than specificity of the pharmacophore (what is the ratio of active to inactive hits in the hit list). To some extent, the second optimization function considers this distinction. In each of our optimizations with this dataset, both the yield and the specificity increased as a result of optimization, but this may not always be the case.

25.6. Summary

We have described a simple approach to pharmacophore development and optimization which can be implemented using software that is normally used for other applications (modeling, cluster analysis, optimization). Using a well-known example, we have demonstrated how either topological or property-based pharmacophores can be identified and optimized. Some improvements to this approach are fairly obvious, including:

- Implementing a genetic algorithm to control the addition and exclusion of points from the pharmacophore—this is already a feature of some commercial systems.[34]

- Faster and more biologically-relevant overlapping of structures-perhaps using extended receptor—interaction points rather than the atoms of the structures themselves.

- Integration with property-calculating routines, to define a greater variety of pharmacophore points.

- Improved display of clustered pharmacophore points—perhaps via "interactive" dendrograms, circular dendrograms, or minimal spanning trees.

- Management of the various aspects of pharmacophore development from a JAVA-based interface—we currently use a simple html approach with limited capability.

- Storage of optimized queries in a relational database, for use as filters in high-throughput and virtual screening.

We believe that pharmacophores and 3D searching will always be important aspects of the drug discovery process. A shift in emphasis from searching to screening and filtering applications is inevitable. In the absence of specific drug-receptor complexes, and sometimes even when these are known, large 3D databases of drug molecules contain unique information that can be mined effectively using techniques similar to what we have described.

Acknowledgements

We gratefully acknowledge the assistance of Richard Briggs Jr., for Cheshire scripts, and Mark Surles and Len Wanger for providing a beta copy of Sculpt 3.0.

References

1. P Gund: **Pharmacophoric pattern searching and receptor mapping.** In: *Ann Rep Med Chem*, Vol. 14, Chapter 29, New York: Academic Press, 1979:299-308.

2. Raves ML, Harel M, Pang Y-P, Silman I, Kozikowski AP, Sussman JL: **Structure of acetylcholinesterase complexed with the nootropic alkaloid, 9-0-huperzine A.** *Nature Struct Biol* 1997, 4:57-63.

3. Henry DR, Güner OF: **Techniques for searching databases of three-dimensional (3D) structures with receptor-based queries.** In: *Electronic Conference on Trends in Organic Chemistry (ECTOC-1).* Rzepa HS, Goodman JS, eds. Royal Society of Chemistry publications, 1995; http://www.ch.ic.ac.uk/ectoc/papers/Güner/

4. Clark DE, Westhead DR, Sykes RA, Murray CW: **Active-site-directed 3D database searching: Pharmacophore extraction and validation of hits.** *J Computer-Aided Mol Des* 1996, **10**:397-416.

5. Greene J, Kahn S, Savoj H, Sprague P, Teig S: **Chemical function queries for 3D database search.** *J Chem Inf Comput Sci* 1994, 34:1297-1308.

6. Daveau C, Bureau R, Baglin I, Prunier H, Lancelot J-C, Rault S: **Definition of a pharmacophore for partial agonists of serotonin 5-HT3 receptors.** *J Chem Inf Comput Sci* 1999, **39**:362-369. (A recent example using the Catalyst® pharmacophore development and 3D searching program. Molecular Simulations Inc., San Diego, California.)

7. Güner OF, Henry DR, Pearlman RS: **Use of flexible queries for searching conformationally flexible molecules in databases of three-dimensional structures.** *J Chem Inf Comput Sci* 1992, **32**:101-109.

8. Van Drie JH: **"Shrink-Wrap" surfaces: A new method for incorporating shape into pharmacophoric 3D database searching.** *J Chem Inf Comput Sci* 1997, **37**:38-42.

9. Hahn M: **Three-dimensional shape-based searching of conformationally flexible compounds.** *J Chem Inf Comput Sci* 1997, **37**:80-86.

10. Masek BB, Merchant A, Matthew JB: **Molecular shape comparison of angiotensin II receptor antagonists.** *J Med Chem* 1993, **36**:1230-1238.

11. Franke R: **Heuristic Approach to Topological Pharmacophores, Section11.2.6.** In: *Theoretical Drug Design Methods.* New York: Elsevier, 1984:297-310.

12. Marshall GR, Berry CD, Bosshard HE, Dammkoehler RA, Dunn DA: **The conformational parameter in drug design: the active-analog approach.** In: *Computer-Assisted Drug Design.* Olson EC, Christoffersen RE, eds. ACS Symposium Ser. 112, American Chemical Society, 1979:205-226.

13. Martin YC, Bures MG, Danaher EA, DeLazzer J, Lico I, Pavlik PA: **A fast new approach to pharmacophore mapping and its application to dopaminergic and benzodiazepine agonists.** *J Comput-Aided Mol Des* 1993, **7**:83-102.

14. Golender V, Vesterman B, Vorpagel E: **APEX-3D expert system for drug design.** *Network Science* 1996, http://www.netsci.org/Science/Compchem/feature09.html

15. Talele T, and Kulkarni VM: **Three-dimensional quantitative structure-activity relationship (QSAR) and receptor mapping of cytochrome P-450 inhibiting azole antifungal agents.** *J Chem Inf Comput Sci* 1999, **39**:204-210. A recent example using the APEX-3D pharmacophore development program.

16. Sprague PW: **Automated chemical hypothesis generation and database searching with Catalyst.** *Perspectives in Drug Discovery and Design* 1995, **3**:1-20.

17. Walters FH, Morgan SL, Parker LR, Deming SN: *Sequential Simplex Optimization: A technique for Improving Quality and Productivity in Research, Development, and Manufacturing.* Boca Raton, Florida: CRC Press LLC, 1991; also online at http://www.multisimplex.com.

18. Goldberg DE: *Genetic Algorithms in Search, Optimization, and Machine Learning.* New York: Addison-Wesley, 1989.

19. Willett P, **Genetic algorithms in molecular recognition and design.** *TIBTECH, Elsevier Science* 1995, **13**:516-521.

20. Henry DR, Miller MA, Güner OF: **Optimization of pharmacophore search queries for structure-based drug design.** American Chemical Society, 213th National Meeting, April 13-17, 1997, paper COMP-39.

21. Surles M, Richardson J, Richardson D, Brooks F: **Sculpting proteins interactively.** *Protein Science* 1994, **3**:198-210. (Sculpt® is a Trademarked program developed and marketed by MDL Information Systems, Inc., San Diego, California, USA.)

22. Durant JL, Briggs RL Jr, Nassau D, Leland BA, Sasse T, Nourse JG. **Cheshire: A new scripting language and its use in characterizing databases.** *Fifth International Conference on Chemical Structures*, Noordwijkerhout, the Netherlands, June, 1999.

23. Kaufman L, Rousseeu PJ: *Finding Groups in Data-An Introduction to Cluster Analysis.* New York: Wiley, 1990:280-311.

24. *Protein Data Bank,* Research Collaboratory for Bioinformatics; http://www.rcsb.org/pdb/.

25. Chen L, Robien W: MCSS: **A new algorithm for perception of maximal common substructures and its application to NMR spectral studies. 1. The algorithm.** *J Chem Inf Comput Sci* 1992, **32**:501-506.

26. Bron C, Kerbosch R: **Algorithm 457: Finding all cliques of an undirected graph.** *Communications of the ACM* 1973, 16:575-577. (Also found at http://www.netlib.org/tomspdf/457.pdf. Improvements on Bron-Kerbosch have been posted at ftp://dimacs.rutgers.edu/pub/challenge/graph/solvers/.)

27. Kearsley SS, Smith G: **SEAL, the steric and electrostatic alignment method for molecular fitting.** *Tetrahedron Comp Methodol* 1992, **3**:615-633.

28. Smith GM: **QCPE Program 567, Steric and Electrostatic Alignment Molecular Superposition Program.** Quantum Chemistry Program Exchange, Department of Chemistry, Indiana University, Bloomington, Indiana.

29. Davies K, Upton R: **3D pharmacophore searching.** *Network Science,* September, 1995; http://www.netsci.org/Science/Cheminform/feature02.html.

30. James A, Weininger D, Delany J: **Daylight Theory Manual, Daylight 4.62.** Daylight Chemical Information Systems, Inc, 1997; http://www.daylight.com.

31. *SYBYL®* is a Trademarked program developed and marketed by Tripos, Inc., St Louis, Missouri, USA.

32. *ISIS®* is a Trademarked program developed and marketed by MDL Information Systems, Inc., San Leandro, California, USA.

33. Pickett SD, Mason JS, McLay IM: Diversity profiling and design using 3D **pharmacophores: Pharmacophore-derived queries (PDQ).** *J Chem Inf Comput Sci* 1996, **36**:1214-1223.

34. *GASP* is a program developed and marketed by Tripos, Inc., St Louis, Missouri, USA.

35. Sprague PW, Hoffmann R: **CATALYST pharmacophore models and their utility as queries for searching 3D databases.** In: *Computer Assisted Lead Finding and Optimization-Current Tools for Medicinal Chemistry.* Van de Waterbeemd H, Testa B, Folkers G. eds. Basel: VHCA, 1997:230-240.

36. McGregor MJ, Muskal SM: **Pharmacophore fingerprinting. 1. Application to QSAR and focused library design.** *J Chem Inf Comput Sci* 1999, **39**:569-574.

37. Dalby A, Nourse JG, Hounshell WD, Gushurst AK, Grier DL, Leland BA, Laufer J: **Description of several chemical structure file formats used by computer programs developed at Molecular Design Limited.** *J Chem Inf Comput Sci* 1992, **32**:244-255.

38. Cannon RL, Dave JV, Bezdek JC: **Efficient implementation of the fuzzy c-means clustering algorithms.** *IEEE Trans Pattern Analysis and Machine Intell* 1986, **PAM1-8**:248-255.

39. Press WH, Flannery BP, Teukolsky SA, Vetterling WT: *Numerical Recipes in C.* New York: Cambridge University Press, 1988:305-315.

40. *MACCS-Drug Data Report (MDDR)* is a drug database available from MDL Information Systems, Inc. San Leandro, California, USA.

41. Güner OF, Henry, DR: **Metric for analyzing hit lists and pharmacophores.** Preliminary work is presented at the 1998 Charleston Conference as a poster; http://www.netsci.org/Science/Cheminform/feature09.html. (See also Chapter 11.)

42. Mayer D, Naylor CB, Motoc I, Marshall GR: **A unique geometry of the active site of angiotensin-converting enzyme consistent with structure-activity studies.** *J Comput-Aided Mol Des* 1987, **1**:3-16.

26

Effect of Variable Weights and Tolerances on Predictive Model Generation

Jon Sutter, Osman Güner, Rémy Hoffmann, Hong Li, and Marvin Waldman

Abstract

Catalyst is a program suite that, among other things, automatically generates pharmacophores using only experimentally obtainable ligand information—2D structure and biological activity. The HypoGen algorithm in Catalyst creates initial pharmacophores that are common among the active compounds but not among the inactive compounds, and optimizes the pharmacophores using simulated annealing. Each pharmacophore is scored using a cost function that accounts for its complexity, the deviation from ideal chemical weights for each chemical feature, and the differences between the predicted and measured activities. The pharmacophores can be used to predict the activity of unknown compounds or to search for new possible leads contained in 3D chemical databases. In previous versions of Catalyst, HypoGen only considered pharmacophores that consisted of features with constant weights (equal activity contribution) and tolerances (equal allowable distance from matching features of a lead compound). This chapter discusses new techniques in which HypoGen considers pharmacophores with variation among the individual feature weights and tolerances.

26

Effect of Variable Weights and Tolerances on Predictive Model Generation

Jon Sutter,[†] Osman Güner,[†] Rémy Hoffmann,[‡]
Hong Li,[∇] and Marvin Waldman[†]

[†]*Molecular Simulations Inc., San Diego, California*
[‡]*Molecular Simulations SARL, Parc Club Orsay Université,
Orsay Cédex, France*
[∇]*ChemInnovation Software, Inc.,San Diego, California*

26.1. Background

The Catalyst software package[1] includes two algorithms that automatically generate pharmacophore models, HipHop and HypoGen. HipHop[2] seeks pharmacophore models based on common features present among active compounds. It can be used when only a few compounds are known to be active (the exact activity values are not needed). The HypoGen algorithm, discussed in Chapter 10, is more appropriate to use if a training set of molecules with a range of known activity values exists. It creates pharmacophores based on how well they correlate estimated activities with measured activities in a training set. The pharmacophore models produced by either HipHop or HypoGen can be used to search 3D databases in order to obtain potential leads. HypoGen pharmacophores can also be used in the form of a formula to predict the activity of unknown leads.

Standard HypoGen (all previous versions) only considers pharmacophores that contain features with equal weights and tolerances. Each
feature (e.g., hydrogen-bond acceptor, positive ionizable group, etc.)
contributes an equal amount to the activity estimate. Similarly, each
chemical feature in the HypoGen pharmacophore requires a match to a
corresponding ligand atom to be within the same distance (tolerance).
In practice, HypoGen works very well using these assumptions.[3-4]
However, it is conceivable that certain chemical features may contribute
more to the activity or may quickly lose potency with increasing distance from the corresponding receptor site. Allowing the weights and
tolerances to vary in HypoGen could create pharmacophores more suited to encode the subtle nature of the receptor-ligand interactions, thus
improving correlation to activity and search results. This chapter will
discuss the addition of variable feature weights and tolerances to
HypoGen, and will present the results of a validation study which used
the new enhancements.

26.2. Methodology

HypoGen seeks pharmacophore models from training set data that correlates estimated activities with measured activities well. The estimated
activity values are computed using regression information obtained
from a simple regression of geometric fit values versus activity of the
training set members. The greater the geometric fit value, the more
active the compound. The geometric fit is based on two factors: 1) the feature weight and 2) how well the chemical features of the pharmacophore
overlap with the subject molecule. The pharmacophore is mapped to
each molecule considering several different mappings and configurations and the maximum geometric fit is used in the regression.

It is known that molecules can adjust their conformations in order to
bind to a receptor site—therefore each molecule in the training set is
represented by a collection of energetically reasonable conformations
(maximum 256). HypoGen was designed to work best on drug-like
compounds (molecular weights between 100 and 1000). In other words,
large molecules requiring more than 256 conformations to accurately

sample the conformational space are not good candidates for HypoGen. The molecules should not contain more degrees of torsional freedom than are found in tetrapeptides.

Before running HypoGen, the user must select a training set. This is possibly the most important step and should be done carefully; obviously, HypoGen can only create pharmacophores that are as good as the data entered. Ideally the training set should contain at least 16 compounds, span four orders of magnitude in activity range, contain no redundant information, and contain no molecules that are inactive due to excluded volume problems.

The next step is to select a maximum of five generalized chemical features that HypoGen will use to build the pharmacophores. The user can choose from 11 generalized chemical features supplied by Catalyst[5] (e.g., hydrogen-bond acceptor, hydrogen-bond donor, positive ionizable groups, etc.) or can create a user defined generalized feature to submit to HypoGen. The algorithm can be forced to select pharmacophores that contain a minimum or maximum number of certain chemical features. For example, the minimum number of hydrogen-bond acceptors (HBA) can be set to two, forcing HypoGen to consider pharmacophores containing at least two HBAs. This is often a good way to reduce the configuration cost if it is too high (see discussion below).

HypoGen generates pharmacophores in three phases: constructive, subtractive, and optimization. In the constructive phase, the pharmacophores that are common to the active compounds in the training set are identified and kept. In the subtractive phase, the pharmacophores that are present among the inactive compounds are removed. The optimization phase uses the well-known algorithm simulated annealing to improve the initial pharmacophores.

In the optimization phase, small perturbations are applied to the initial pharmacophores in an attempt to improve the correlation. The perturbations can include feature translations, rotations, and the removal or addition of features from the pharmacophore. In the recent enhancement, the perturbations can also include changing the relative weight or tolerance of a feature. To keep the number of adjustable parameters reasonable, the relative weights and the tolerances are chosen from a small subset of discrete values found in a parameter file (hypo.data). Throughout the optimization each pharmacophore is assessed using a cost value and the top 10 unique pharmacophores are exported.

26.3. Cost Function

HypoGen distinguishes between many possible pharmacophores by applying a cost analysis. The cost is a quantitative extension of Occam's razor (everything else being equivalent, the simplest model is the best). The simplicity is defined using the minimum description length principle from information theory.[6-8] The overall cost of each pharmacophore is calculated by summing three cost components: a weight, an error, and a configuration component.

The weight component is a value that increases in a gaussian form as the feature weight deviates from an ideal value (2.0). The error component increases as the root mean squared (*rms*) difference between estimated and measured activities for the training set molecules increase. The configuration component is a fixed cost, which depends on the complexity of the pharmacophore space being optimized. It is equal to the entropy of the pharmacophore space. The error and the weight components are estimated using the probability distribution shown in Equation 26.1.

$$P = \frac{1}{(2\pi\sigma^2)^{\frac{1}{2}}} e^{\frac{-x^2}{2\sigma^2}} \Delta \tag{26.1}$$

The error and weight components of the pharmacophore cost are estimated by taking -ln*P* of Equation 26.1 as shown in Equation 26.2.

$$-\ln P = \frac{1}{2}\ln 2\pi + \ln\sigma - \ln\Delta + \frac{x^2}{2\sigma^2} \tag{26.2}$$

where σ and Δ are constant parameters derived from expected values of weights and errors, and x is the deviation from the expected values for each. The deviation x of the error component is the actual minus the predicted scaled activity values for the training set members, and the deviation x for the weight component is the difference between the average of the feature weights and the ideal weight (2.0).

The configuration component is $\log_2 P$ where P is the number of initial pharmacophores created in the constructive phase that also survived the subtractive phase. It has been empirically determined that if the configuration cost is greater than 17.0, HypoGen is more likely to generate pharmacophores that correlate well due to chance. When using standard HypoGen, the user should attempt to keep the configuration cost below 17.0. The degrees of freedom can be reduced by supplying HypoGen as much information about the actual pharmacophores as possible (e.g., minimum or maximum number of certain feature types).

The cost for each pharmacophore is the summation of each component multiplied by a coefficient (the default coefficient is 1.0 for each) as shown in Equation 26.3:

$$Cost = eE + wW + cC \qquad (26.3)$$

where e, w, and c are the coefficients associated with the error (E), weight (W), and configuration (C) components, respectively.

HypoGen also provides two theoretical cost values to assist the user in determining the statistical significance of the optimized pharmacophores. These theoretical cost values are the null cost and the fixed cost. The cost values of the optimized pharmacophores should lie somewhere between these two values. The closer it is to the fixed cost and the further away it is from the null cost, the more statistically significant the pharmacophore is believed to be.

The fixed cost represents the simplest model that fits the data perfectly. If such a pharmacophore existed, the x terms in Equation 26.2 would be zero for both the error and weight components. Therefore, the fixed cost is the first 3 terms of Equation 26.2 plus the configuration cost. It is named the fixed cost because only the 4th term in Equation 26.2 varies. The other three terms, which are used to calculate the cost, are constant. The fixed cost is represented in Equation 26.4:

$$FixedCost = eE(x = 0) + wW(x = 0) + cC \qquad (26.4)$$

The null cost represents the cost of a pharmacophore with no features that estimates every activity to be the average activity. Since the null pharmacophore has no features, there is no contribution from the weight or configuration component. It is computed as shown in Equation 26.5:

$$NullCost = eE(x_{est} = \bar{x}) \qquad (26.5)$$

where x_{est} is the average scaled activity value of the training set members.

It was necessary to modify the cost functions to support the recent enhancements of variable weights and tolerances. First, the additional flexibility had to be addressed. Therefore the configuration cost now accounts for all the possible pharmacophores plus all the possible combinations of relative weights or tolerances for each. The empirically defined upper limit of 17.0 does not apply to the variable weight or variable tolerance modes. This cutoff will have to be reinvestigated in the future for the new modes. Second, an additional term to account for the tolerance was added. As is done for the weight and error components of the cost, the tolerance component of the cost is calculated using Equation 26.2. The σ and Δ values are derived from the discrete choices of possible tolerance values. The x term is computed as the average tolerance value minus the ideal tolerance value (the minimum value in the list). In other words, the optimization will prefer to use a smaller tolerance unless there is an improvement in correlation when increased. The new pharmacophore cost is shown in Equation 26.6,

$$Cost = eE + wW + tT + cC \qquad (26.6)$$

the new fixed cost is shown in Equation 26.7,

$$FixedCost = eE(x = 0) + wW(x = 0) + tT(x = 0) + cC \qquad (26.7)$$

and the null cost stays exactly the same.

26.4. Case Study

In this study, HypoGen was used to develop pharmacophores from a series of 23 5-HT3 antagonists. The activity values of this set of molecules ranged from 0.2 to 1400 nM. This particular set of 5-HT3 antagonists was a good candidate for HypoGen since the molecules had diverse chemical features and the activity range spanned more than 4 orders of magnitude.

Pharmacophore models were selected using combinations of five chemical features: ring aromatic, hydrogen-bond acceptor, hydrogen-bond donor, positive ionizable, and hydrophobic groups. Seven of the

23 molecules were identified as active by HypoGen and were used in the constructive phase to obtain the initial pharmacophores. Three of the 23 molecules were identified as inactive and were used to remove some of the initial pharmacophores in the subtractive phase. The configuration cost was 11.35, which corresponds to approximately 2600 initial pharmacophores. The optimization phase of HypoGen was used to select the top ten scoring pharmacophores by applying small perturbations to the initial pharmacophores. The perturbations differed according to which mode of HypoGen was used—standard, variable weight, or variable tolerance. In this case, using the variable weight or variable tolerance mode improved the top pharmacophore model as evidenced by an improvement in the correlation with activity and an improvement in search results.

First, standard HypoGen was used to generate 10 pharmacophore models. The geometric fit values between the top pharmacophore model and each of the 23 5-HT3 antagonists in the training set correlated well with the activity values. The best pharmacophore had a correlation coefficient (R) of 0.828 and root mean square (rms) error of regression of 1.40. The fixed cost, pharmacophore cost, and null cost were 89.84, 112.7, and 148.9, respectively. The pharmacophore cost was well below the null cost and closer to the fixed cost, which indicated that the correlation was not obtained by chance.

The pharmacophore contained 4 features: 2 hydrophobic groups, 1 hydrogen-bond donor, and 1 ring aromatic group. The tolerance values for each feature were the default values (2.2 Angstroms for the projection point of the hydrogen-bond donor and 1.6 Angstroms for all others). Each generalized chemical feature contributed equally to the activity estimate (weight of 2.2). Plate 26.1 shows the pharmacophore aligned to the most active compound in the training set. Although the correlation to activity was adequate, clearly there was room for improvement. This data set seemed to be an ideal candidate for the variable weight or variable tolerance mode of HypoGen.

Next, variable tolerance HypoGen was used to generate 10 pharmacophore models. The geometric fit values between the top pharmacophore model and each of the 23 5-HT3 antagonists in the training set correlated well with the activity values. The best pharmacophore had an R of 0.866 and rms error of 1.26, which was quite an improvement over the standard HypoGen pharmacophore. The fixed cost, pharmacophore cost, and null cost were 102.6, 122.3, and 148.9, respectively. The increased cost for this pharmacophore over the standard HypoGen pharmacophore is due to the additional penalty added for the variable tolerances, however, the pharmacophore cost is still well below the null cost and closer to the fixed cost.

The best pharmacophore also contained 4 features. However, the feature types were different from those found using standard HypoGen. The variable tolerance pharmacophore model had 2 hydrophobic groups, 1 hydrogen-bond acceptor, and 1 positive ionizable group. Plate 26.2 shows the pharmacophore aligned to the most active compound in the training set. HypoGen only increased the tolerance of one blob and all other tolerances were reduced. The tolerance on the heavy atom blob of the hydrogen-bond acceptor was increased to 1.75 from the default of 1.6 Angstroms. The single blob features (2 hydrophobic and 1 positive ionizable group) were all reduced to 1.3 Angstroms. The blob on the projection point of the hydrogen-bond acceptor was reduced to 1.9 from the default of 2.2 Angstroms. Each feature had an equal contribution to the activity estimate (weight 2.5).

Finally, HypoGen in the variable weight mode was used to generate 10 pharmacophore models. The best pharmacophore had an R of 0.834 and *rms* error of 1.38. There was not a great improvement in the correlation over standard HypoGen using the variable weight mode. It was interesting, though, that the best pharmacophore found was very similar to the variable tolerance pharmacophore. In fact, the exact same four features in nearly the same locations were found. The only significant difference was that the features of the variable weight model used the default tolerances (1.6 and 2.2 Angstroms for all features) and used feature weights of 2.6 for two features, and 2.0 for the other two features. The fixed cost, pharmacophore cost, and null cost were 101.5, 123.9, and 148.9, respectively. Plate 26.3 shows the pharmacophore aligned to the most active compound in the training set.

The improved activity correlation suggested that the pharmacophore models generated by variable weights and variable tolerances were superior. When the pharmacophores were validated via searching a database with known 5-HT3 antagonists, the results corroborated this finding. The search was performed on the 96-4 version of the Derwent's World Drug Index (WDI).[9] Four measures of fitness were used to assess the quality of the queries, the percent yield of actives in the hit list ($\%Y$), percent ratio of the known actives retrieved ($\%A$), the enrichment (E), and the Goodness of Hit list (GH). E is a measure of how much more enriched the result of a query search is over the entire database, and GH is a weighted linear combination of the $\%A$ and $\%Y$. Chapter 11 discusses the $\%A$, $\%Y$, E, and GH measures in more detail.

The WDI database contained 48,405 compounds. In order to obtain meaningful measures of fitness, the search was limited to the 10,318 compounds with known activities (non-empty entry in the Mechanism of Action (MA) field). A search for the keyword "antiserotonins" in the MA field revealed that the database contained 225 5-HT3 antagonists ($\%Y = 2.18$). Each of the three best pharmacophores produced by standard, variable tolerance, and variable weight HypoGen was used as search queries. All searches were performed in the BEST flexible search mode of Catalyst.

The measures of fitness obtained by each query are presented in Table 26.1.

Table 26.1. WDI search results.

Query	*Actives*	*Hits*	*%Y*	*%A*	*E*	*GH*
Database	225	10318	2.18	100.0	1.00	0
Standard	64	1889	3.39	28.4	1.55	0.079
Tolerance	97	1915	5.06	43.1	2.32	0.120
Weight	112	2512	4.46	49.8	2.04	0.120

The row labeled "Database" shows the measures of fitness when the entire database was considered. The row labeled "Standard" shows the results of the search when the best pharmacophore produced by standard HypoGen was used as the search query. Only 64 of 225 (28.4%) of all the active compounds were retrieved in the search. However, the total number of hits was 1889; therefore the $\%Y$ improved to 3.39%. Consequently, the enrichment factor improved to 1.55. Clearly there was an improvement in the search results when either the variable tolerance pharmacophore or the variable weight pharmacophore was used. The number of active compounds retrieved increased for both, 97 and 112, which nearly doubled the $\%Y$ and $\%A$ measures. The enrichment factor and goodness of hit list factor also improved for both pharmacophores.

As stated previously, the best pharmacophore found using the variable tolerance method was practically identical to the pharmacophore found by the variable weight method, and yet there are differences in the search results. Table 26.1 shows that the variable tolerance query is more selective. It retrieves a total of 1915 as opposed to 2512 hits via the variable weight query. This can be attributed to the fact that most of the tolerance values were decreased from the default values. As a result, the $\%Y$ is better for the variable tolerance model. The increased selectivity, however, causes the query to miss more of the actives, and therefore the $\%A$ measure is slightly worse. The GH score, a linear combination of $\%Y$ and $\%A$, rates the queries as being equivalent.

26.5. Conclusions

Variable tolerances in HypoGen should prove to be a useful addition. Using variable tolerances could compensate for deficiencies in the conformational coverage of unusually flexible compounds, and could tighten the tolerances when large values are not needed. The resulting pharmacophore models will likely produce improved search queries.

The variable weights should also be a useful addition, especially when the pharmacophores contain features that obviously contribute more to the activity than the others. The resulting pharmacophore models will likely predict activity values more accurately. A change in relative feature weights will not have a large impact on the results from a database search. The power of the enhancement will come from the fact that novel hypotheses will be found during the optimization, which may be superior. This assumption is supported in the validation study presented in this chapter. In the validation study, the best pharmacophore found using variable tolerance and weight was different and better than the best from standard HypoGen.

It is important to realize that the addition of variable weights or tolerances adds a large number of degrees of freedom to the optimization problem. The number of possible pharmacophore configurations created in the constructive and subtractive phase will be the same when using HypoGen in standard, variable weight, or variable tolerance mode. However, there will be several more possibilities since each feature in each pharmacophore can have n different weight values or tolerance values, where n is the number of possible relative weights or tolerance values. Validation of the pharmacophores obtained using the new modes is very important to ensure that the model's correlation is not due to chance.

References

1. *Catalyst v.4.0*, available from Molecular Simulations Inc., San Diego, California, USA.

2. Barnum D, Greene J, Smellie A, Sprague P: **Identification of common functional configurations among molecules.** *J Chem Inf Comput Sci* 1996, **36**:563-571.

3. Daveu C, Bureau R, Baglin I, Prunier H, Lancelot J, Rault S: **Definition of a pharmacophore for partial agonists of serotonin 5-HT3 receptors.** *J Chem Inf Comput Sci* 1999, **39**:362-369.

4. Grigirov M, Weber J, Tronchet JMJ, Jefford CW, Milhous WK, Maric D: **A QSAR study of the antimalarial activity of some synthetic 1,2,4-tri-oxanes.** *J Chem Inf Comput Sci* 1997, **37**:124-130.

5. Green J, Kahn S, Savoj H, Sprague P, Teig S: **Chemical function queries for 3D database search.** *J Chem Inf Comput Sci* 1994, **34**:1297-1308.

6. Rissanen J: **Modeling by shortest data description.** *Automatica* 1978, **14**:465-471.

7. Rissanen J: **A universal prior for integers and estimation by minimum description length.** *Ann Stat* 1983, **11**:416-431.

8. Rissanen J: **Stochastic complexity and modeling.** *Ann Stat* 1986, **14**:1080-1100.

9. *World Drug Index v.96.02*, available from Derwent Information Ltd., London, UK.

PART V

The Future of Pharmacophore Research

- **Future Direction in Pharmacophore Discovery**

27

Future Directions in Pharmacophore Discovery

John H. Van Drie

Abstract

The evolution of the field of pharmacophore discovery is briefly reviewed. The key factors for a successful method is described as: objectivity, completeness, robustness, use of computational controls, statistical measures of pharmacophore quality, and the prospective use of those pharmacophores. The idea is introduced that "not all datasets are created equal", i.e., some datasets are easy for any pharmacophore discovery method to handle, some are hard. The interplay between conformational analysis methods and pharmacophore discovery methods is discussed. And, finally, some speculation is offered on the frontiers of this field.

27

Future Directions in Pharmacophore Discovery

John H. Van Drie

Pharmacia & Upjohn, Kalamazoo, Michigan

27.1. Introduction

"There is a time to sow, and a time to reap." This Biblical maxim is appropriate to the state of the field of pharmacophore discovery. We have seen throughout the 1990s an explosion of ideas, methods, and interest in this field, with much creativity displayed. These contributions have come from investigators coming from many disciplines. Now it is time to take stock: to evaluate critically what stands before us, to inject rigor into these analyses, and to facilitate the placement of these methods into the hands of researchers closely tied to experimental efforts in the pharmaceutical industry.

It is difficult for a newcomer to get an overall grasp of this field; hence, this volume will serve an important compendium of some of this work. The field of pharmacophore discovery still awaits a critical review, with a thorough citation of all of the work and critique and comparison of the various methods. Although predecessor work may be cited,[1] in my own mind I tend to trace the beginnings of interest in this field to our days at BioCAD, where we first introduced the Catalyst software in 1992. Even as we began demo'ing early versions of that software, a splurge of similar methodology arose. DISCO was the first of this crew,[2] and in short order each of the vendors were offering their own method. Dissatisfaction with these methods has stimulated many new investigators, some of whom are represented in this volume.

Unfortunately, BioCAD was not a commercial success, but as the company folded in 1994, the Catalyst software was acquired by MSI. Interest in using Catalyst continues, and many of us persist in attempting to find better methodologies to implement the vision articulated at BioCAD: use a structure-activity dataset to discover a pharmacophore, and use that pharmacophore both to guide the design of new analogs and to discover new leads via 3D database searching. Though the roots of pharmacophore discovery were largely in the commercial software vendor arena, the symposium that led to this volume demonstrates that we are now seeing research from many quarters, including the pharmaceutical industry and academia.

As Peter Gund relates in this volume (see Chapter 1), the use of 3D pharmacophores in computer-aided drug discovery dates back to his work in 3D database searching in the 1970s. It is refreshing to see the current variety of both methods for pharmacophore discovery and ways of using pharmacophores. This volume documents a large slice of that work. One sees pharmacophores used now in the following ways:

- as the query for a 3D database search, as has long been done;
- to overlay structurally distinct molecules with similar biological activities, to guide the design of new analogs, and to allow the SAR (structure-activity relationship) of one series to inform the chemist about possibilities in another series;
- to guide the design of targeted combinatorial libraries, in a manner which has been termed *structure-based combinatorial chemistry*[3];
- to analyze the data emerging from HTS (high-throughput screening).[4]

As we look to future directions in pharmacophore discovery, it is reasonable to anticipate that more applications of pharmacophore methodologies will be found. More aggressive use of these methods in real-life applications will doubtlessly drive the field toward better, more robust, and more reliable methods. Notice in particular that the last two bullets above demand pharmacophore discovery methodologies that are highly automated and capable of handling large numbers of molecules; these are not characteristics of any commercial packages today, though some published methods satisfy these criteria.

We also need to agree on a name for this field. One of the first ACS sessions devoted to this field called it "pharmacophore mapping"; this term emphasizes its roots in the receptor mapping work of Garland Marshall, et al. Others have labeled it "pharmacophore identification," "pharmacophore perception," or "pharmacophore determination." My own bias is against such terms, because they imply that a pharmacophore exists and that it is only a matter of the computer finding it. Not all SAR datasets have a pharmacophore, and my own work with DANTE[5] emphasizes the need to discover if a pharmacophore exists. Hence my preference for the term "pharmacophore discovery."

Another evolving aspect of this field, and of computer-aided drug discovery in general, is how software methods are distributed. In the early days, most software was developed in academia, and distributed for nominal sums, e.g., through the QCPE (quantum chemistry program exchange). The software vendors emerged in the scene beginning in 1984, and by the mid-90s became almost the sole source of software of this type. It saddens me to see young people entering the field whose education seems to have come exclusively from software vendors; reading the scientific literature evidently is a fading pastime. Until recently, it has seemed like a quaint anachronism to take publications and rewrite the software from scratch based on the published method.

This is changing. I am familiar with at least one academic who formerly distributed his software via a vendor, but now prefers to distribute it himself. MOE, from Chemical Computing Group (www.chemcomp.com), is a Molecular Operating Environment which encourages researchers to quickly develop their own applications based on a high-level language, SVL, and a toolbox of chemistry routines. OpenEye Software is another vendor (www.eyesopen.com) offering both end-user software and a toolkit for developers. And of course Daylight Chemical Information Systems continues to provide a chemistry toolkit (www.daylight.com); it was the precursor to this toolkit that allowed me to develop ALADDIN quickly. Hopefully, this evolution will spur innovation in the field and will allow a plethora of methods like those described in this volume to more readily reach a wide audience.

One final comment: I know of at least one academic who applied for grant funding to work on pharmacophore discovery methods. This grant was denied, because one reviewer claimed that this was a solved problem, citing DISCO. Let me say emphatically: *Pharmacophore discov-*

ery is not a solved problem. We need contributions from every source, academic, the pharmaceutical industry, and the commercial vendors. This volume demonstrates that, if anything, this field is wide open and in a high state of flux.

What follows is divided into these topics:

- Goals for a Pharmacophore Discovery Method (criteria by which we can decide if method A is better than method B)
- Not All Datasets Are Created Equal (some thoughts on differences in datasets)
- Conformational Analysis and its Relation to Pharmacophore Discovery
- Frontiers in Pharmacophore Discovery

27.2. Goals for a Pharmacophore Discovery Method

What are we trying to achieve in pharmacophore discovery?

If we do not have a clear answer to that question, it will be impossible for us to make progress; we will be unable to judge whether method A is better than method B. Here, I will give my own answer to that question, by articulating the criteria by which one can decide which method is better; obviously this answer reflects my own biases and opinions.

27.2.1. Objectivity

First, our pharmacophores must represent an objective description of those structural characteristics common to a class of active molecules, and possibly also those characteristics which discriminate active from inactive molecules. When we introduced the ALADDIN language for describing pharmacophores for 3D database searching,[6] one of our initial goals was to produce an objective description of a pharmacophore. One aspect of an objective description is that it can be evaluated by a non-expert against an arbitrary molecule; clearly this is a requirement for a 3D database search query, where the computer is the non-expert. Frequently, the pharmacophores now in use satisfy this requirement, by following the approach we first used in ALADDIN—a series of features defined using substructural criteria connected by a set of geometric constraints between pairs of features.

It might seem that one could take this criterion of objectivity for granted. Nonetheless, one sometimes sees in publications of pharmacophore methods a series of overlays of molecules. In my opinion, this does *not* represent an objective description, i.e., one that can be articulated in the absence of those molecules. I have also seen at least one published example of a pharmacophore which claimed to be a chiral pharmacophore—one which discriminated an active molecule from its inactive enantiomer. However, this pharmacophore was comprised of a set of features connected by distance constraints. It is mathematically impossible for a pharmacophore composed solely of distances to be chiral; it appeared that the authors were relying on some unstated, i.e., unobjective, criteria in performing the chiral discrimination.

One key advantage of objective pharmacophores is that they allow straightforward comparison of two pharmacophores that have been produced by different methods. With an objective description, one can easily identify how similar two pharmacophores are and where they differ.

27.2.2. Completeness

Our understanding of what must be included in a pharmacophore continues to slowly evolve. The pharmacophores generated by my DANTE methodology include: functional groups ("features"), the inter-feature distances and the angular relationships where appropriate, and shape constraints (sterically forbidden regions). Much of the early un-automated pharmacophore modeling in the 1980s emphasized the importance of the angular relationships of hydrogen-bond donors, etc.; surprisingly, these lessons have been frequently ignored in the modern automated pharmacophore discovery methods. I recall clearly that in our days at BioCAD, we showed the first prototypes of Catalyst, which included these orientational constraints, and then proceeded to ship Version 1.0 without such constraints. There was a large hue and cry, and ultimately by V 2.0, these orientational constraints re-emerged. One no longer hears these complaints about pharmacophores composed solely of features and inter-feature distances, but one should.

The issue of shape constraints, or sterically forbidden regions, has long been a sore point. Again, the early un-automated pharmacophore modeling in the 1980s usually included such sterically forbidden regions. When Scott Kahn and I joined BioCAD in 1990, we were surprised to discover that we had both independently discovered a novel shape representation, what we both called a "shrink-wrap representation"; we were both eager to see this employed in our pharmacophore discovery module. This never appeared in Catalyst. V 2.0 of Catalyst did, however, include the possibility for very primitive user-added shape constraints, but no tools were provided for the automated determination of shape constraints. Ultimately, this "shrink-wrap representation" of shape appeared in my DANTE pharmacophore discovery method[5c]; the forbidden regions thus determined may be converted into the shape constraints in a Catalyst 3D database search.[3]

It is very encouraging to see the work in this volume describing the determination of Catalyst shape constraints from a protein structure.[7] It is also encouraging to see work that involves pharmacophore methods for automatically determining shape constraints. I view this only as a beginning, and anticipate much more work in the smooth integration of shape into the pharmacophore discovery field.

Both orientational constraints or shape constraints are useful in achieving chiral pharmacophores, i.e., ones which discriminate an active molecule from its inactive enantiomer

23.2.3. Robustness

Molecular modeling began in the 1980s as a discipline which involved much hand-tweaking by a sophisticated user interacting with the computer. Automated pharmacophore discovery methods arose with the promise of avoiding this hand-tweaking, with quality results hopefully emerging directly from the input dataset. Nonetheless, many of these automated pharmacophore discovery methods are used in the old spirit, with a lot of hand-tweaking to get quality results.

This promise of automated pharmacophore discovery methods must be realized if they are to have an impact beyond the coterie of molecular modelers. In my opinion, the reason for so much tweaking is that the these methods in general are rarely robust. Frequently, much time is spent on deciding which molecules should be included in the dataset (to "teach" the computer), and which should be held back (to avoid exciting known problems in the method). We must make our methods more robust. It is not clear from what appears in this volume how robust many of these methods are. This issue of robustness really hits home when one attempts to extend pharmacophore discovery to the analysis of HTS data and combi-chem; here the flow of data is large and fast, and lack of robustness ensures failure.

27.2.4. Computational Controls

In the field of biology, control experiments are mandatory. One is interacting with a complicated system, and even if the system response is consistent with one's hypothesis, one must design control experiments that rule out confounding effects, i.e., behaviors in the system contrary to one's hypothesis but still able to give rise to results consistent with one's hypothesis. In chemistry, our training is different. For example, one shines some electromagnetic radiation on a molecule, and reports the result. It is foreign to us as chemists to systematically apply computational controls to evaluate every computational result that may lead to an experimental test.

Yet work in drug discovery is more akin to the biology model of a complicated system, and hence our methods should be subject to the greater scrutiny of computational controls.

It is difficult to convey in a few words the importance of computational controls; hang around some cell biologists for a while to get a better appreciation of that. Some of the types of computational controls used to evaluate early versions of the DANTE pharmacophore methodology were:[5a] add steadily larger amounts of conformational "noise" to the conformations (e.g., add a random number in the range [-1Å, +1Å] to all atom positions) and see how robust the output is to such changes; add a random molecule to the dataset or change an activity value at random, and see how robust the output is to such changes; give a dataset of totally random molecules as input, and see what kind of output if any emerges. Try these controls on your favorite pharmacophore discovery method—you will probably be surprised by the results. Some of the most creative things done by cell biologists are the design of control experiments. For example, the discovery of G-proteins came about from a cleverly designed control experiment which yielded an unanticipated result.[8] We in computer-aided drug discovery need to be equally creative about control experiments.

27.2.5. Statistical Measures of Quality

I contend that it is inherent in the pharmacophore discovery problem that most datasets are consistent with multiple pharmacophores. In mathematical terms, most datasets admit multiple solutions. In my opinion, it is not sufficient to find a pharmacophore in a dataset, i.e., one structural pattern consistent with the activity. In general, there are many such patterns. One must find the *right* one—the one which will prospectively predict well.

There has been limited recognition of this problem in the literature. Demeter et al.[9] acknowledge this problem, and use the ability of a pharmacophore to yield a well-scoring CoMFA analysis as a measure of quality. In my own work,[5] a statistical test is used, *the principle of selectivity*, to rank the statistical significance of the multiple pharmacophores which are consistent with the input data. The work of Güner and Henry in this volume represents yet another step in this direction of trying to statistically evaluate a pharmacophore.

27.2.6. Prospective Application of Pharmacophores

Nonetheless, no amount of retrospective analysis, jackknifing, bootstrapping, or statistical wizardry will ever replace the *sine qua non* of computer-aided drug discovery: the prospective application of our methods. In other words, we must apply our methods to guide the chemist in the decision "what molecule should I make next?" prior to that decision. This is the ultimate final arbiter of what makes method A better than method B—the ability to more accurately and more creatively predict what molecule should be made next to improve the molecule's characteristics *vis-à-vis* the target profile. This is one advantage to pharmacophore discovery methods that feed directly into a 3D database search: This is a simple way to perform prospective tests, by searching a database of compounds in inventory which can be quickly tested. Furthermore, this is one of the reasons I find so exciting the application of pharmacophore methods to combinatorial chemistry via structure-based combi-chem: one gets a direct readout of one's success, as gauged by the proportion of molecules in a designed library that are active.

27.3. Not All Datasets Are Created Equal

My own experience in using Catalyst for four years while at BioCAD, and in using DANTE for the last five years at Pharmacia & Upjohn, is that some datasets are easy, some are hard. Listening to the talks which gave rise to this volume, a significant appreciation for this fact did not emerge. In my opinion, one dataset that is one of the easiest is the dataset of D2 antagonists. Any pharmacophore discovery method that cannot quickly and effortlessly nail that to the floor should be cast aside.

Another easy dataset is the set of ACE inhibitors used by Mayer et al.[1] This SAR is the result of a decade or more of ACE inhibitor development, including many fairly rigid compounds whose affinity is below 10 nM. By contrast, the set of peptidic millimolar ACE inhibitors known to Ondetti & Cushman prior to the discovery of Captopril (see reference[5a]) is a very tricky and subtle dataset, which is a challenge to any methodology.

One of the first datasets we received while at BioCAD were a series of PAF antagonists, later published by Girotra et al.[10] This is an extraordinarily difficult dataset; it may be one of these datasets where a good pharmacophore does not really exist.

In general, the following are characteristics of easy datasets:

- many high-affinity molecules, < 10 nM
- molecules that are relatively rigid or feature-poor (e.g., few heteroatoms)
- organic molecules, synthesized in the course of a directed SAR program
- biological activity assayed by an enzymatic or cloned receptor assay with full dose-response curve, with kinetic evaluation

On the other hand, the following are characteristics of difficult datasets:

- none of the molecules are very potent, e.g., all are > 1 μM

- the molecules are highly flexible and feature-rich, e.g., peptides
- the biological activity may measure multiple mechanisms of action (e.g., competitive and non-competitive inhibitors), or may be far-removed from the molecular site of action (e.g., a functional assay like a muscle-strip contraction, which measures both ability to bind to a receptor and the ability to traverse membrane boundaries)
- the biological activity has been coarsely measured, e.g., a single-point HTS assay

As potential customers of Catalyst evaluated our software, it was striking that some groups were quite happy with the results, while others were not; in part this may be attributed to the different datasets that were being applied. Similarly, it is difficult to compare different pharmacophore discovery methods, as a common set of standards about datasets does not exist for comparison; some are reporting results on easy datasets, while others are reporting on difficult ones. Peter Willett has advocated the development of some common datasets against which methods developers can compare their methods; this is eminently sensible, and something towards which to look forward. I have advocated rating datasets in the manner that canoeists rank whitewater rivers: Class I is the smooth water for a Sunday paddle with the family, while Class V is a supremely challenging river, appropriate only for experts in full gear.

27.4. Conformational Analysis

We see two different approaches in various pharmacophore discovery methods: those that have conformational analysis performed externally by a separate package, and those that integrate the conformational exploration with the pharmacophore discovery. Catalyst and DANTE are examples of the former; the work of Dammkoehler, Shands et al.,[11] GASP,[12] and SCAMPI[13] are examples of the latter.

My own bias has been to keep these two algorithms separate, with a "firewall" between them, though that is just a bias. One advantage of keeping them separate is that, as new algorithms appear in exhaustive conformational analysis, these can be simply "plugged in"; the 1999 Anaheim ACS meeting had a session devoted to innovations in conformational analysis—it is clear that the pace of innovation here is high. One argument in favor of integrating conformational analysis with pharmacophore discovery is that this allows for a more directed exploration of conformational space.

It is difficult to assess whether this is merely a software design issue, or whether this has implications to the scientific basis of pharmacophore discovery.

27.5. Frontiers

Where are we headed in pharmacophore discovery?

First and foremost, I anticipate seeing these methods used more and more in real-life settings in drug discovery efforts in the pharmaceutical industry. This, more than anything, will drive the development of the field, and force us all to pay attention to the bottlenecks and weaknesses of existing methods.

I also anticipate a steadily widening circle of applications. I consider the use in the analysis of HTS data one of the most innovative new applications of such methodology.

We are beginning to see some innovations in the representation of pharmacophores (the term "representation" used in the sense of artificial-intelligence/expert-systems research). The notion of a "maximum common 3D substructure" presented in Chapter 23 is quite intriguing, and is an area of research I hope we will see develop more fully. The notion of features being selected from a standard library (H-bond donor, acceptor, negative and positive charges, aromatic ring, and hydrophobe) is an idea that I introduced to BioCAD, mainly as a "hack" to get us going quickly; it has astonished me to see how this idea was copied and continues to persist without elaboration or refinement. I look forward to improvements here. Some of the efforts with recursive partitioning[14] or phylogenetic-like trees[3] hint at some possibilities here.

Most efforts at dealing with shape are still too primitive, in my opinion. My own work with inferring the shape of receptor sites in DANTE via the shrink-wrap method convinces me that this is an important aspect of the overall pharmacophore; if a molecule has an atom bumping into the wall of the receptor, no amount of fiddling with the features in the pharmacophore can account for this. Furthermore, this is a very common aspect of most SAR datasets.

One new idea which emerged from a more refined understanding of shape constraints is that of *terra incognita*, regions that an SAR has not explored.[3] It is sometimes as important to steer new exploration towards unexplored regions than it is to steer exploration away from sterically forbidden regions. This is an aspect of pharmacophore discovery that needs to be more fully elaborated.

One largely overlooked problem arises when multiple binding modes exist among the dataset, which leads to one portion of the dataset belonging to one pharmacophore, the other portion to another pharmacophore. As datasets get larger, and are less carefully filtered by users, this problem will inevitably grow. The algorithm used in DANTE[5a] is in principle capable of recognizing multiple pharmacophores, though in practice this does not work as well as one would desire. The efforts at Bioreason[4] represent a novel and innovative way of handling this problem, by clustering the molecules by topological criteria and submitting those clusters to pharmacophore discovery.

The fact that there frequently exist many pharmacophores all consistent with the data is a problem that inevitably will attract more attention. It is critical that more effort is made to devise and apply statistical measures to sift through these multiple solutions. My own attempt to do this[5a] has never been cited in the literature; I take this as evidence for how little appreciation there is of this issue today. My own view: It is unlikely that any method will be useful in prospective applications if it does not acknowledge these multiple solutions and discard the statistically meaningless solutions.

I sincerely hope that we will see an ever-widening circle of contributors to the pharmacophore discovery field. As the pace of innovation within the commercial software vendors has slowed, evidently due to market pressures, that pace has picked up among researchers in CADD groups in the pharmaceutical industry. We in the pharmaceutical industry are under our own set of market pressures, however, which may open the way for greater contributions from academic institutions. Besides the funding issue mentioned above, the main obstacle to academics in this area is that much of the data is still largely unpublished, in the hands of the pharmaceutical industry researchers.

Finally, it is time for us to critically assess our progress in the pharmacophore discovery field; to clarify precisely what problem we are trying to solve; and to introduce rigor. We must avoid reinventing the wheel when building upon predecessor work, and we must clarify the mathematical character and the statistical assumptions underpinning our work.

References

1. Mayer D, Naylor CB, Motoc I, Marshall GR: **A unique geometry of the active site of angiotensin-converting enzyme consistent with structure-activity studies.** *J Comput-Aided Mol Des* 1987, **1**:3-16.

2. Martin YC, Bures MG, Danaher EA, DeLazzer J, Lico I, Pavlik PA: **A fast new approach to pharmacophore mapping and its application to dopaminergic and benzodiazepine agonists.** *J Comput-Aided Mol Des* 1993, **7**:83-102.

3. Van Drie JH, Nugent RA: **Addressing the challenges of combinatorial chemistry.** *SAR and QSAR in Environ Res* 1998, **9**:1-21. (proceedings of a meeting held in Ispra, Italy, 1/97).

4. Elling JW, Bassett, SI, Nutt RF: **Pharmacophore model generation from high-throughput screening datasets.** Talk presented at 217th ACS National Meeting in Anaheim, March 21-25,1999.

5. (a) Van Drie JH: **Strategies for the determination of pharmacophoric 3D database queries.** *J Comput-Aided Mol Des* 1997, **11**:39-52; (b) Van Drie JH: **An inequality for 3D database searching and its use in evaluating the treatment of conformational flexibility.** *J Comput-Aided Mol Des* 1996, **10**:623-630; (c) Van Drie JH: **"Shrink-wrap" surfaces: A new method for incorporating shape into pharmacophoric 3D database searching.** *J Chem Inf Comp Sci* 1997, **37**:38-42.

6. Van Drie JH, Weininger D, Martin YC: **ALADDIN: An integrated tool for computer-assisted molecular design and pharmacophore recognition from geometric, steric, and substructure searching of three-dimensional molecular structures.** *J Comput-Aided Mol Des* 1989, **3**:225--251; see also Van Drie JH: **3D Database Searching in Drug Discovery.** *Netsci*, http://www.netsci.org/Science/Cheminform/feature06.html.

7. Greenidge PA, Carlsson B, Bladh LG, Gillner M: **Pharmacophores incor-porating numerous excluded volumes defined by X-ray crystallo-graphic structure in three-dimensional database searching: Application to the thyroid hormone receptor.** *J Med Chem* 1998, **41**:2503-2512, and their contribution to this volume.

8. Linder ME, Gilman AG: **G-proteins.** *Sci Am* 1992, **267**:56-61.

9. Demeter DA, Weintraub HJR, Knittel JJ: **The Local Minima Method of pharmacophore determination: A protocol for predicting the bioactive conformation of small, conformationally flexible molecules.** *J Chem Inf Comp Sci* 1998, **38**:1125-1136.

10. Girotra NN, Biftu T, Ponpipom MM, Acton JJ, Alberts AW, Bach TN, Ball RG, Bugianesi RL, Parsons WH, Chabala JC, et al: **Development, synthesis, and biological evaluation of (-)-trans-(2S,5S)-2-[3-[(2-oxopropyl)sul-fonyl]-4-n-propoxy-5-(3-hydroxypropoxy)-phenyl]-5-(3,4,5-trimethoxy-phenyl)tetrahydrofuran, a potent orally active platelet-activating fac-tor (PAF) antagonist and its water-soluble prodrug phosphate ester.** *J Med Chem* 1992, **35**:3474-3482.

11. Dammkoehler RA, Karasek SF, Shands EF, Marshall GR: **Constrained search of conformational hyperspace.** *J Comput-Aided Mol Des* 1989, **3**:3-21.

12. Jones G, Willett P, and Glen RC: **A genetic algorithm for flexible molec-ular overlay and pharmacophore elucidation.** *J Comput-Aided Mol Des* 1995, **9**:532-549.

13. Chen X, Rusinko III A, Tropsha A, Young SS: **Implementation of fast conformational search strategies for 3-D pharmacophore identification using Scampi.** 217th ACS National Meeting in Anaheim, March 21-25,1999.

14. Young SS, Hawkins DA: **Using recursive partitioning to analyze a very large SAR dataset.** *SAR and QSAR in Environ Res* 1998, **8**:183-193. (pro-ceedings of a meeting held in Ispra, Italy, 1/97).

Index

%A, 197-202, 206, 207, 216, 217, 220, 222-223, 225, 331, 333, 509-510
%Y, 197-203, 206, 207, 215-217, 219, 220, 222-223, 225, 231, 331, 509-510
.chm file, 403
.pka file, 117
.pky file, 117

2D keys, 113
3-center keys, 119
3D keys, 112
3D QSAR—see QSAR
3D query, 112, 114, 124, 210, 252
3D searching, xv, xvi, 51, 60, 65, 111, 113, 199, 200, 204, 221, 231, 232, 333, 480, 481, 484, 489, 493
3D substructure, 433, 435, 480, 529
4-center keys, 116
5-HT3 antagonists, 77, 79, 102, 218, 506-509

Absorption, Distribution, Metabolism, and Excretion (ADME), 275, 278, 282, 284, 286, 288, 290, 291
Accessibility, 8, 118
ACD—see Available Chemicals Directory
ACDD—see Available Chemicals Directory database
ACE—see Angiotensin converting enzyme
ACE inhibitors—see Angiotensin converting enzyme inhibitors
Active analog approach, xvi, 20, 24, 25, 32, 33, 38-41, 43, 481
Active site, 17, 41, 42, 71, 131, 132, 203, 208, 221, 222, 226, 275, 276, 278, 279, 284, 285, 312-315, 341-343, 345, 412-417, 421, 422, 482
Adaptive pharmacophore searching, 124
ADME—see Absorption, Distribution, Metabolism, and Excretion

Adverse drug reactions (AORs), 274
AG—see Auxiliary groups
Aladdin, xvi, 60, 519
Aligning 3D structures, 341
AM1, 53
Analog-based design, 20, 221, 341
Angiotensin converting enzyme (ACE), 42, 418, 421, 423, 471, 485, 491-492
Angiotensin converting enzyme inhibitors (ACE inhibitors), 40, 42, 54, 179, 205, 459, 460, 466, 467, 469, 470, 488, 491-492, 525
Angiotensin II antagonists, 103, 207, 442, 449
Angiotensin II blockers, 207
Angiotensin II receptor, 449
Angiotensin inhibitors, 206
Antihypertensive, 206
Anti-pharmacophore shielding (APS), 458, 459, 462-473
Antiserotonins, 219
AORs—see Adverse drug reactions
APEX-3D, xvii, xviii, 133-142, 145-148, 304
APS—see Anti-pharmacophore shielding
Arotinoid, 329
Atom types, 8, 90, 96, 99, 110, 159, 242, 355, 360, 437
Automated method of generation of pharmacophore, 342
Auxiliary groups (AG), 458, 459, 462-467, 470, 472
Available Chemicals Directory (ACD), 9, 19, 227, 357, 418, 421, 423
Available Chemicals Directory database (ACDD), 418, 421, 423

Basic skeleton, 470-472
Bayesian statistics, 134
Binding affinity, 388, 390, 404
Binding
  data, 397
  energy, 395-397, 404